Introduction to Modern Algebra

COLLEGE MATHEMATICS SERIES

Neal H. McCoy

Professor of Mathematics
Smith College

Introduction to Modern Algebra

BOSTON: ALLYN AND BACON, INC.

First printing.........................May, 1960
Second printing......................August, 1960
Third printing...... ....June, 1961
Fourth printing.....................November, 1961
Fifth printing ....August, 1962
Sixth printing........................January, 1963
Seventh printing........................August, 1963

Library of Congress Catalog Card Number: 60–11416

Dedicated to the memory of my son

PAUL

Preface

This book is designed as a text for a *first* course in modern abstract algebra. Since many students find such a course fairly difficult, it has been my goal to make the exposition as clear and simple as possible but, at the same time, sufficiently precise and thorough to furnish an honest introduction to the methods and results of abstract algebra.

A few preliminary concepts are introduced in the first chapter, and then in the second chapter rings are defined and discussed in considerable detail. Integral domains and fields are presented in later chapters. Although a very brief discussion of the Peano Axioms is given in an optional section, the viewpoint of the book is to *assume* that the system of integers has those properties which make it an ordered integral domain in which the set of positive elements is well-ordered. A number of other properties of the integers are proved in Chapter 4, including some of those usually established in elementary courses in the theory of numbers. The various number fields of elementary algebra are derived in detail. In particular, the field of real numbers is treated quite thoroughly in Chapter 6 although, as indicated at the beginning of that chapter, some of this material may be omitted at the option of the instructor. Later chapters contain introductions to other important topics in algebra as follows: polynomials, groups, vector spaces, systems of linear equations, determinants, linear transformations and matrices.

There is enough material in the book for a two-semester course meeting three times a week. The first seven chapters, with the possible omission of part of Chapter 6 on the real numbers and the possible inclusion of part of Chapter 8 on polynomials, can be covered in a one-semester course in which the emphasis is on the construction of the various number systems.

Carefully selected exercises, designed to be of assistance in the development of an understanding of the material presented, appear at the end of most sections. Experience has shown that almost all of these exercises should be assigned, particularly in the first few chapters.

I have taught a preliminary version of this book to a Smith College class at the undergraduate level, and Professor W. H. Durfee has taught about half of it to a Mount Holyoke College class at the same level. In addition, I have taught various preliminary versions of parts of the first few chapters in three Summer Institutes for High School Teachers, two at the State University of Iowa and one at Randolph-Macon Woman's College, and also in an Academic Year Institute at the University of North Carolina. I am greatly indebted to all those former students who by their questions and difficulties have helped to improve the exposition in various ways. Professor Durfee also made several valuable suggestions as a result of his experience in teaching part of the material.

It would not be possible to list all of those to whom I am indebted in a direct or indirect way. However, I would like to mention a special indebtedness to my colleague, Professor R. E. Johnson. Although, for the most part, I did not discuss with him the choice of topics or the way in which they were to be presented, nevertheless, over the years we have had many discussions on various topics in abstract algebra and on the pedagogical problems involved in teaching this subject matter. Accordingly, he has had a substantial, although partially indirect, influence on this book. I have also taught his excellent text in this same field and have been consciously influenced by it in certain ways, and no doubt have been unconsciously influenced in other ways as well. In addition, I am grateful to him for substantial help in reading the galley proofs.

Finally, it is a pleasure to express my appreciation to my wife, Ardis, without whose inspiration and encouragement this book would never have been written.

Northampton, Mass.   NEAL H. McCOY

Contents

5. FIELDS AND THE RATIONAL NUMBERS   72

6. THE FIELD OF REAL NUMBERS   88

7. THE FIELD OF COMPLEX NUMBERS   112

8. POLYNOMIALS   126

9. GROUPS   166

10. VECTOR SPACES   195

11. SYSTEMS OF LINEAR EQUATIONS   221

12. DETERMINANTS   246

Contents

Introduction

to

Modern

Algebra

1

Some Fundamental Concepts

The outstanding characteristic of modern algebra, and indeed also of many other branches of modern mathematics, is its extensive use of what is known as the axiomatic or postulational method. The method itself is not new, since it was used by Euclid (about 300 B.C.) in his construction of geometry as a deductive science. However, in many ways the modern viewpoint is quite different from Euclid's, and the power of the method did not become apparent until this century.

We shall not attempt to give here any description or analysis of the postulational method, but the material of the next few chapters will illustrate the ideas involved. This first brief chapter will present a few basic concepts to be used repeatedly, and will introduce some convenient notation. Although we shall give a few illustrations of each concept as it is introduced, many more illustrations and examples will appear later.

1.1 SETS

The concept of *set* (class, collection, aggregate) is fundamental in mathematics as it is in everyday life. A related concept is that of *element* of a set. We make no attempt to define these terms but shall presently give some examples that will illustrate the sense in which they are being used.

First of all, we may say that a set is made up of elements. In order to give an example of a set we need, therefore, to exhibit its elements or to give some rule that will specify its elements. We shall often find it convenient to denote sets by capital letters and elements of sets by lower-case letters. If a is an element of the set A, we may indicate this fact by writing $a \in A$ (read, "a is an element of A"). Also, $a \notin A$ will mean that a is not an element of the set A. If both a and b are elements of the set A, we may write $a, b \in A$.

If P is the set of all positive integers, $a \in P$ means merely that a is a positive integer. Certainly, then, it is true that $1 \in P$, $2 \in P$, and so on. If B is the set of all triangles in a given plane, $a \in B$ means that a is one of the triangles in this plane. If C is the set of all books in the Library of Congress, then $a \in C$ means that a is one of these books. We shall presently give other examples of sets.

If A and B are sets with the property that every element of A is also an element of B, we call A a *subset* of B and write $A \subseteq B$ (read, "A is contained in B"). Perhaps we should point out that for every set A it is true that $A \subseteq A$ and hence, according to our definition, one of the subsets of A is A itself. If $A \subseteq B$ and also $B \subseteq A$, then A and B have exactly the same elements and we say that these sets are *equal*, and indicate this by writing $A = B$. If it is not true that $A = B$, we may write $A \neq B$. If $A \subseteq B$ and $A \neq B$, then we say that A is a *proper subset* of B and indicate this fact by the notation $A \subset B$ (read "A is properly contained in B"). Clearly, $A \subset B$ means that every element of A is an element of B and, moreover, B contains at least one element which is not an element of A.

Sometimes, as has been the case so far, we may specify a set by stating in words just what its elements are. Another way of specifying a set is to exhibit its elements. Thus, $\{x\}$ indicates the set which consists of the single element x, $\{x, y\}$ the set consisting of the two elements x and y, and so on. We may write $A = \{1, 2, 3, 4\}$ to mean that A is the set whose elements are the positive integers 1, 2, 3, and 4. If P is the set of all positive integers, by writing

$$K = \{a; \ a \in P, a \text{ divisible by } 2\},$$

we shall mean that K consists of all elements a having the properties indicated after the semicolon, that is, a is a positive integer and is divisible by 2. Hence, K is just the set of all *even* positive integers. We may also write

$$K = \{2, 4, 6, 8, \cdots\},$$

the dots indicating that all even positive integers are included in this set. As another example, if

$$D = \{a; \ a \in P, a < 6\},$$

then it is clear that $D = \{1, 2, 3, 4, 5\}$.

For many purposes, it is convenient to allow for the possibility that a set may have no elements. This fictitious set with no elements we shall call the *empty set*. According to the definition of subset given above, the empty set is a subset of every set. Moreover, it is a proper subset of every set except the empty set itself.

If A and B are sets, the elements that are in both A and B form a set called the *intersection* of A and B, denoted by $A \cap B$. Of course, if A and B have no elements in common, $A \cap B$ is the empty set.

If A and B are sets, the set consisting of those elements which are elements either of A or of B (or of both), is a set called the *union* of A and B, denoted by $A \cup B$.

As examples of the concepts of intersection and union, let $A = \{1, 2, 3\}$, $B = \{2, 4, 5\}$, and $C = \{1, 3, 6\}$. Then we have $A \cap B = \{2\}$, $A \cap C = \{1, 3\}$, $B \cap C$ is the empty set, $A \cup B = \{1, 2, 3, 4, 5\}$, $A \cup C = \{1, 2, 3, 6\}$, and $B \cup C = \{1, 2, 3, 4, 5, 6\}$.

Although we have defined the intersection and the union of only *two* sets, it is easy to extend these definitions to any number of sets, as follows. The *intersection* of any number of given sets is the set consisting of those elements which are in all the given sets, and the *union* is the set consisting of those elements which are in at least one of the given sets.

The next concept to be introduced may be illustrated by the familiar idea of coordinates of a point in a plane. A point is determined by an ordered pair (x, y) of real numbers. The word *ordered* is meant to imply that the order of writing the two numbers x and y is important; that is, that (x, y) is to be considered as a different pair than (y, x) unless, of course, x and y happen to be equal real numbers. If K denotes the set of all real numbers, the set of all ordered pairs of elements of K is frequently called the *product set* of K by K and designated by "$K \times K$." More generally, if A and B are any sets, the set of all ordered pairs (a, b), where $a \in A$ and $b \in B$, is the *product set* of A by B, designated by "$A \times B$." It may happen, of course, that A and B are identical sets, as in the illustration given above. Actually, we shall not need to make much use of the notation for a product set, but shall find occasion to refer to ordered pairs. As indicated here, these are merely elements of a certain product set.

As another example of a product set, let $A = \{1, 2, 3\}$, and

$B = \{u, v\}$. Then $A \times B$ consists of all ordered pairs of elements (a, b), where $a \in A$, $b \in B$. That is, we have

$$A \times B = \{(1, u), (1, v), (2, u), (2, v), (3, u), (3, v)\}.$$

<hr>

EXERCISES

1. If $A = \{a, b, c\}$, $B = \{c, x, y\}$, and $C = \{x, z\}$, determine each of the following sets: $A \cap B$, $A \cap C$, $B \cap C$, $A \cup B$, $A \cup C$, $B \cup C$, $A \times B$, $A \times C$, $B \times C$.

2. Let P be the set of all positive integers, and define subsets of P as follows:

$$F = \{a;\ a \in P, a < 10\},$$
$$G = \{a;\ a \in P, a > 5\},$$
$$H = \{a;\ a \in P, a \text{ divisible by } 3\}.$$

Determine each of the following sets: $F \cap G$, $F \cap H$, $G \cap H$, $F \cup G$, $F \cup H$, $G \cup H$.

3. Exhibit the four different subsets of a set with two elements. How many subsets does a set with three elements have? A set with four elements?

4. Find a general formula for the number of subsets of a set with n elements, where n is an arbitrary positive integer.

1.2 MAPPINGS

As a first illustration of the concept to be introduced in this section, let C be the set of all books in the Library of Congress and P the set of all positive integers. Corresponding to each book there is a unique positive integer; namely, the number of pages in the book. That is, to each element of C there corresponds in this way a unique element of P. This is an example of a mapping of the set C into the set P. As another illustration, let N be the set of all names occurring in a given telephone directory, and L the set of the twenty-six letters of the alphabet. We may then associate with each name the first letter of the surname, and this then defines a mapping of N into L. Additional examples will be given after the following definition.

1.1 Definition. A *mapping* of a set A into a set B is a correspondence that associates with each element a of A a unique element a' of B. This mapping may be indicated by writing $a \rightarrow a'$, and we shall call a' the *image* of a under this mapping. If every element of B is the image of some element of A, we may speak of a mapping of A *onto* B.

[margin handwritten note: onto]

As another example of a mapping, let $S = \{1, 2, 3, 4\}$ and $T = \{x, y, z\}$. Then

1.2
$$1 \to x, \quad 2 \to y, \quad 3 \to x, \quad 4 \to y$$

defines a mapping of S into T. It is not a mapping of S onto T since there exists an element of T, namely z, which is not the image of any element of S under this mapping.

The mapping

1.3
$$1 \to x, \quad 2 \to x, \quad 3 \to y, \quad 4 \to z$$

of S into T is a mapping of S onto T since under this mapping every element of T is the image of some element of S. In each of the mappings 1.2 and 1.3, there exist at least two different elements of S that have the same image in T. A most important kind of mapping is one in which different elements have different images and, moreover, the mapping is *onto*. Such a mapping has a special name according to the following definition.

1.4 Definition. A mapping $a \to a'$ of a set A *onto* a set B is called a *one-one* mapping of A onto B if distinct elements of A have distinct images in B.

[margin handwritten note: one-one]

If $T = \{x, y, z\}$ as above, and $U = \{r, s, t\}$, then

1.5
$$x \to r, \quad y \to t, \quad z \to s$$

is an example of a one-one mapping of T onto U. It is clear that now

1.6
$$r \to x, \quad s \to z, \quad t \to y$$

defines a one-one mapping of U onto T, and in this mapping the same elements of U and T are associated as in the mapping 1.5. Of course, this is always true. That is, if $a \to a'$ is a one-one mapping of A onto B, then $a' \to a$ defines a one-one mapping of B onto A.

Although we have defined mappings of a set A into (or onto) a set B, the sets A and B may be identical. For example, if P is the set of all positive integers and $n \in P$, then $n \to n^2$ defines a mapping of P into P. It is not a mapping of P onto P since, for example, the element 2 of P is not the image of any element of P. If I is the set of all integers (positive, negative, and zero), and $i \in I$, the mapping $i \to i + 1$ is easily seen to define a mapping of I onto I. This is a one-one mapping of I onto I since if $i, j \in I$, $i \neq j$ implies that $i + 1 \neq j + 1$.

The present terminology may be new to the reader, but the general idea of a mapping has no doubt already been met in elementary mathematics. A *function*, as the word is often used, is merely a mapping of the set K of real numbers (or of some subset of K) into K. For example, the function f defined by $f(x) = x^2 + x + 1$ is the mapping which associates with the real number x the real number $x^2 + x + 1$. In our present notation, this function f is the mapping $x \rightarrow x^2 + x + 1$ of K into K.

-- *E X E R C I S E S*

1. If I is the set of all integers and $i \in I$, which of the following mappings of I into I are mappings of I onto I? Which are one-one mappings of I onto I?

    (a) $i \rightarrow i + 3$,   (d) $i \rightarrow 2i - 1$,
    (b) $i \rightarrow i^2 + i$,   (e) $i \rightarrow -i + 5$,
    (c) $i \rightarrow i^3$,   (f) $i \rightarrow i - 4$.

2. If K is the set of all real numbers and $x \in K$, which of the following mappings of K into K are mappings of K onto K? Which are one-one mappings of K onto K?

    (a) $x \rightarrow 2x - 1$,   (d) $x \rightarrow x^3$,
    (b) $x \rightarrow 1 - x$,   (e) $x \rightarrow x^2 + x$,
    (c) $x \rightarrow x^2$,   (f) $x \rightarrow 4x$.

3. If K is the set of all real numbers, use the fact that every cubic equation with real coefficients has a real root to show that $x \rightarrow x^3 - x$ defines a mapping of K onto K. Is this a one-one mapping?

4. If P is the set of all positive integers and $n \in P$, show that $n \rightarrow 2n$ is a one-one mapping of P onto the set E of all *even* positive integers.

1.3   EQUIVALENCE RELATIONS

The concept of an equivalence relation, to be defined presently, plays a very important role in modern algebra. Accordingly, we present it in this preliminary chapter even though we shall not have need of it until the last section of Chapter 4. Before giving the definition, let us explain what we mean by a relation.

If I is the set of all integers, and $i < j$ has the usual meaning for $i, j \in I$, then "$<$" is an example of a relation defined on I. This statement only means that for every ordered pair (i, j) of elements of I, $i < j$ is either true or false. With the usual meanings of these symbols, "$\leq$" and "$=$" are other relations defined on I.

In general, let A be a given set. We say that a *relation* "$\sim$" is defined on A if for each ordered pair (a, b) of elements of A, $a \sim b$ is meaningful and is either true or false. If this is false, we may write $a \not\sim b$. For the present, we are not concerned with relations in general but only with those relations which have the particular properties stated in the following definition.

1.7 Definition. A relation "$\sim$" defined on a set A is called an *equivalence relation* if it has the following three properties, where a, b, and c are arbitrary elements of A:

(1) $a \sim a$ (*reflexive property*),
(2)   If $a \sim b$, then $b \sim a$ (*symmetric property*),
(3)   If $a \sim b$ and $b \sim c$, then $a \sim c$ (*transitive property*).

If "$\sim$" is an equivalence relation, we may find it convenient to read $a \sim b$ as "a is equivalent to b."

The relation "$<$" on the set I of all integers is not an equivalence relation since it has neither the reflexive property nor the symmetric property. The relation "$\leq$" has the reflexive property but not the symmetric property. Of course, "$=$" is an equivalence relation on I, as is perhaps suggested by the word "equivalence." Other examples of equivalence relations will be given presently. However, let us point out how we shall use the familiar symbol "$=$" of equality. If a and b are elements of any set A and we write $a = b$, *unless otherwise explicitly stated we shall always mean that these are identical elements of A.* That is, a and b are different symbols for the same element of A. It is then trivial that equality as so defined satisfies the three defining properties of an equivalence relation.

There are many equivalence relations other than equality in the sense just described. We shall now give a few examples, but many more will occur in later chapters of this book. Let T be the set of all triangles in a fixed plane, and let a and b be arbitrary elements of T. Then "$\sim$" is an equivalence relation on T if we agree to define "$\sim$" in any one of the following ways:

(i) $a \sim b$ to mean "a is congruent to b,"
(ii) $a \sim b$ to mean "a is similar to b,"
(iii) $a \sim b$ to mean "a has the same area as b,"
(iv) $a \sim b$ to mean "a has the same perimeter as b."

As another example of an equivalence relation, let I be the set of all integers, and let us define $a \equiv b$ to mean that $a - b$ has 3 as a factor;

that is, that there exists an integer n such that $a - b = 3n$. It is then readily verified that "$\equiv$" has the three defining properties of an equivalence relation. Furthermore, every integer is equivalent to one of the three integers 0, 1, 2. In this connection, consider the following three subsets of I:

$$J = \{\cdots, -9, -6, -3, 0, 3, 6, 9, \cdots\},$$
$$K = \{\cdots, -8, -5, -2, 1, 4, 7, 10, \cdots\},$$
$$L = \{\cdots, -7, -4, -1, 2, 5, 8, 11, \cdots\}.$$

It will be observed that every integer is in exactly one of these subsets. In other words, the union of these three subsets is I and the intersection of any two of them is the empty set. Moreover, J can be characterized as the set of all elements of I that are equivalent to 0 (or to any other element of J), and similar characterizations can be given for K and L. The sets J, K, and L are examples of a concept which we proceed to define.

1.8 Definition. Let A be a set and "$\sim$" an equivalence relation defined on A. If $a \in A$, the subset of A which consists of all elements x of A such that $x \sim a$ is called an *equivalence set*. This equivalence set will frequently be denoted by $[a]$.

This definition of the equivalence set $[a]$ can be written formally as follows:

1.9
$$[a] = \{x;\ x \in A,\ x \sim a\}.$$

In the above example, note that $J = [0]$, $K = [1]$, and $L = [2]$; also that $[0] = [3] = [6]$, and so on. Hence there are just the three different equivalence sets.

To return to the general definition, let us consider a few properties of equivalence sets. First, since $a \sim a$ by the reflexive property of an equivalence relation, we always have $a \in [a]$; that is, $[a]$ is the equivalence set which contains a. Other properties of equivalence sets are the following, where a, b, c, and d are arbitrary elements of the set A:

(i)   If $b \in [a]$, then $[b] = [a]$,

(ii) $[a] = [b]$ if and only if $a \sim b$,

1.10   (iii)   If $[a] \cap [b]$ is not the empty set, then $[a] = [b]$,

(iv) $[a] \cap [b]$ is the empty set if and only if $a \nsim b$,

(v)   If $c \in [a]$, $d \in [b]$, and $[a] \neq [b]$, then $c \nsim d$.

We shall prove (i) and leave the proofs of the others as exercises. Suppose, then, that $b \in [a]$. According to 1.9, this implies that $b \sim a$. To show that $[b] = [a]$, we shall show that $[b] \subseteq [a]$ and also that $[a] \subseteq [b]$. Let $x \in [b]$. Then $x \sim b$ and since $b \sim a$ it follows from the transitive property of an equivalence relation that $x \sim a$ and hence that $x \in [a]$. Since every element x of $[b]$ is also an element of $[a]$, we have shown that $[b] \subseteq [a]$. To go the other way, let $y \in [a]$, which means that $y \sim a$. Since $b \sim a$, we know by the symmetric property of an equivalence relation that $a \sim b$. Now we have that $y \sim a$ and $a \sim b$, and the transitive property assures us that $y \sim b$. Hence, we have $y \in [b]$, and it follows that $[a] \subseteq [b]$. We have therefore shown that $[b] = [a]$, and 1.10(i) has been proved.

Since always $a \in [a]$, it is clear that every element of A is in some equivalence set; that is, that A is the union of all its different equivalence sets. Moreover, Property 1.10(i) assures us that each element of A is in exactly one equivalence set.

_____ **E X E R C I S E S**

1. Prove 1.10(ii)–(v) in detail, and state the reason for each step.

2. Let I be the set of all integers, and define $a \equiv b$ to mean that $a - b$ has 5 as a factor. Prove that "$\equiv$" is an equivalence relation on I and exhibit all the different equivalence sets.

1.4 OPERATIONS

There is just one other term that we wish to introduce in this preliminary chapter. First, we consider a familiar concept as follows. Let I be the set of all integers. Associated with each ordered pair (i, j) of elements of I there is a uniquely determined element $i + j$ of I. Accordingly, we say that addition, denoted by "$+$", is an operation on I. More precisely, we may call it a *binary* operation to emphasize that it is defined for each ordered *pair* of elements of I. The general definition is as follows.

1.11 Definition.* Let A be a given set. A *binary operation* "$\circ$" on A is a correspondence that associates with each ordered pair (a, b) of elements of A a uniquely determined element $a \circ b$ of A.

We shall seldom have occasion to use any unfamiliar symbol to denote an operation. For the most part, we shall find it convenient to call an operation "addition" or "multiplication," and to use the familiar notations, $a + b$ and $a \cdot b$ (or simply ab).

*A more formal definition is that a binary operation on A is a mapping of $A \times A$ into A. Thus a binary operation "$\circ$" on A can be described as a mapping $(a, b) \rightarrow a \circ b$ of $A \times A$ into A.

2

Rings

In this chapter we shall introduce the important class of algebraic systems that are called *rings*, give a large number of examples, and then establish some fundamental properties of any ring. All the properties that are used to define a ring are suggested by simple properties of the integers, and we begin by pointing out some of these properties. The following section is therefore of a preliminary nature and is merely intended to furnish a partial motivation of the material to follow.

2.1 FORMAL PROPERTIES OF THE INTEGERS

The simplest numbers are the numbers 1, 2, 3, $\cdots$, used in counting. These are called the "natural numbers" or the "positive integers." Addition and multiplication of natural numbers have simple interpretations if we consider a natural number as indicating the number of elements in a set. For example, suppose that we have two piles of stones, the first one containing m stones and the second one n stones. If the stones of the first pile are placed on the second pile, there results a pile of $n + m$ stones. If, instead, the stones of the second pile are placed on the first pile, we get a pile of $m + n$ stones. It thus seems quite obvious that

$$m + n = n + m$$

for every choice of m and n as natural numbers. This property of the natural numbers is an example of what we may call a *law* or a *formal property*.

Multiplication of natural numbers may be introduced as follows. If one has m piles, each of which contains n stones, and all the stones are placed in one pile, the resulting pile will contain mn stones. Some other very familiar formal properties of the natural numbers are the following, where m, n, and k are arbitrary natural numbers:

$$(m + n) + k = m + (n + k),$$
$$mn = nm,$$
$$(mn)k = m(nk),$$
$$m(n + k) = mn + mk.$$

Historically, the natural numbers were no doubt used for centuries before there was any consideration of their formal properties. However, in modern algebra it is precisely such formal properties that are of central interest. Some of the reasons for this changed viewpoint will become evident later on in this chapter as well as in succeeding chapters.

Of course, if m and n are natural numbers, there need not be a natural number x such that $m + x = n$. In order to be able to solve all equations of this kind, we need to have available the negative integers and zero along with the positive integers. The properties with which we shall be concerned in the next section are suggested by well-known properties of the system of *all* the integers (positive, negative, and zero). Near the end of the next chapter we shall be ready to give what may be called a characterization of the system of all integers although, for the most part, we shall merely assume a familiarity with the simpler properties of this system. In later chapters, the other number systems of elementary algebra will be derived in detail. However, even before they are presented in a logical way we shall not hesitate to illustrate parts of our general theory by examples from these familiar number systems.

2.2 DEFINITION OF A RING

The concepts to be presented in this section are of fundamental importance, although a full realization of their generality will probably not become apparent until the examples of the following section are carefully studied.

We begin with a nonempty set R on which there are defined two binary operations, which we shall call "addition" and "multiplication," and for which we shall use the familiar notation. Accordingly, if $a, b \in R$, then $a + b$ and ab (or $a \cdot b$) are uniquely determined elements of the set R. We now assume the following properties or laws, in which a, b, and c are arbitrary elements, distinct or identical, of R:

P_1: $a + b = b + a$ (*commutative law of addition*),

P_2: $(a + b) + c = a + (b + c)$ (*associative law of addition*),

P_3: There exists an element 0 of R such that $a + 0 = a$ for every element a of R (*existence of a zero*),

P_4: If $a \in R$, there exists $x \in R$ such that $a + x = 0$
  (*existence of additive inverses*).

P_5: $(ab)c = a(bc)$ (*associative law of multiplication*),

P_6: $a(b + c) = ab + ac$, $(b + c)a = ba + ca$ (*distributive laws*).

Under all these conditions R is said to be a *ring*. Let us repeat this definition in the following formal way.

2.1 Definition. If R is a nonempty set on which there are defined binary operations of addition and multiplication such that Properties P_1–P_6 hold, we say that R is a *ring* (with respect to these definitions of addition and multiplication).

The element of R designated by "0" and called a *zero* in P_3 is not to be thought of as necessarily being the number zero of elementary algebra, but is just an element of R having the property stated in P_3. In order to emphasize this fact we shall, in some of the examples of the next section, use a different symbol for the zero of a ring. We may point out that P_3 does not assert that a ring has only *one* zero, but later on we shall prove that it has only one. Similarly, P_4 does not assert that an element a of R has only *one* additive inverse, but this will also be proved eventually.

All the properties used to define a ring are certainly familiar properties of the integers. Hence, with the usual definitions of addition and multiplication, the set of all integers is a ring. Henceforth, this ring will be denoted by "I". For this ring, the zero whose existence is asserted in P_3 is the familiar number zero.

Now let E be the set of all *even* integers (positive, negative, and zero). Using, of course, addition and multiplication as already defined in I, we see that the sum of two elements of E is an element of E, and similarly for the product of two elements. Hence, the operations of addition and multiplication, originally defined on the larger set I, are also operations *on the set E*. This fact is often expressed by saying that E is *closed* under these operations. It is easy to verify that E is itself a ring.

If all elements of a ring S are contained in a ring R, it is natural to call S a *subring* of R. It is understood that addition and multiplication of elements of S are to coincide with addition and multiplication of these elements considered as elements of the larger ring R. Naturally, a set S of elements of R cannot possibly be a subring of R unless S is closed under the operations of addition and multiplication on R since, otherwise, we would not have operations *on the set S*. We see that E, as defined above, is a subring of the ring I. However, the set of all odd integers cannot be a subring of I since this set is not closed under addition; that is, the sum of two odd integers is not always (in fact, is never) an odd integer.

A ring may have many properties other than those required by the definition. For example, consider the following property, which may or may not hold in a given ring R:

P_7: If $a, b \in R$, then $ab = ba$ (*commutative law of multiplication*).

A ring which has this property is called a *commutative* ring. If P_7 does not hold, that is, if there exist at least two elements c, d of R such that $cd \neq dc$, R is said to be a *noncommutative* ring.

Another property of interest is the following:

P_8: There exists an element e of R such that $ea = ae = a$ for every element a of R (*existence of a unity*).

If such an element exists, it is called a *unity* (or identity or unit element) of R, and R is said to be a *ring with unity*.

We may emphasize that a ring need not have either of the properties P_7 or P_8. However, most of the rings that we shall study in detail will have both of these properties. The ring I is an example of a commutative ring with unity, whereas the ring E of all even integers is a commutative ring without a unity. A few cases of noncommutative rings will occur among the examples of the next section. Naturally, they will have to be quite different from the familiar number systems.

2.3   EXAMPLES OF RINGS

In order to give an example of a ring R, it is necessary to specify the elements of R and to define the operations of addition and multiplication on R so that Properties P_1–P_6 hold. The ring I of integers has been mentioned as a well-known example of a ring. Other examples are the ring of all real numbers and the ring of all complex numbers, with the usual definitions of addition and multiplication. It will be recalled that the *rational numbers* are those numbers which can be expressed in the form m/n, where m and n are integers with $n \neq 0$. With respect to the familiar definitions of addition and multiplication of rational numbers, the set of all rational numbers is also a ring. Clearly, the ring I is a subring of the ring of all rational numbers; the ring of all rational numbers is a subring of the ring of all real numbers; and the ring of all real numbers is a subring of the ring of all complex numbers. All these number systems will be considered in detail in later chapters.

We proceed to give some other, less familiar, examples of rings. For the most part, we shall not write out the verifications of the Properties P_1–P_6. Some of these verifications will be required in the next list of exercises. The purpose of these examples is to clarify the concept of a ring and to show that there are rings of many different kinds.

Example 1. Let S be the set of all real numbers of the form $x + y\sqrt{2}$, where x, $y \in I$, with addition and multiplication defined in the usual way. It may be verified that S is closed under these operations. Actually, S is a commutative ring with unity. Of course, it is a subring of the ring of all real numbers.

Example 2. Let T be the set of all real numbers of the form $u + v\sqrt[3]{2} + w\sqrt[3]{4}$, where u, v, and w are rational numbers. Using the usual definitions of addition and multiplication, T is a commutative ring with unity.

Example 3. Let $R = \{u, v, w, x\}$; that is, R consists of just these four elements. We define addition and multiplication in R by means of the following tables.

(+)	u	v	w	x		(·)	u	v	w	x
u	u	v	w	x		u	u	u	u	u
v	v	u	x	w		v	u	v	w	x
w	w	x	u	v		w	u	w	w	u
x	x	w	v	u		x	u	x	u	x

These we read as follows. For example, we find $v + x$ by looking in the addition table at the intersection of the row which contains v as its left-hand element and the column which contains x at the top. Since w appears in this position, we have $v + x = w$. Other examples are: $w + w = u$, $x + w = v$, $vw = w$, $xx = x$. It would take too much calculation to verify the associative laws and the distributive laws, and we shall now merely state that they do hold. From the addition table, it is seen that the zero of the ring R is the element u; and from the multiplication table it follows that v is the unity. The reader may verify that this is a commutative ring. This ring R differs from previous examples in that it has only a finite number (four) of elements.

Example 4. Let C be the set of all functions which are continuous on the closed interval, $0 \leq x \leq 1$, with the usual definitions of addition and multiplication of functions. Since a sum or product of two continuous functions is a continuous function, C is closed under these operations. It can be shown that C is a ring. What is the zero of C? Does it have a unity?

Example 5. The set $T = \{0, 1\}$ is a ring of two elements if addition and multiplication are defined by the following tables.

(+)	0	1
0	0	1
1	1	0

(·)	0	1
0	0	0
1	0	1

Clearly, 0 is the zero of this ring and 1 is the unity. Hence, this ring has *only* a zero and a unity.

Example 6. Let $K = \{a, b, c, d\}$ with addition and multiplication defined by the following tables.

(+)	a	b	c	d
a	a	b	c	d
b	b	a	d	c
c	c	d	a	b
d	d	c	b	a

(·)	a	b	c	d
a	a	a	a	a
b	a	b	c	d
c	a	a	a	a
d	a	b	c	d

The ring K is our first example of a noncommutative ring. From the multiplication table we see, for example, that $cd = a$, whereas $dc = c$. Does this ring have a unity? What is the zero?

Example 7. For later reference, we give still another example of a ring with four elements a, b, c, and d. In this case, we define addition and multiplication as follows:

(+)	a	b	c	d
a	a	b	c	d
b	b	a	d	c
c	c	d	a	b
d	d	c	b	a

(·)	a	b	c	d
a	a	a	a	a
b	a	b	c	d
c	a	c	d	b
d	a	d	b	c

It will be observed that the addition table coincides with the addition table of the preceding example. However, the multiplication table is quite different. This ring is another example of a commutative ring.

Example 8. Let L be the set of all ordered triples of elements of I. That is, L is the set of all symbols of the form (a, b, c), where $a, b, c \in I$. We make the following definitions:

$$(a, b, c) + (d, e, f) = (a + d, b + e, c + f),$$
$$(a, b, c)(d, e, f) = (ad, bd + ce, cf).$$

To avoid any possible confusion, we may again state that we consider two elements of a set to be equal only if they are identical. Hence, if

ordered triples ring

(a, b, c) and (d, e, f) are elements of L, then $(a, b, c) = (d, e, f)$ means that $a = d$, $b = e$, and $c = f$.

It is easy to verify that $(0, 0, 0)$ is the zero of the ring L, and that $(1, 0, 1)$ is a unity. This is another noncommutative ring since, for example,

$$(0, 1, 0)(1, 0, 0) = (0, 1, 0),$$

whereas

$$(1, 0, 0)(0, 1, 0) = (0, 0, 0).$$

Let us verify one of the distributive laws for this ring. If (a, b, c), (d, e, f), and (g, h, i) are elements of L, let us show that

$$(a, b, c)((d, e, f) + (g, h, i)) = (a, b, c)(d, e, f) + (a, b, c)(g, h, i).$$

The equality of these expressions is a consequence of the following simple calculations:

$$
\begin{aligned}
(a, b, c)((d, e, f) + (g, h, i)) &= (a, b, c)(d + g, e + h, f + i) \\
&= (a(d + g), b(d + g) + c(e + h), c(f + i)),
\end{aligned}
$$

and

$$
\begin{aligned}
(a, b, c)(d, e, f) + (a, b, c)(g, h, i) &= (ad, bd + ce, cf) + (ag, bg + ch, ci) \\
&= (ad + ag, (bd + ce) + (bg + ch), cf + ci).
\end{aligned}
$$

The right sides of these equations are equal in view of certain simple properties of the integers. What properties are involved?

Example 9. Let W be the set of all symbols of the form

$$\begin{bmatrix} a & b \\ c & d \end{bmatrix},$$

where a, b, c, and d are arbitrary elements of I. Our definitions of addition and multiplication are as follows:

$$\begin{bmatrix} a & b \\ c & d \end{bmatrix} + \begin{bmatrix} e & f \\ g & h \end{bmatrix} = \begin{bmatrix} a + e & b + f \\ c + g & d + h \end{bmatrix},$$

$$\begin{bmatrix} a & b \\ c & d \end{bmatrix} \cdot \begin{bmatrix} e & f \\ g & h \end{bmatrix} = \begin{bmatrix} ae + bg & af + bh \\ ce + dg & cf + dh \end{bmatrix}.$$

With respect to these definitions of addition and multiplication, W is a ring. It is called the *ring of all matrices of order two over the integers*. The reader may verify, by examples, that the commutative law of multiplication does not hold and hence that W is a noncommutative ring. More general matrices will be considered in a later chapter.

We may point out that the elements of W are ordered quadruples of elements of I, and could just as well have been written in the form

(a, b, c, d). However, the above notation is more convenient and is the traditional one.

  Example 10.   This final example is of a type quite different from any of the previous examples. Let A be a given set, and let R be the set of *all* subsets of A, including the empty set and the entire set A. We shall now denote elements of R by lower-case letters—even though they are sets of elements of A.

  Our definitions of addition and multiplication are as follows. If $a, b \in R$, $a + b$ is the set of all elements of A that are in subset a or in subset b, *but not in both*. Also, we define $ab = a \cap b$, the intersection of a and b; in other words, it is the set of elements in both a and b. We may observe that $a + b$ is not, in general, the union of the sets a and b, but it will be this union whenever $a \cap b$ is the empty set.

  We now assert that with these definitions of addition and multiplication, R is a commutative ring with unity. We shall verify some of the necessary properties, and leave the others as exercises.

  Let us introduce a convenient, but purely symbolic, way of visualizing the meaning of the operations of addition and multiplication. In Figure 1, the elements of a are thought of as the points within the

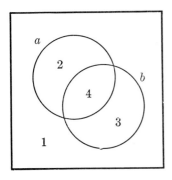

Figure 1

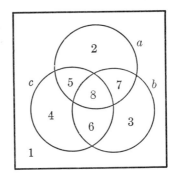

Figure 2

circle a; similarly, the elements of b are represented by the points in the circle b. Then ab is represented by the intersection of these circles, that is, by the region marked 4 in the figure. Evidently, $a + b$ is represented by the points in region 2 together with those in region 3. Region 1 represents those points of A which are in neither a nor b.

  The commutative laws of addition and multiplication are obvious, as is also the associative law of multiplication. Let us consider the associative law of addition, and let a, b, and c be arbitrary elements of R. In Figure 2, $a + b$ is represented by regions 2, 3, 5, and 6. Since c is made up of regions 4, 5, 6, and 8, it follows that $(a + b) + c$ is represented by regions 2, 3, 4, and 8. This pictorial representation suggests that $(a + b) + c$ consists of those elements of A which are in exactly one of the subsets a, b, and c; together with those which are in all three. This fact can be proved in a logical way without the use of diagrams, but the diagrams aid in suggesting the logical steps involved. To complete the proof of the associative law of addition, we need to characterize the set $a + (b + c)$. We omit the details, but it is not difficult to verify that we again get the set represented by regions 2, 3, 4, and 8. Hence, $(a + b) + c = a + (b + c)$, as we wished to show.

If we denote the empty set by "0", it follows that $a + 0 = a$, and the empty set is the zero of the ring R. Moreover, the subset of A consisting of A itself is the unity of the ring (why?). If $a \in R$. it is interesting to observe that $a + a = 0$, and thus a is its own additive inverse. Another unusual property of this ring is that $a \cdot a = a$ for every element a of R. We shall refer to this ring as the *ring of all subsets of the set A*.

EXERCISES

1. Which of the following are rings with respect to the usual definitions of addition and multiplication? In this exercise, the ring of all even integers is denoted by E.

   (a) The set of all positive integers.

   (b) The set of all integers (positive, negative, and zero) that are divisible by 3.

   (c) The set of all real numbers of the form $x + y\sqrt{2}$, where $x, y \in E$.

   (d) The set of all real numbers of the form $x + y\sqrt{5}$, where $x, y \in I$.

   (e) The set of all real numbers of the form $x + y\sqrt{2}$, where x and y are rational numbers.

   (f) The set of all real numbers of the form $x + y\sqrt[3]{2}$, where $x, y \in I$.

   (g) The set of all real numbers of the form $x + y\sqrt[3]{2} + z\sqrt[3]{4}$, where $x, y, z \in I$.

   (h) The set of all real numbers of the form $x + y\sqrt{2}$, where $x \in E$ and $y \in I$.

   (i) The set of all real numbers of the form $x + y\sqrt{2}$, where $x \in I$ and $y \in E$.

(*j*) The set of all real numbers of the form $x + y\sqrt{3}$, where $x \in E$ and $y \in I$.

(*k*) The set of all rational numbers that can be expressed in the form m/n where $m \in I$ and n is a positive odd integer.

2. What is the additive inverse of each element of the ring R of Example 3?

3. Verify that the subset $S = \{u, w\}$ of the ring R of Example 3 is a subring of R. Show that, except for the notation employed, this is the ring of Example 5.

4. For the ring R of Example 3, use the tables to verify each of the following:

$$(u + v) + w = u + (v + w),$$
$$(v + w) + x = v + (w + x),$$
$$w(v + x) = wv + wx,$$
$$(w + v)x = wx + vx,$$
$$(xv)w = x(vw).$$

5. For the ring L of Example 8, verify the other distributive law and the associative law of multiplication.

6. For the ring W of Example 9, verify the associative law of multiplication and the distributive laws. What is the zero of this ring? Verify that

$$\begin{bmatrix} 1 & 0 \\ 0 & 1 \end{bmatrix}$$

is a unity of W. Give examples to show that W is a noncommutative ring.

7. For the ring R of Example 10, complete the proof of the associative law of addition.

8. For the ring R of Example 10, verify that if a, b, $c \in R$, then $a(b + c) = ab + ac$. How do you know without further calculation that the other distributive law must also hold?

9. It can be shown that the set $\{a, b, c, d\}$ is a ring if addition and multiplication are defined by the following tables.

(+)	*a*	*b*	*c*	*d*
a	*a*	*b*	*c*	*d*
b	*b*	*c*	*d*	*a*
c	*c*	*d*	*a*	*b*
d	*d*	*a*	*b*	*c*

(·)	*a*	*b*	*c*	*d*
a	*a*	*a*	*a*	*a*
b	*a*	*c*	*a*	*c*
c	*a*	*a*	*a*	*a*
d	*a*	*c*	*a*	*c*

Is this a commutative ring? Does it have a unity? What is the zero of this ring? What is the additive inverse of each element of this ring?

10. Show that neither of the following can possibly be the addition table for a ring consisting of the set $\{a, b, c, d\}$ of four elements.

(+)	a	b	c	d
a	a	b	c	a
b	b	c	d	a
c	c	d	a	b
d	a	a	b	c

(+)	a	b	c	d
a	a	b	c	d
b	b	c	a	d
c	c	a	d	b
d	b	c	d	a

11. Define addition of integers in the usual way, but define the "product" of any two integers to be zero. Is the set of all integers a ring with respect to addition and this new "multiplication"?

12. If a and b are integers, let us define $a \oplus b$ to be ab, and $a \odot b$ to be $a + b$. Is the set of all integers a ring with respect to the operations "$\oplus$" of "addition" and "$\odot$" of "multiplication"?

13. A set $A = \{x\}$ with one element has just two subsets, and so the ring of all subsets of A, as defined in Example 10, is a ring with two elements. Make addition and multiplication tables for this ring, and compare it with the ring of Example 5.

14. Make addition and multiplication tables for the ring of all subsets of the set $A = \{x, y\}$ having two elements. Verify that by a proper choice of notation, this ring is the ring of Example 3.

15. The following is an addition table and part of a multiplication table for a ring of four elements. Make use of the distributive laws to fill in the rest of the multiplication table.

(+)	a	b	c	d
a	a	b	c	d
b	b	a	d	c
c	c	d	a	b
d	d	c	b	a

(·)	a	b	c	d
a	a	a	a	a
b	a	—	—	a
c	a	—	c	—
d	a	b	c	—

Is this ring a commutative ring? Does it have a unity?

16. If a and b are any integers let us give the following new definitions of "addition" and "multiplication," indicated respectively by "$\oplus$" and "$\odot$":

$$a \oplus b = a + b - 1, \qquad a \odot b = a + b - ab.$$

Verify that with respect to these definitions of "addition" and "multiplication," the set of all integers is a commutative ring with unity. What is the zero of this ring?

2.4 SOME PROPERTIES OF ADDITION

So far we have given the definition of a ring and have presented a number of examples of rings of many different kinds. It should by now be clear that when we think of an arbitrary ring we should not necessarily think of one of our familiar number systems. Accordingly, we cannot consider any properties of a ring as being obvious, except those actually used in the definition. In this section and the next we shall give proofs of a number of properties of any ring. In the present section, we consider only properties of addition, and hence will use in our proofs only the properties P_1–P_4.

First, let us prove the following result.

2.2 Theorem. *The zero of a ring R, whose existence is asserted by P_3, is unique.* ~~assume not, let $a = o$, RAA~~

By this statement, we mean the following. If $0, 0' \in R$ such that for every element a of R,

$$(1) \qquad a + 0 = a,$$

and also

$$(2) \qquad a + 0' = a,$$

then $0 = 0'$. The proof is as follows. Since Equation (1) is true for every element a of R, we may replace a in this equation by $0'$. Hence, we have that

$$(3) \qquad 0' + 0 = 0'.$$

In like manner, it follows from Equation (2) that

$$(4) \qquad 0 + 0' = 0.$$

Since, by the commutative law of addition, $0' + 0 = 0 + 0'$, it follows from Equations (3) and (4) that $0 = 0'$, and the proof is completed.

In view of this result, we are justified in speaking of *the* zero of a ring. An element which is not the zero may naturally be called a *nonzero* element.

We next prove the following theorem.

2.3 Theorem. (Cancellation Laws of Addition) *If a, b, and c are elements of a ring R, the following are true:*

(i) $\qquad$ *If $a + c = b + c$, then $a = b$,*

(ii) $\qquad$ *If $c + a = c + b$, then $a = b$.*

add. inverse of c.

We proceed to prove the first statement of this theorem. Let us therefore assume that

(5) $\qquad$ $a + c = b + c.$

By P_4, there exists an element t of R such that

(6) $\qquad$ $c + t = 0.$

Now it follows from Equation (5) that

(7) $\qquad$ $(a + c) + t = (b + c) + t.$

But

$$(a + c) + t = a + (c + t) \qquad \text{(assoc. law)},$$
$$= a + 0 \qquad \text{(Equation (6))},$$
$$= a \qquad \text{(definition of 0)}.$$

Similarly,

$$(b + c) + t = b + (c + t)$$
$$= b + 0 = b.$$

From these calculations, and Equation (7), we see that $a = b$, as we wished to show.

In view of the commutative law of addition, part (ii) of the theorem follows at once from part (i), and we therefore omit the proof.

The next result follows almost immediately.

2.4 Corollary. *The additive inverse of an element a of a ring R, whose existence is asserted by Property P_4, is unique.*

To prove this statement, suppose that $a + x = 0$ and that $a + y = 0$. Then $a + x = a + y$, and one of the cancellation laws of addition shows at once that $x = y$.

Since each element a of R has exactly one additive inverse, we shall find it convenient to denote this additive inverse by $-a$, and shall also often write $b + (-a)$ in the form $b - a$. It may be helpful to have in mind a verbal definition of $-a$ as follows, "$-a$ is the element of R which when added to a gives 0." That is, if $a + x = 0$ (or, equally well, $x + a = 0$), it follows that $x = -a$.

Since $a + (-a) = 0$, we see also that a is the additive inverse of $-a$, that is, that $-(-a) = a$. We have thus established the first of the following, where a, b, and c are arbitrary elements of a ring:

2.5

(i) $\qquad -(-a) = a,$

(ii) $\qquad -(a+b) = -a-b,$

(iii) $\qquad -(a-b) = -a+b,$

(iv) $\qquad (a-b)-c = a-(b+c).$

$\left.\begin{array}{c}\\\\\\\\\end{array}\right\}$ *prove by copying reasoning*

Let us next prove the second of these statements. Now $-(a+b)$ is, by definition, the additive inverse of $a+b$, and we proceed to verify as follows that also $-a-b$ is the additive inverse of $a+b$:

$$
\begin{aligned}
(a+b)+(-a-b) &= (a+b)+((-a)+(-b)) && \textit{(notation),}\\
&= [(a+b)+(-a)]+(-b) && \textit{(assoc. law),}\\
&= [a+(b+(-a))]+(-b) && \textit{(assoc. law),}\\
&= [a+(-a+b)]+(-b) && \textit{(comm. law),}\\
&= [(a+(-a))+b]+(-b) && \textit{(assoc. law),}\\
&= (0+b)+(-b) && \textit{(def. of } -a\textit{),}\\
&= b+(-b) && \textit{(def. of 0),}\\
&= 0 && \textit{(def. of } -b\textit{).}
\end{aligned}
$$

We therefore see that both $-(a+b)$ and $-a-b$ are additive inverses of $a+b$. Hence, the uniqueness of the additive inverse implies that

$$-(a+b) = -a-b,$$

and the proof is completed. The proofs of the other two parts of 2.5 will be given as exercises in the next list of exercises.

The final theorem of this section is the following.

2.6 Theorem. *If a and b are elements of a ring R, the equation $a+x = b$ has in R the unique solution $x = b-a$.*

It is easy to verify that $x = b-a$ *is* a solution. For

$$
\begin{aligned}
a+(b-a) &= a+(-a+b) && \textit{(comm. law),}\\
&= (a+(-a))+b && \textit{(assoc. law),}\\
&= 0+b = b.
\end{aligned}
$$

The *uniqueness* of the solution follows from one of the cancellation laws. For if we have $a+x = b$ and $a+y = b$, then $a+x = a+y$, and this implies that $x = y$.

2.5 SOME OTHER PROPERTIES OF A RING

In this section we shall establish some properties of a ring that involve multiplication only, and some that involve both addition and multiplication.

First, we prove the following result.

2.7 Theorem. *If a ring R has a unity, it is unique.*

The proof is much like the proof of the uniqueness of the zero. Suppose that $e, e' \in R$ such that for every element a of R,

(1) $$ea = ae = a,$$

and also

(2) $$e'a = ae' = a.$$

In particular, Equation (1) must hold for $a = e'$, that is, we must have

(3) $$ee' = e'e = e'.$$

Similarly, by setting $a = e$ in Equation (2), we obtain

(4) $$e'e = ee' = e.$$

Equations (3) and (4) then imply that $e = e'$, and there is only one unity. If a ring has a unity, we may therefore properly speak of *the* unity of a ring.

We next make the following definition.

2.8 Definition. Let a be an element of a ring R with unity e. If there exists an element s of R such that

$$as = sa = e,$$

then s is called a *multiplicative inverse* of a.

One of the defining properties of a ring states that every element has an additive inverse. However, simple examples show that the situation may be quite different for multiplicative inverses. In the ring of all real numbers it is true that every nonzero element has a multiplicative inverse. In the ring I of all integers there are exactly two elements that have multiplicative inverses, namely, 1 and -1. In the ring of all subsets of a given set A (Example 10), the only element that has a multiplicative inverse is the unity e of the ring; that is, the subset consisting of the entire set A. For if a and b are elements of this ring, ab (which we defined to be $a \cap b$) is a proper subset of A if either a or b is a proper subset of A. Hence, $ab = e$ only if $a = e$ and $b = e$.

In view of these examples, it is clear that we must never take it for granted that an element of a ring necessarily has a multiplicative inverse. However, the following result is easy to establish.

2.9 Theorem. *If an element a of a ring R with unity e has a multiplicative inverse, it is unique.*

Suppose that both s and t are multiplicative inverses of the element a. Then, using the fact that $sa = e$ and the associative law of multiplication, we see that

$$s(at) = (sa)t = et = t.$$

But since $at = e$, it is also true that

$$s(at) = se = s,$$

and it follows that $s = t$.

In case a has a multiplicative inverse, it is customary to designate this multiplicative inverse by "a^{-1}". However, we shall not make much use of this notation until Chapter 5.

It will be recalled that the zero of a ring has been defined in terms of addition only. However, we shall now prove the following theorem, which has a familiar form.

2.10 Theorem. *For each element a of a ring R, we have*

$$a \cdot 0 = 0 \cdot a = 0.$$

Since $a + 0 = a$, it follows that

$$a(a + 0) = a \cdot a.$$

But, by one of the distributive laws,

$$a(a + 0) = a \cdot a + a \cdot 0.$$

Hence,

$$a \cdot a + a \cdot 0 = a \cdot a.$$

Now we know that $a \cdot a + 0 = a \cdot a$ and, by Theorem 2.6, we conclude that $a \cdot 0 = 0$.

In case R is a commutative ring, it follows from what we have just proved that also $0 \cdot a = 0$. If R is not commutative, a proof that $0 \cdot a = 0$ can easily be given using the other one of the distributive laws. This proof will be left as an exercise.

The following can now be verified in turn for arbitrary elements a, b, and c of a ring:

(i) $\qquad\qquad\qquad a(-b) = -(ab),$

(ii) $\qquad\qquad\qquad (-a)b = -(ab),$

2.11 (iii) $\qquad\qquad\qquad (-a)(-b) = ab,$

(iv) $\qquad\qquad\qquad a(b - c) = ab - (ac),$

(v) $\qquad\qquad\qquad (b - c)a = ba - (ca).$

The proof of (i) goes as follows. We have

$$a(b + (-b)) = a \cdot 0 = 0.$$

However, by one of the distributive laws, we know that

$$a(b + (-b)) = ab + a(-b).$$

Hence,

$$ab + a(-b) = 0.$$

But since ab has a unique additive inverse $-(ab)$, it follows that $a(-b) = -(ab)$. The proofs of the other parts of 2.11 will be left as exercises.

In view of 2.11 (i) and (ii), we see that

$$-(ab) = (-a)b = a(-b).$$

Accordingly, in later sections we shall usually write simply $-ab$ for any one of these equal expressions.

We have several times used the concept of a *subring* of a given ring. The following theorem, whose proof will be left as an exercise for the reader, gives a way to determine whether a set of elements of a ring is actually a subring.

2.12   Theorem.   *Let R be a ring and S a nonempty subset of the set R. Then S is a subring of R if and only if the following conditions hold:*

(i)   *S is closed under the operations of addition and multiplication defined on R,*

(ii)   *If $a \in S$, then $-a \in S$.*

——————————————————— **E X E R C I S E S**

1.   Prove 2.5 (iii) and (iv).

2.   If a and b are elements of the ring of all subsets of a given set (Example 10), show that (i) $a = -a$, and (ii) the equation $a + x = b$ has the solution $x = a + b$.

3.   Complete the proof of Theorem 2.10 by showing that $0 \cdot a = 0$ for every element a of any ring.

4.   Prove 2.11 (ii)–(v).

5.   If a, b, c, and d are elements of a ring, prove each of the following:

(*i*) $(a + b)(c + d) = (ac + ad) + (bc + bd)$,

(*ii*) $(a + b)(c + d) = (ac + bc) + (ad + bd)$,

(*iii*) $(a - b)(c - d) = (ac + bd) - (bc + ad)$,

(*iv*) $(a + b)(c - d) = (ac + bc) - (ad + bd)$,

(*v*) $(a - b)(c + d) = (ac + ad) - (bc + bd)$,

(*vi*) $(a(-b))(-c) = a(bc)$.

6. Verify that every nonzero element of the ring of Example 7 has a multiplicative inverse.

7. Show that an element (a, b, c) of the ring L of Example 8 has a multiplicative inverse if and only if $a = \pm 1$ and $c = \pm 1$.

8. (i) Find the multiplicative inverse of the element

$$\begin{bmatrix} 2 & 5 \\ 1 & 3 \end{bmatrix}$$

of the ring W of Example 9.
(ii) Show that the element

$$\begin{bmatrix} 1 & 2 \\ 0 & 3 \end{bmatrix}$$

of the same ring W does not have a multiplicative inverse in W.

9. Let R be a ring with unity. If a and b are elements of R that have multiplicative inverses, show that ab has a multiplicative inverse by verifying that $(ab)^{-1} = b^{-1}a^{-1}$.

10. Prove Theorem 2.12.

11. Show that the set of all elements of the ring W of Example 9 of the form

$$\begin{bmatrix} x & 0 \\ y & z \end{bmatrix},$$

where $x, y, z \in I$ is a subring of the ring W.

12. If S and T are subrings of a ring R, show that $S \cap T$ is a subring of R.

13. (i) Give the addition table and multiplication table for a ring with exactly one element.
(ii) If a ring R has more than one element and has a unity e, show that $e \neq 0$.

2.6 GENERAL SUMS AND PRODUCTS

The operations of addition and multiplication are *binary* operations, that is, they apply to *two* elements only. Let us now consider how we can give a meaning to sums or products of three or more elements of a ring.

If a_1, a_2, and a_3 are elements of a ring, let us define $a_1 + a_2 + a_3$ as follows:

2.13 $$a_1 + a_2 + a_3 = (a_1 + a_2) + a_3.$$

However, by the associative law of addition, it then follows that

2.14 $$a_1 + a_2 + a_3 = a_1 + (a_2 + a_3),$$

and therefore a sum of three elements is independent of the way parentheses might be introduced to indicate the manner of association of the elements.

Now that we have defined a sum of three elements of a ring, let us define a sum of four elements as follows:

2.15 $$a_1 + a_2 + a_3 + a_4 = (a_1 + a_2 + a_3) + a_4.$$

The associative law of addition then shows that

2.16 $$a_1 + a_2 + a_3 + a_4 = (a_1 + a_2) + (a_3 + a_4),$$

and also that

2.17 $$a_1 + a_2 + a_3 + a_4 = a_1 + (a_2 + a_3 + a_4).$$

These calculations verify that the sum of four elements is also independent of the way in which the elements may be associated.

It seems fairly clear that similar statements hold for sums of more than four elements. A general proof can be given by the method of mathematical induction. This method of proof will be discussed in the next chapter, at which time we shall return to a further consideration of the material of this section. Although we shall not now give a proof, we proceed to formulate a statement which generalizes what we have said above about sums of three or four elements, as well as some similar statements also involving products.

We have in 2.13 and 2.15 defined the sum of three or four elements of a ring. In general, if k is a positive integer such that

$$a_1 + a_2 + \cdots + a_k$$

has been defined, we define

2.18 $$a_1 + a_2 + \cdots + a_k + a_{k+1} = (a_1 + a_2 + \cdots + a_k) + a_{k+1}.$$

It should then appear that this gives us a definition of the sum of any number n of elements of a ring. Such a definition is called a *recursive* definition, and definitions of this kind will be considered more carefully in the next chapter.

We shall not write out the details, but in precisely the same way it is possible to give a recursive definition of a product of any number n of elements of a ring.

We now state the following theorem, which generalizes several of the properties used in the definition of a ring.

2.19 Theorem. *Let n be an arbitrary positive integer, and let $a_1, a_2, \cdots, a_n$ be elements of a ring R.*

(i) Generalized associative laws. *For each positive integer r such that $1 \leq r < n$, we have*

2.20 $$(a_1 + a_2 + \cdots + a_r) + (a_{r+1} + \cdots + a_n) = a_1 + a_2 + \cdots + a_n,$$

and

2.21 $$(a_1 a_2 \cdots a_r)(a_{r+1} \cdots a_n) = a_1 a_2 \cdots a_n.$$

(ii) Generalized distributive laws. *If $b \in R$, we have*

2.22 $$b(a_1 + a_2 + \cdots + a_n) = ba_1 + ba_2 + \cdots + ba_n,$$

and

2.23 $$(a_1 + a_2 + \cdots + a_n)b = a_1 b + a_2 b + \cdots + a_n b.$$

(iii) Generalized commutative laws. *If $i_1, i_2, \cdots, i_n$ are the integers $1, 2, \cdots, n$ in any order, then*

2.24 $$a_{i_1} + a_{i_2} + \cdots + a_{i_n} = a_1 + a_2 + \cdots + a_n.$$

In case R is a commutative ring, we have also

2.25 $$a_{i_1} a_{i_2} \cdots a_{i_n} = a_1 a_2 \cdots a_n.$$

It will be observed that if $n = 3$ in 2.20, then necessarily $r = 1$ or $r = 2$ and the truth of 2.20 in these cases is asserted by 2.14 and 2.13. Similarly, if $n = 4$, it follows that $r = 1, 2,$ or 3. These three cases of 2.20 have been verified in 2.17, 2.16, and 2.15.

Let us explain the notation used in the generalized commutative laws. As an example, let $n = 3$, and let $i_1 = 3$, $i_2 = 1$, $i_3 = 2$. Then 2.24 states that

$$a_3 + a_1 + a_2 = a_1 + a_2 + a_3.$$

This special case can readily be verified as follows:

$$
\begin{aligned}
a_3 + a_1 + a_2 &= (a_3 + a_1) + a_2 && (def.), \\
&= a_3 + (a_1 + a_2) && (assoc.\ law), \\
&= (a_1 + a_2) + a_3 && (comm.\ law), \\
&= a_1 + a_2 + a_3 && (def.).
\end{aligned}
$$

As stated above, a general proof of any part of the above theorem requires the use of mathematical induction, and this method of proof will be discussed later. However, the theorem should seem fairly obvious; for the time being we shall merely assume it without proof. In particular, Theorem 2.19 (i) assures us that we can introduce parentheses in a sum or product to indicate association in any way we wish without changing the value of the respective sum or product. Accordingly, we shall henceforth usually omit such parentheses entirely. Some special cases of the theorem will be assigned as exercises at the end of this section.

We next observe that positive integral exponents may be defined in any ring R in the usual way. If a is an arbitrary element of R, we may define $a^1 = a$, $a^2 = a \cdot a$, and, in general, if k is a positive integer such that a^k has been defined, we define $a^{k+1} = a^k \cdot a$. The following familiar laws of exponents now hold, where m and n are arbitrary positive integers:

2.26
(i) $$a^m \cdot a^n = a^{m+n},$$
(ii) $$(a^m)^n = a^{mn}.$$

Suppose, now, that a, $b \in R$. Then $(ab)^2 = (ab)(ab)$, and if $ba \neq ab$, $(ab)^2$ may not be equal to $a^2 b^2$. However, if $ba = ab$, it does follow that $(ab)^2 = a(ba)b = a(ab)b = a^2 b^2$. In general, it is not difficult to show that if R is a *commutative* ring and m is any positive integer, then

2.27
$$(ab)^m = a^m \cdot b^m.$$

We may remark that *negative* integral exponents can be defined if we restrict attention to elements which have multiplicative inverses. However, we shall postpone any consideration of negative exponents until a later chapter.

We now introduce a convenient notation for *multiples* that parallels the exponent notation for *powers*. If $a \in R$, let us define $1a = a$, $2a = a + a$, and, in general, if k is a positive integer such that ka has been defined, we define $(k+1)a = ka + a$. If 0 is the zero integer, we define $0a$ to be the zero element of R. Actually, there will be no confusion if the same symbol is used to designate the zero integer and the zero of the ring. Since every element of a ring has an additive inverse, we can easily introduce negative multiples as well as positive multiples. If m is a positive integer, we define $(-m)a$ to be $m(-a)$. Then $(-m)a$ is also seen to be equal to $-(ma)$. Thus, for example,

$$(-2)a = 2(-a) = -a - a = -(a + a) = -(2a).$$

The reader may easily convince himself of the truth of the following, it being understood that m and n are any integers (positive, negative, or zero) and that a and b are arbitrary elements of any ring R:

(i) $\qquad ma + na = (m + n)a,$

(ii) $\qquad m(na) = (mn)a,$

(iii) $\qquad m(a + b) = ma + mb,$

(iv) $\qquad m(ab) = (ma)b = a(mb),$

(v) $\qquad (ma)(nb) = (mn)(ab).$

It should perhaps be emphasized that ma is a convenient way of indicating a certain sum of elements of R. However, since the integer m is not necessarily itself an element of R, it is not correct to think of ma as the product of two elements of R. Hence, for example, 2.28 (iii) is not necessarily a consequence of one of the distributive laws.

Again, complete proofs of 2.26, 2.27, and 2.28 require the use of mathematical induction.

_____ E X E R C I S E S

1. Verify the truth of 2.20 for the case in which $n = 5$, and therefore $r = 1, 2, 3,$ or 4.

2. Verify 2.22 for the case in which $n = 3$.

3. Verify 2.24 for the case in which $n = 4, i_1 = 3, i_2 = 1, i_3 = 4, i_4 = 2.$

4. If R is a commutative ring, verify 2.27 for the case in which $m = 3$.

5. If a is any element of the ring of Example 3, verify that $2a = 0$. (The zero of the ring is u.)

6. In the ring W of Example 9, let

$$A = \begin{bmatrix} 1 & 2 \\ 0 & 0 \end{bmatrix},$$

and

$$B = \begin{bmatrix} 0 & 1 \\ 0 & 1 \end{bmatrix}.$$

Verify that $(AB)^2 \neq A^2B^2$.

7. If x and y are any elements of the ring K of Example 6, verify that $(xy)^2 = x^2y^2$, even though this is not a commutative ring.

8. Show that, by a suitable change of notation, 2.26 (i) can be considered to be a special case of 2.21.

9. Show that, by a suitable change of notation, 2.28 (i) can be considered to be a special case of 2.20.

10. Show that, by a suitable change of notation, 2.28 (iv) can be obtained from 2.22 and 2.23.

11. A ring R is called a *Boolean ring* if $a^2 = a$ for every element a of R. If R is a Boolean ring and $a \in R$, prove that $2a = 0$. Then prove that R is necessarily a commutative ring. [Hint: Consider $(a+b)^2$.]

2.7 ISOMORPHISMS

There is just one additional concept which we wish to introduce in this chapter. Let us first give a simple illustration by considering two particular rings of four elements. Let $K = \{a,\, b,\, c,\, d\}$ be the ring of Example 6 with addition and multiplication tables, which we here repeat for convenience.

(+)	a	b	c	d		($\cdot$)	a	b	c	d
a	a	b	c	d		a	a	a	a	a
b	b	a	d	c		b	a	b	c	d
c	c	d	a	b		c	a	a	a	a
d	d	c	b	a		d	a	b	c	d

Now let L be the ring consisting of the set $\{i,\, j,\, k,\, l\}$ with addition and multiplication defined by the following tables.

(+)	i	j	k	l		($\cdot$)	i	j	k	l
i	k	l	i	j		i	i	j	k	l
j	l	k	j	i		j	k	k	k	k
k	i	j	k	l		k	k	k	k	k
l	j	i	l	k		l	i	j	k	l

At first glance, these rings may not seem to be closely related, but it is not difficult to verify that they are identical except for the notation used. If, in the tables for K we replace a by k, b by i, c by j, and d by l, the tables will coincide with the tables for L except for the order in which the elements are written down. We may express this in a way which does not involve explicit mention of the tables. Let us consider the one-one mapping

2.29 $a \to k, \qquad b \to i, \qquad c \to j, \qquad d \to l$

of the set K onto the set L. If x represents any element of K, let us denote by x' the image of x under the mapping 2.29, so that the mapping 2.29 is suggested by writing $x \to x'$. For example, if $x = a$, then $x' = k$, and so on. Now the fact that under the mapping $x \to x'$ the addition and multiplication tables for K are transformed into those for L merely states that if $x, y \in K$, then under the mapping 2.29, $x + y \to x' + y'$

and $xy \rightarrow x'y'$. This fact is sometimes expressed by saying that the operations of addition and multiplication are *preserved* under the mapping 2.29.

The remarks just made show that the mapping 2.29 is an isomorphism of K onto L according to the following general definition.

2.30 Definition. A one-one mapping $x \rightarrow x'$ of a ring R onto a ring S is called an *isomorphism* of R onto S if the operations of addition and multiplication are preserved under this mapping, that is, if for arbitrary elements a, b of R, the following hold:

2.31
$$a + b \rightarrow a' + b', \qquad ab \rightarrow a'b'.$$

If there exists an isomorphism of R onto S, we also say that R is *isomorphic to S*.

It may be observed that there is an alternate way of writing relations 2.31. For, under the notation being used, the image of $a + b$ is $(a + b)'$, and similarly the image of ab is $(ab)'$. Hence, 2.31 may be written in the form:

2.32
$$(a + b)' = a' + b', \qquad (ab)' = a'b'.$$

If the mapping $x \rightarrow x'$ is an isomorphism of R onto S, then $x' \rightarrow x$ defines a one-one mapping of S onto R, which is also an isomorphism of S onto R. Accordingly, if R is isomorphic to S, then also S is isomorphic to R, and we shall sometimes say that R and S are *isomorphic rings*.

It should be clear that two rings that are isomorphic differ only in the notation used to indicate the elements of the rings. Accordingly, isomorphic rings are sometimes said to be *abstractly identical*. The following theorem should now seem fairly obvious.

2.33 Theorem. *If $x \rightarrow x'$ defines an isomorphism of the ring R onto the ring S, the following are true:*

    (i)   *If 0 is the zero of R and $0 \rightarrow 0'$, then $0'$ is the zero of S,*
    (ii)   *If $a \in R$, then $-a \rightarrow -a'$,*
    (iii) *If R has a unity e and $e \rightarrow e'$, then S has e' as unity,*
    (iv) *R is a commutative ring if and only if S is a commutative ring.*

Let us give a formal proof of part (i). If b' is any element of S, there exists one (and only one) element b of R such that $b \rightarrow b'$. Now, by 2.31, we have $b + 0 \rightarrow b' + 0'$. But $b + 0 = b$, and hence also $b + 0 \rightarrow b'$. It follows that $b' + 0' = b'$ for every element b' of S, and hence that $0'$ is the zero of S. Actually, in view of Theorem 2.6, we would have had to prove only that $b' + 0' = b'$ for some *one* element b' of S.

The other parts of this theorem will be left as exercises.

1. Prove Theorem 2.33 (ii), (iii), (iv).

2. In the ring K of Example 6 (used in the illustration at the beginning of this section) show that $\{a, b\}$ is a subring which is isomorphic to the ring of Example 5.

3. Does the ring of Exercise 9 of Section 2.3 have a subring isomorphic to the ring of Example 5?

4. It was shown in a previous exercise that the set P of all elements of the ring W of Example 9 of the form

$$\begin{bmatrix} x & 0 \\ y & z \end{bmatrix},$$

where $x, y, z \in I$, is a subring of the ring W. Verify that the mapping

$$\begin{bmatrix} x & 0 \\ y & z \end{bmatrix} \to (x, y, z)$$

of P onto the ring L of Example 8 is an isomorphism of P onto L.

5. Show that the set of all elements of the ring L of Example 8 of the form $(x, 0, x)$, where $x \in I$, is a subring of L that is isomorphic to the ring I of integers.

6. Let R and S be given rings, and let T be the product set $R \times S$, that is, T is the set of all ordered pairs (r, s), $r \in R$, $s \in S$. Verify that T is a ring if we define:

$$(r_1, s_1) + (r_2, s_2) = (r_1 + r_2, s_1 + s_2)$$

and

$$(r_1, s_1)(r_2, s_2) = (r_1 r_2, s_1 s_2).$$

What is the zero of T? Under what conditions will T have a unity? Show that T has a subring isomorphic to R and a subring isomorphic to S.

3

Integral Domains

The properties which we used to define a ring were suggested by simple properties of the integers. However, since we have had numerous examples of commutative rings with unity that bear little resemblance to the ring of integers, it is clear that the system of integers must have some other properties in addition to those which make it a commutative ring with unity. Accordingly, in order to specify in some sense *all* the properties of the ring of integers, we need to consider some properties not mentioned in the previous chapter. In the present chapter we proceed to restrict the rings studied and, eventually, shall have enough properties listed that, in a sense to be described precisely later on, the *only* system which has all these properties is the ring of integers. We may then say that we have obtained a characterization of the ring of integers.

One of the properties that we shall require in characterizing the ring of integers is a property which leads in a natural way to the method of proof by mathematical induction. Accordingly, we shall introduce this important method of proof and use it to establish a few of the results that were stated without proof in Section 2.6.

We shall conclude the chapter with a few remarks about an alternate method of approaching the study of the integers in which all the familiar properties are derived from a few simple properties of the *positive* integers only.

3.1 DEFINITION OF INTEGRAL DOMAIN

We have proved that if 0 is the zero of a ring R, then $a \cdot 0 = 0 \cdot a = 0$ for every element a of R. Of course, this is a familiar property of our elementary number systems. However, in some of the rings previously mentioned there exist elements c and d, both of which are different from zero, such that $cd = 0$. For example, in the ring of Example 3 of the preceding chapter we have $wx = u$, where u is the zero. As another example, consider the ring of all subsets of a given set (Example 10). The empty set is the zero of this ring and, by the definition of multiplication in this ring, if c and d are subsets whose intersection is the empty set, then $cd = 0$. As a first step in the program of this chapter we wish to rule out rings of this type. Moreover, we shall restrict attention to commutative rings with unity. Accordingly, it will be convenient to make the following definition.

3.1 Definition. A commutative ring D with more than one element and having a unity is called an *integral domain* if it has the following additional property:

P_9: If $r, s \in D$ such that $rs = 0$, then $r = 0$ or $s = 0$.

The requirement that an integral domain must have more than one element is merely to assure us that it has at least one nonzero element.

The reader may now verify that, in addition to the rings of Examples 3 and 10 mentioned above, the rings of Examples 4 and 6 of the preceding chapter are not integral domains because Property P_9 does not hold. On the other hand, the rings of Examples 1, 2, 5, and 7 are integral domains. Other, more familiar, examples of integral domains are the ring of integers, the ring of rational numbers, the ring of real numbers, and the ring of complex numbers.

The following theorem will suggest an alternate way of characterizing an integral domain.

3.2 Theorem. *Property P_9 holds in an arbitrary ring R if and only if R has the following property:*

P_9': *If $a, b, c \in R$ such that $ac = bc$ and $c \neq 0$, then $a = b$*
$$(cancellation\ law\ of\ multiplication).$$

Suppose, first, that R has Property P_9, and that $ac = bc$ with $c \neq 0$. We thus have that $ac - bc = 0$ and, by 2.11(v), it follows that $(a - b)c = 0$. Since $c \neq 0$, Property P_9 implies that $a - b = 0$; that is, that $a = b$. We have therefore shown that Property P_9' holds. On the other hand, let us now assume that Property P_9' holds in the ring R, and suppose that r, $s \in R$ such that $rs = 0$. Since $0s = 0$, we then have that $rs = 0s$. If $s \neq 0$, Property P'_9 shows that we must have $r = 0$. Hence $r = 0$ or $s = 0$, and therefore Property P_9 holds in R.

In view of this theorem, Property P'_9 could be used in place of P_9 in the definition of an integral domain. In particular, the cancellation law of multiplication always holds in an integral domain.

3.2 ORDERED INTEGRAL DOMAINS

One important property of the integers that has not been mentioned so far is that they can be *ordered*. If we think of the integers as being exhibited in the following way

$$\cdots, -4, -3, -2, -1, 0, 1, 2, 3, 4, \cdots,$$

and a and b are integers, we say that "a is greater than b" if a occurs to the right of b in the above scheme. It is clear that "a is greater than b" means merely that $a - b$ is a positive integer. This observation suggests that the concept of "order" can be defined in terms of the concept of "positive." We therefore make the following definition.

3.3 Definition. An integral domain D is said to be an *ordered integral domain* if D contains a subset D_p with the following properties:

(i)   If $a, b \in D_p$, then $a + b \in D_p$ (*closed under addition*),

(ii) If $a, b \in D_p$, then $ab \in D_p$ (*closed under multiplication*),

(iii) For each element a of D exactly *one* of the following holds:
$$a = 0, \quad a \in D_p, \quad -a \in D_p \qquad (\textit{trichotomy law}).$$

The elements of D_p are called the *positive* elements of D. The nonzero elements of D that are not in D_p are called the *negative* elements of D.

Obviously, the set I_p of positive integers has the properties required of D_p in the above definition, and hence I is an ordered integral domain. However, there are other ordered integral domains such as, for example, the integral domain of all rational numbers or the integral domain of all real numbers.

Now let D be any ordered integral domain, and let D_p be the set of positive elements of D, that is, the set having the three properties stated in the preceding definition. If $c, d \in D$, we *define* $c > d$ (or $d < c$) to mean that $c - d \in D_p$. Then it is clear that $a > 0$ means that $a \in D_p$, that is, that a is a positive element of D. Similarly, $a < 0$ means that $-a \in D_p$ or that a is a negative element of D. The three properties of Definition 3.3 can then be restated in the following form:

3.4   (i)   If $a > 0$ and $b > 0$, then $a + b > 0$,
(ii) If $a > 0$ and $b > 0$, then $ab > 0$,
(iii) If $a \in D$, then exactly one of the following holds:
$$a = 0, \quad a > 0, \quad a < 0.$$

It is now not difficult to verify the following additional properties of inequalities:

3.5   (i)   If $a > b$, then $a + c > b + c$ for every $c \in D$,
(ii) If $a > b$ and $c > 0$, then $ac > bc$,
(iii) If $a > b$ and $c < 0$, then $ac < bc$,
(iv) If $a > b$ and $b > c$, then $a > c$,
(v) If $a \neq 0$, then $a^2 > 0$.

The proof of the first of these is as follows. If $a > b$, we have $a - b > 0$. However, $a + c - (b + c) = a - b$ and we see at once that $a + c - (b + c) > 0$, that is, that $a + c > b + c$.

Let us now prove 3.5(v). If $a \neq 0$, then by the form 3.4(iii) of the trichotomy law, either $a > 0$ or $-a > 0$. If $a > 0$, it follows from 3.4(ii) that $a^2 > 0$. If $-a > 0$, the same argument shows that $(-a)^2 > 0$. Since, by 2.11(iii), $(-a)^2 = a^2$, it follows again that $a^2 > 0$. Proofs of the other parts of 3.5 will be left as exercises.

It is obvious that one can define $a \geq b$ (or $b \leq a$) to mean that either $a = b$ or $a > b$, without specifying which. We shall henceforth use this notation whenever convenient to do so. If $a \geq 0$, it is sometimes convenient to say that a is *nonnegative*. By writing $a < b < c$, we shall mean that $a < b$ and that also $b < c$.

In any ordered integral domain it is possible to introduce the concept of absolute value in the usual way as follows.

3.6 Definition.   Let D be any ordered integral domain and $a \in D$. The *absolute value* of a, written as "$| a |$", is defined as follows:

(i)   If $a \geq 0$, then $| a | = a$,
(ii) If $a < 0$, then $| a | = -a$.

From this definition it follows that $| 0 | = 0$ and that if $a \neq 0$, then $| a | > 0$.

_____ **E X E R C I S E S**

The letters a, b, c, and d represent elements of an ordered integral domain.

1. Prove 3.5(ii), (iii), (iv).

2. Show that if $a > b$, then $-a < -b$.

3. Show that if $a > b$ and $c > d$, then $a + c > b + d$.

4. Show that if a, b, c, and d are all positive with $a > b$ and $c > d$, then $ac > bd$.

5. Show that if $a > 0$ and $ab > ac$, then $b > c$.

6. Prove that $|ab| = |a| \cdot |b|$.

7. Show that $-|a| \le a \le |a|$.

8. Prove that $|a + b| \le |a| + |b|$.

9. If e is the unity of an ordered integral domain, prove that we must have $e > 0$. Then show that $me > 0$ for every positive integer m.

10. Use the results of the preceding exercise to show that the rings of Examples 5 and 7 of the preceding chapter are not ordered integral domains.

3.3 A CHARACTERIZATION OF THE RING OF INTEGERS

We need one further condition to characterize the ring of integers among the ordered integral domains. We first make the following general definition.

.7 Definition. A set S of elements of an ordered integral domain is said to be *well-ordered* if each nonempty subset U of S contains a least element, that is, if for each nonempty subset U of S there exists an element a of U such that $a \le x$ for every element x of U.

It is apparent that the set of all positive integers is well-ordered, and we shall presently find that this property is precisely what distinguishes the ring of integers from other ordered integral domains. The rational numbers will be considered in detail later on in this book, but we may observe now that the set of positive rationals is not well-ordered. In fact, the set of all positive rational numbers has no least element. For if r is any positive rational number, then $r/2$ is also a positive rational number and $r/2 < r$. Hence there can be no least positive rational number.

As preparation for the next theorem, we now prove the following result.

.8 Lemma. *Let D be an ordered integral domain such that the set D_p of positive elements of D is well-ordered. If e is the unity of D, then*

$$D_p = \{me; \ m \ a \ positive \ integer\},$$

and

$$D = \{ne; \ n \ an \ arbitrary \ integer\}.$$

We recall that $a \in D_p$ can also be expressed by writing $a > 0$. It is clear that $e > 0$ since $e^2 = e$, and $e^2 > 0$ by 3.5(v). Now since $e > 0$, it follows from 3.3(i) that $2e = e + e > 0$. Then $3e = e + 2e > 0$, and so on. Hence, $me \in D_p$ for every positive integer m.* We now proceed to show that every element of D_p is necessarily of this form.

First, since D_p is well-ordered, D_p itself has a least element. Actually, e is this least element. For suppose that c is the least element of D_p and that $0 < c < e$. It follows by 3.5(ii) that $0 < c^2 < c$, since $ce = c$. Hence $c^2 \in D_p$ and $c^2 < c$. However, this violates the assumption that c is the least element of D_p, and it follows that the least element of D_p is the unity e.

We can now complete the proof that every element of D_p is of the form me for some positive integer m. Suppose that this is false, and let U be the nonempty set of elements of D_p that are not of this form. Then U must have a least element, say d. We have proved that e is the least element of D_p, and hence we must have $d > e$, or $d - e > 0$. Hence, $d - e \in D_p$ and, since $e > 0$, it follows that $d - e < d$ and hence that $d - e \notin U$; therefore $d - e = m_1e$ for some positive integer m_1. It then follows that $d = e + m_1e = (1 + m_1)e$, and $1 + m_1$ is a positive integer. But d, being an element of U, is *not* of this form, and we have a contradiction. It follows that U must be the empty set, that is, that every element of D_p is of the required form.

It is now easy to complete the proof of the lemma. If $a \in D$, and $a \notin D_p$, then 3.3(iii) implies that $a = 0$ or $-a \in D_p$. If $a = 0$, then $a = 0 \cdot e$. If $-a \in D_p$, then by what we have just proved, $-a = m_2e$ for some positive integer m_2. It follows that $a = (-m_2)e$, and so every element of D is of the form ne, where n is an integer (positive, negative, or zero).

We can now easily establish the following theorem, which is the principal result of this section.

3.9 Theorem. *Let both D and D' be ordered integral domains with the property that the set of all positive elements is well-ordered. Then D and D' are isomorphic.*

Suppose that e and e' are the respective unities of D and D'. In view of the lemma, we know that

*A formal proof of this rather obvious statement can be given using only the fact, which we are here assuming, that the ring of integers is itself an ordered integral domain in which the set of positive elements is well-ordered. See Theorem 3.11 at the beginning of the next section.

$$D = \{ne; \ n \text{ an arbitrary integer}\},$$
and
$$D' = \{ne'; \ n \text{ an arbitrary integer}\}.$$

First, let us show that each element of D is *uniquely* expressible in the form ne. Suppose that $n_1 e = n_2 e$ with $n_1 \neq n_2$, and let us seek a contradiction. If the notation is so chosen that $n_1 > n_2$, then $n_1 - n_2$ is a positive integer and $(n_1 - n_2)e = 0$. However, this contradicts the lemma which states that for each positive integer m, $me \in D_p$ and therefore $me > 0$. Of course, each element of D' is also uniquely expressible in the form ne'.

We can now easily establish the theorem by showing that the mapping

3.10 $$ne \rightarrow ne'$$

is an isomorphism of D onto D'. By what we have just proved, this is a one-one mapping of D onto D' since distinct elements of D have distinct images in D'. Moreover, under this mapping we have

$$n_1 e + n_2 e = (n_1 + n_2)e \rightarrow (n_1 + n_2)e' = n_1 e' + n_2 e',$$
and
$$(n_1 e)(n_2 e) = (n_1 n_2)e \rightarrow (n_1 n_2)e' = (n_1 e')(n_2 e').$$

Hence, addition and multiplication are preserved and the mapping 3.10 is therefore an isomorphism. This completes the proof of the theorem.

Another way of stating the theorem is to say that, except for the notation used, there is *only one* ordered integral domain with the property that the set of positive elements is well-ordered. Since the ring of integers is such an integral domain, we thus have a complete characterization of the ring of integers. Although there are other properties of the ring of integers that are just as obvious as the ones previously used, we shall not need to assume any additional properties. Accordingly, when we shall speak of a proof of any property of the ring of integers we shall mean a proof *based on the fact that the ring of integers is an ordered integral domain in which the set of positive elements is well-ordered.* Of course, we shall use the familiar notation for the integers and shall make free use of the fact, established in the proof of the last theorem, that the unity 1 of the ring of integers is the smallest positive integer. In the next chapter we shall proceed to establish a number of properties of the integers. However, we now pause to discuss in some detail the important method of proof called a "proof by mathematical induction."

3.4 MATHEMATICAL INDUCTION

We first establish the following result, which is the basis of proofs by mathematical induction.

3.11 Theorem. *Let K be a set of positive integers with the following two properties:*

(i) $1 \in K$,

(ii) *If k is an arbitrary positive integer such that $k \in K$, then also $k + 1 \in K$.*

Then K consists of the set of all *positive integers.*

To prove this theorem, let us assume that there is a positive integer not in K, and obtain a contradiction. Let U be the set of all positive integers not in K and therefore, by our assumption, U is not empty. Then, by the well-ordering property, U must contain a least element m. Since, by (i), we have $1 \in K$, clearly $m \neq 1$ and it follows that $m > 1$ and therefore $m - 1 > 0$. Moreover, $m - 1 \in K$ since m was chosen to be the least element of U. Now, by (ii) with $k = m - 1$, we see that $m \in K$. But $m \in U$, and we have obtained the desired contradiction. The proof is therefore completed.

The most frequent application of Theorem 3.11 is to a proof of the following kind. Suppose that there is associated with each positive integer n a *statement* (or proposition) S_n, which is either true or false, and suppose we wish to prove that the statement S_n is true for every positive integer n. Let K be the set of all positive integers n such that S_n is a true statement. If we can show that $1 \in K$, and that whenever $k \in K$, then also $k + 1 \in K$, it will follow from Theorem 3.11 that K is the set of all positive integers. Since $n \in K$ merely means that S_n is true, we may reformulate these remarks in the following convenient form.

3.12 Induction Principle. *Suppose that there is associated with each positive integer n a statement S_n. Then S_n is true for every positive integer n provided the following hold:*

(i) S_1 *is true,*

(ii) *If k is an arbitrary positive integer such that S_k is true, then also S_{k+1} is true.*

A proof making use of the Induction Principle (or of Theorem 3.11) is usually called a proof by induction or by mathematical induction.

We may remark that there is another useful form of the Induction Principle in which condition (ii) is replaced by a somewhat different condition. (See Exercise 8 at the end of this section.)

As a first illustration of the language and notation just introduced, we consider a simple example from elementary algebra. If n is a positive integer, let S_n be the statement that

$$2 + 4 + 6 + \cdots + 2n = n(n + 1),$$

it being understood that the left side is the sum of the first n positive even integers. We now prove that S_n is true for every positive integer n, by verifying (i) and (ii) of 3.12. Clearly, S_1 is true since S_1 merely states that $2 = 1 \cdot 2$. Suppose, now, that k is any positive integer such that S_k is true, that is, such that the following is true:

$$2 + 4 + 6 + \cdots + 2k = k(k + 1).$$

Then, by adding the next even integer, $2(k + 1)$, to both sides we obtain

$$2 + 4 + 6 + \cdots + 2k + 2(k + 1) = k(k + 1) + 2(k + 1)$$
$$= (k + 1)(k + 2).$$

However, this calculation shows that S_{k+1} is true, and hence we have verified both (i) and (ii) of 3.12. The Induction Principle then assures us that S_n is true for every positive integer n.

We now consider again part of the material of Section 2.6, and we first illustrate by a simple example how a recursive definition really involves the Induction Principle. The recursive definition of a^n, which was given earlier, may be stated in the following formal way.

13 Definition. If a is an element of a ring R, we define $a^1 = a$. Moreover, if k is a positive integer such that a^k is defined, we define $a^{k+1} = a^k \cdot a$.

Now let S_n be the statement, "a^n is defined by 3.13." The Induction Principle then shows that S_n is true for every positive integer n, that is, that a^n is defined by 3.13 for every positive integer n.

Let us now prove (2.26(i)) that if m and n are arbitrary positive integers, then

14 $$a^m \cdot a^n = a^{m+n}.$$

Let S_n be the statement that for the positive integer n, 3.14 is true for *every* positive integer m. Then, by definition of a^{m+1}, we see that $a^m \cdot a^1 = a^{m+1}$, and hence S_1 is true. Let us now assume that k is a positive integer such that S_k is true, that is, such that

15 $$a^m \cdot a^k = a^{m+k}$$

for every positive integer m. Then

$$
\begin{aligned}
a^m \cdot a^{k+1} &= a^m \cdot a^k \cdot a && \text{(by def. of } a^{k+1}), \\
&= a^{m+k} \cdot a && \text{(by 3.15)}, \\
&= a^{m+k+1} && \text{(by def. of } a^{(m+k)+1}).
\end{aligned}
$$

We have now shown that S_{k+1} is true, and the Induction Principle then assures us that S_n is true for every positive integer n. Thus we have given a formal proof of the very familiar law of exponents stated in 3.14. In the above proof we have tacitly made use of the associative law of multiplication. As a matter of fact, it was pointed out in the preceding chapter that 3.14 is actually a special case of the generalized associative law of multiplication.

As a further illustration of the use of mathematical induction in proving the results stated in Section 2.6, we shall prove the generalized associative law of addition (2.20). For convenience of reference, let us first restate in a slightly different notation the recursive definition (2.18) of a sum of more than two elements of a ring. If l is a positive integer and b_1, b_2, $\cdots$, b_{l+1} are elements of a ring such that

$$b_1 + b_2 + \cdots + b_l$$

is defined, we define

3.16 $$b_1 + b_2 + \cdots + b_{l+1} = (b_1 + b_2 + \cdots + b_l) + b_{l+1}.$$

Now let S_n be the statement that for arbitrary elements a_1, a_2, $\cdots$, a_n of a ring and for each positive integer r such that $1 \leq r < n$, we have

3.17 $$(a_1 + \cdots + a_r) + (a_{r+1} + \cdots + a_n) = a_1 + a_2 + \cdots + a_n.$$

To establish the generalized associative law of addition, we need to prove that S_n is true for every positive integer n. Clearly, S_1 and S_2 are true, and we verified S_3 and S_4 in Section 2.6. We complete the proof by showing that if k is a positive integer such that S_k is true, then also S_{k+1} is true. Otherwise expressed, if S_k is true and r is an integer such that $1 \leq r < k + 1$, we shall show that

3.18 $$(a_1 + \cdots + a_r) + (a_{r+1} + \cdots + a_{k+1}) = a_1 + a_2 + \cdots + a_{k+1}.$$

The case in which $r = k$ is true at once by definition (3.16) of the right side of 3.18. Suppose, then, that $r < k$. As a special case of 3.16, we have

$$a_{r+1} + \cdots + a_{k+1} = (a_{r+1} + \cdots + a_k) + a_{k+1}.$$

This is used in the first step of the following calculation:

$$
\begin{aligned}
(a_1 + \cdots + a_r) &+ (a_{r+1} + \cdots + a_{k+1}) \\
&= (a_1 + \cdots + a_r) + ((a_{r+1} + \cdots + a_k) + a_{k+1}) \\
&= ((a_1 + \cdots + a_r) + (a_{r+1} + \cdots + a_k)) + a_{k+1} \quad (\textit{by assoc. law}), \\
&= (a_1 + \cdots + a_k) + a_{k+1} \quad (\textit{by } S_k), \\
&= a_1 + \cdots + a_{k+1} \quad (\textit{by } 3.16).
\end{aligned}
$$

This calculation establishes 3.18 and completes the proof.

In a similar manner the other results that were stated in Section 2.6 can be established by induction. Some of them are listed in the following set of exercises.

——————————————————— *E X E R C I S E S*

1. Prove the generalized distributive law (2.22):
$$b(a_1 + a_2 + \cdots + a_n) = ba_1 + ba_2 + \cdots + ba_n.$$

2. Prove (2.26(ii)) that for arbitrary positive integers m and n,
$$(a^m)^n = a^{mn}.$$

3. If a and b are elements of a commutative ring, prove (2.27) that
$(ab)^m = a^m b^m$ for every positive integer m.

4. If n is a positive integer and $a_1, a_2, \cdots, a_n$ are elements of an integral domain such that $a_1 a_2 \cdots a_n = 0$, show that some one of the a's is zero.

5. Prove (2.28(iii)) that for every integer m (positive, negative, or zero),
$$m(a + b) = ma + mb.$$
[Hint: For negative m, set $m = -n$ and prove for every positive integer n.]

6. Prove (2.28(iv)) that for every integer m,
$$m(ab) = (ma)b = a(mb).$$

7. Prove (2.28(i)) that for all integers m and n,
$$ma + na = (m + n)a.$$
[Hint: Make a number of cases as follows: either m or n is zero; both m and n are positive; one of m, n is positive and the other negative; both m and n are negative.]

8. Use the fact that the set of positive integers is well-ordered to prove the following alternate form of the Induction Principle:
Suppose that there is associated with each positive integer n a statement S_n. Then S_n is true for every positive integer n provided the following hold:
(i) S_1 is true,
(ii)   If k is a positive integer such that S_i is true for every positive integer $i < k$, then also S_k is true.

3.5 THE PEANO AXIOMS (OPTIONAL)

So far, we have merely *assumed* that the system of all integers has the properties of an ordered integral domain in which the set of positive elements is well-ordered. In this section we shall briefly indicate how it is possible to assume as a starting point only a few simple properties of the natural numbers (positive integers) and then to *prove* all the other properties that are required. This program was first carried out by the Italian mathematician, G. Peano, and the simple properties with which we start are therefore called Peano's Axioms. If we denote by "N" the set of all natural numbers, these axioms may be stated as follows.

Axiom 1. $1 \in N$.

Axiom 2. To each element m of N there corresponds a unique element m' of N called the *successor* of m.

Axiom 3. For each $m \in N$ we have $m' \neq 1$. (That is, 1 is not the successor of any natural number.)

Axiom 4. If $m, n \in N$ such that $m' = n'$, then $m = n$.

Axiom 5. Let K be a set of elements of N. Then $K = N$ provided the following two conditions are satisfied:

    (i) $1 \in K$,
    (ii) If $k \in K$, then $k' \in K$.

This last axiom is essentially our Theorem 3.11 and is the basis of proofs by mathematical induction. In this approach to the study of the natural numbers it is taken as one of the defining properties or axioms.

Using only these five simple axioms, it is possible to *define* addition and multiplication on N and then to *prove* that N has all the properties of an integral domain except that it does not have a zero and its elements do not have additive inverses. We proceed to give the definitions of addition and multiplication, but shall not carry out the rest of the program. The details can be found in many algebra texts.

The definition of addition is as follows.

3.19 Definition. Let m be an arbitrary element of N. First, we define $m + 1 = m'$. Moreover, if $k \in N$ such that $m + k$ is defined, we define $m + k' = (m + k)'$.

By Axiom 5, it follows that the set of all elements n of N such that $m + n$ is defined by 3.19 is the set of *all* elements of N. In other words, an operation of addition is now defined on N.

The operation of multiplication is defined in a similar way as follows.

3.20 Definition. Let m be an arbitrary element of N. First, we define $m \cdot 1 = m$. Moreover, if $k \in N$ such that $m \cdot k$ is defined, we define $m \cdot k' = m \cdot k + m$.

It is also possible to define an order relation on N as follows. If $m, n \in N$, we define $m > n$ to mean that there exists an element k of N such that $m = n + k$. It can then be proved that ">" has all the properties that we would expect it to have when applied to the positive elements of an ordered integral domain. Moreover, the set N is well-ordered according to our Definition 3.7 of this concept.

Up to this point we have outlined a program for using Peano's Axioms to establish all the familiar properties of the natural numbers or positive integers. In order to obtain the *ring* of all integers we still have to introduce into the system the negative integers and zero. This can be done by a method quite similar to that which we shall use in Chapter 5 to construct the rational numbers from the integers. Accordingly, we postpone any further discussion of this program until Section 5.7 at the end of Chapter 5.

4

Some Properties of the Integers

Now that we have obtained a characterization of the ring I of integers, in this chapter we proceed to establish a number of simple properties of this system. In giving illustrative examples we shall naturally make use of our familiar decimal notation, but the proofs will be based only on the fact that the ring of integers is an ordered integral domain in which the set of positive elements is well-ordered. In particular, mathematical induction will play a central role in many of the proofs, although we shall frequently omit some of the details.

4.1 DIVISORS AND THE DIVISION ALGORITHM

We begin with the following familiar definition.

4.1 Definition. If $a, b \in I$, b is said to be a *divisor* (or *factor*) of a if there exists $c \in I$ such that $a = bc$. If b is a divisor of a, we say also that a is *divisible by* b or that a is a *multiple of* b.

The following observations are easy consequences of this definition. Since $0 = b \cdot 0$ for every $b \in I$, we see that every integer b is a divisor of zero. Moreover, it is apparent that if $a \in I$, then ± 1 and $\pm a$ are divisors of a. If b is a divisor of a, so that $a = bc$ for some integer c, it is clear that $-a = b(-c)$ and b is also a divisor of $-a$. It follows that a and $-a$ have precisely the same divisors. As a consequence, in problems about divisors there is frequently no real loss of generality in restricting attention to positive integers only.

We next observe that if the positive integer b is a divisor of the positive integer a, then $b \le a$. For if $a = bc$, then c is also a positive integer, and therefore $c \ge 1$. Multiplying this inequality by the positive integer b, we see that $bc \ge b$ or $a \ge b$.

In view of the preceding remarks, it is obvious that the only divisors of ± 1 are ± 1.

The following concept is an important one in studying divisibility properties of the integers.

4.2 Definition. A nonzero integer p other than 1 or -1 is called a *prime* if its only divisors are ± 1 and $\pm p$.

If $n > 1$, it follows from this definition that n is *not* a prime if and only if there exist positive integers n_1 and n_2, with $1 < n_1 < n$ and $1 < n_2 < n$, such that $n = n_1 n_2$.

It is obvious that $-p$ is a prime if and only if p is a prime. The first few positive primes are

$$2, 3, 5, 7, 11, 13, 17, 19, \cdots.$$

One of the principal reasons for the importance of the primes is that every integer other than 0, 1, and -1 is a prime or can be expressed as a product of primes. This is sometimes taken for granted in arithmetic, and no doubt seems almost obvious. However, the fact that any integer can be so expressed and in only one way, in a sense to be made precise later, is not trivial to prove and is so important that it is often called the "Fundamental Theorem of Arithmetic." We shall return to this theorem in a later section of this chapter.

We proceed to a consideration of the following result.

4.3 Division Algorithm. *If $a, b \in I$ with $b > 0$, there exist unique integers q and r such that*

4.4 $$a = qb + r, \qquad\qquad 0 \le r < b.$$

Before giving a detailed proof, we can make the existence of q and r appear plausible by use of a geometric argument. Consider a coordinate line with the multiples of b marked off as in Figure 3. Then if a is marked off, it either falls on a multiple of b, say qb, or it falls between two successive multiples of b, say qb and $(q + 1)b$. (In the figure,

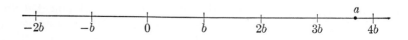

Figure 3

$q = 3$.) In either case, there exists an integer q such that $qb \leq a < (q+1)b$. If we set $r = a - qb$, then $a = qb + r$ and it is clear that $0 \leq r < b$.

Let us now give a proof which does not make use of geometric intuition. An outline of the proof is as follows. Since 4.4 can be written in the form $r = a - qb$, we consider those nonnegative integers of the form $a - xb$, where $x \in I$, and shall show that one of them is necessarily less than b. This one we shall then identify with the integer r, whose existence we wish to establish. In order to carry out the details, let S be the set of integers defined as follows:

$$S = \{a - xb;\ x \in I,\ a - xb \geq 0\}.$$

First, we show that the set S is not empty. Now $b \geq 1$, since b is assumed to be a positive integer. It follows that $|a| \cdot b \geq |a|$, and hence that $a + |a| \cdot b \geq a + |a| \geq 0$. Hence, by using $x = -|a|$, we see that S contains the integer $a + |a| \cdot b$, and is therefore not empty. If $0 \in S$, clearly 0 is the least element of S. If $0 \notin S$, S is a nonempty set of positive integers and therefore has a least element, since the set of positive integers is well-ordered. Hence, in either case, S has a least element, say r. There must then exist an integer q such that $a - qb = r$. We therefore have $a = qb + r$, where $0 \leq r$, and we proceed to show that also $r < b$. Let us suppose, on the contrary, that $r \geq b$. Then $r - b \geq 0$ and, since $r - b = a - (q+1)b$, we see that $r - b \in S$. But since $b > 0$, $r - b < r$ and we have a contradiction of the fact that r is the least element of S. Hence, $r < b$, and this completes the proof that there exist integers q and r satisfying 4.4. It remains to be proved that they are unique.

Suppose that q and r satisfy 4.4, and that also

$$a = q_1 b + r_1, \qquad\qquad 0 \leq r_1 < b$$

Then $qb + r = q_1 b + r_1$, and it follows that

4.5 $$b(q - q_1) = r_1 - r.$$

Using the fact that the absolute value of a product is the product of the absolute values (Exercise 6, Section 3.2), and that $|b| = b$, we obtain

$$b \cdot |q - q_1| = |r_1 - r|.$$

But, since $0 \leq r < b$ and $0 \leq r_1 < b$, we must have $|r_1 - r| < b$ and it follows that $b \cdot |q - q_1| < b$. Since $|q - q_1|$ is a nonnegative integer, this implies that $|q - q_1| = 0$, that is, that $q = q_1$; and 4.5 then shows that also $r = r_1$. We have therefore proved the uniqueness of the integers q and r satisfying 4.4.

The unique integers q and r which satisfy 4.4 are called, respectively, the *quotient* and the *remainder* in the division of a by b. It is important to observe that a is divisible by b if and only if the remainder in the division of a by b is zero.

In a numerical case, at least if $a > 0$, the actual calculation of q and r can be carried out by the familiar process of long division. The method is easily adapted also to the case in which a is negative.

_____ **E X E R C I S E S**

1. Show that if $x = y + z$, and d is a divisor of any two of the integers x, y, and z, it is also a divisor of the third.

2. If a and b are nonzero integers such that each is a divisor of the other, show that $a = \pm b$.

3. If p and q are positive primes such that p is divisible by q, show that $p = q$.

4. If n is a positive integer and p_1, p_2, $\cdots$, p_n are distinct positive primes, show that the integer $(p_1 p_2 \cdots p_n) + 1$ is divisible by none of these primes.

5. For each of the following pairs of integers find the quotient and the remainder in the division of the first integer by the second, and verify Equation 4.4:

    (i) $1251, 78$ (ii) $31, 158$ (iii) $4357, 418$ (iv) $-168, 15$.

6. Prove the following generalized form of the Division Algorithm. If $a, b \in I$ with $b \neq 0$, there exist unique integers q and r such that $a = qb + r$, $0 \leq r < |b|$. [Hint: Make use of the case already proved in which b was assumed to be positive.]

4.2 DIFFERENT BASES (OPTIONAL)

In this section we give a simple application of the Division Algorithm and, in contrast to most of the material of this chapter, we are here primarily concerned with the matter of notation. The topic here presented is independent of the rest of this chapter, but may be of some interest in itself.

It is customary to use the integer 10 as the base of our number system. By this we mean that when we write 4371, for example, it is understood to stand for $4 \cdot 10^3 + 3 \cdot 10^2 + 7 \cdot 10 + 1$. The numbers 4, 3, 7, and 1 are called the *digits* of this number. The possible digits of a number are then the ten integers 0, 1, 2, $\cdots$, 9. Actually, any positive integer greater than 1 can be used as a base in the way in which we ordinarily use 10. By this statement we mean the following.

4.6 Theorem. *Let b be a positive integer greater than 1. If a is any positive integer, there exists a nonnegative integer m such that a can be expressed uniquely in the form*

4.7
$$a = r_m b^m + r_{m-1} b^{m-1} + \cdots + r_1 b + r_0.$$

where $0 < r_m < b$ and $0 \le r_i < b$ for $i = 0, 1, \cdots, m - 1$.

The proof is carried out by repeated use of the Division Algorithm. If $a < b$, we have the desired form at once with $r_0 = a$ and $m = 0$. If $a \ge b$, we may write

4.8
$$a = q_0 b + r_0, \qquad\qquad 0 \le r_0 < b,$$

by the Division Algorithm, and clearly $q_0 > 0$. If $q_0 < b$, we set $r_1 = q_0$ and have the form 4.7 with $m = 1$. On the other hand, if $q_0 \ge b$, we apply the Division Algorithm to q_0 and b, and obtain

$$q_0 = q_1 b + r_1, \qquad\qquad q_1 > 0, 0 \le r_1 < b.$$

Substituting in 4.8, we get

4.9
$$a = q_1 b^2 + r_1 b + r_0.$$

Now if $q_1 < b$, we set $r_2 = q_1$ and have the desired expression 4.7 with $m = 2$. If $q_1 \ge b$, we write

$$q_1 = q_2 b + r_2, \qquad\qquad q_2 > 0, 0 \le r_2 < b,$$

and it follows from 4.9 that

$$a = q_2 b^3 + r_2 b^2 + r_1 b + r_0.$$

If $q_2 < b$, we set $r_3 = q_2$ and are through. A repetition of this process must finally yield the desired result. For

$$a > q_0 > q_1 > q_2 > \cdots,$$

and if $q_k \ge b$, then $q_{k+1} > 0$ and so there is a first one of these q's, say q_{m-1}, such that $0 < q_{m-1} < b$. We then set $r_m = q_{m-1}$, and a is expressed in the form 4.7. Actually, the words, "a repetition of this process" really imply that a complete proof would require use of mathematical induction.

The *uniqueness* of the form 4.7 follows from the uniqueness of the various remainders when the Division Algorithm is used.

Just as we omit the powers of 10 in the usual notation, we may specify a number a with reference to the base b by giving in order the "digits" $r_m, r_{m-1}, \cdots, r_1, r_0$. In order to indicate the base being used, let us specify the number a, given by 4.7, by writing $(r_m r_{m-1} \cdots r_1 r_0)_b$. If no base is indicated, it will be understood that the base is 10. For example, $(3214)_5$ really means

$$3 \cdot 5^3 + 2 \cdot 5^2 + 1 \cdot 5 + 4,$$

and it is readily verified that $(3214)_5 = 434$. The indicated proof of Theorem 4.6 gives an easy way to write a number, given in the base 10, using any other base. It is only necessary to use repeated divisions by the base, as here illustrated for the case in which we wish to write 434 using the base 5. Here the remainders in the successive divisions are written off to the right, and the divisions are carried out until the last quotient is less than 5. We conclude, therefore, that $434 = (3214)_5$, which agrees with our previous calculations.

```
5 | 434
5 | 86    4
5 | 17    1
    3     2
```

It is possible to carry out all the usual operations of arithmetic using entirely some fixed base other than 10. As an illustration, let us use base 5. In order to add or multiply any two numbers we need only learn addition and multiplication tables for the integers less than 5. In designating an integer less than 5, it is not necessary to indicate whether the base is 5 or 10. However, we have $5 = (10)_5$, $3 + 4 = (12)_5$, $3 \cdot 4 = (22)_5$, and so on. The reader may verify the addition and multiplication given below, following the usual procedure of arithmetic but using base 5 throughout.

$(3142)_5$

$(1224)_5$

$(4421)_5$

ADDITION

$(3204)_5$

$(23)_5$

$(20122)_5$

$(11413)_5$

$(134302)_5$

MULTIPLICATION

Of course, any other base can be used just as well as 5. However, the only base other than 10 that is in use to any extent is the base 2, and this system is called the *binary* system. The possible "digits" in the binary system are just 0 and 1, and expressing a number in this system involves expressing it as a sum of *different* powers of 2. For example, $(1011)_2 = 2^3 + 2 + 1$. The binary system is a most convenient one for use with many of the modern high-speed computing machines. Some of these machines are so constructed that information can be fed into the machine in the usual decimal system. The machine then expresses the given numbers in the binary system, carries out the calculations in the binary system, changes the results back into the decimal system, and automatically prints the answers.

_____ *E X E R C I S E S*

1. Write each of the following numbers using the base 5 and also using the base 2:

$$24, \quad 116, \quad 412, \quad 3141, \quad 2384.$$

2. Carry out the following additions using the indicated base:

$$(1130)_5 \quad (2143)_5 \quad (101101)_2$$
$$\underline{(432)_5} \quad \underline{(1434)_5} \quad \underline{(11011)_2}$$

3. Carry out the following multiplications using the indicated base:

$$(143)_5 \quad (4312)_5 \quad (10101)_2$$
$$\underline{(244)_5} \quad \underline{(324)_5} \quad \underline{(1101)_2}$$

4.3 GREATEST COMMON DIVISOR

We now return to our general program of establishing properties of the integers that are independent of the notation being used. First, we make the following definition.

4.10 Definition. The positive integer d is called the *greatest common divisor* (g.c.d.) of the nonzero integers a and b if the following conditions are satisfied:

(i) d is a divisor of both a and b,
(ii) Every divisor of both a and b is a divisor of d.

We shall presently show that two nonzero integers a and b always have a g.c.d. Moreover, it is easy to see that they can have only *one* g.c.d. For if d and d_1 are positive integers, each of which satisfies both conditions of the preceding definition, each is a divisor of the other and therefore $d = d_1$. We may emphasize that, in order to have the convenience of a unique g.c.d., we have required the g.c.d. of two integers to be the *positive* integer satisfying conditions (i) and (ii) of the definition.

In proving the existence of the g c.d. we shall make use of the following concept.

.11 Definition. If $a, b \in I$, we say that an integer of the form

$$ax + by, \qquad\qquad x, y \in I,$$

is a *linear combination* of a and b.

The existence of the g.c.d., and also one of its important properties, will be established in the following theorem.

.12 Theorem. *If a and b are nonzero integers, the least positive integer which is expressible as a linear combination of a and b is the g.c.d. of a and b. That is, if d is the g.c.d. of a and b, there exist integers x_1 and y_1 such that*

$$d = ax_1 + by_1,$$

and d is the smallest positive integer which is expressible in this form.

For convenience of reference, let us define the set S as follows:

$$S = \{ax + by;\ x, y \in I,\ ax + by > 0\}.$$

Hence S is just the set of all positive integers that are expressible as linear combinations of a and b. Since, for example, $a^2 + b^2$ is an element of S, it is clear that S is not empty. Accordingly, there must exist a smallest positive integer d in the set S. Since $d \in S$, there exist integers x_1 and y_1 such that

.13
$$d = ax_1 + by_1.$$

We next show that d is a divisor of a. By the Division Algorithm, there exist integers q and r such that

$$a = qd + r, \qquad\qquad 0 \leq r < d.$$

Using Equation 4.13, we then find that

$$r = a - qd = a - q(ax_1 + by_1)$$
$$= a(1 - qx_1) + b(-qy_1).$$

It is now clear that if $r > 0$, then $r \in S$. But since $r < d$ and d is the least element of S, we conclude that $r = 0$. Hence, $a = qd$, and d is a divisor of a. In a similar way it can be shown that d is a divisor of b. Hence, d satisfies condition 4.10(i).

It is quite easy to see that d also satisfies condition 4.10(ii). For, suppose that c is a common divisor of a and of b, and hence that

$a = a_1c$, $b = b_1c$ for certain integers a_1 and b_1. Then, using Equation 4.13, we obtain

$$d = a_1cx_1 + b_1cy_1 = (a_1x_1 + b_1y_1)c,$$

and c is a divisor of d. This completes the proof of the theorem.

Although the preceding theorem establishes the existence of the g.c.d., its proof does not suggest a method for actually computing the g.c.d. of two given integers. We next present a procedure, known as the *Euclidean Algorithm*, which will be useful in this connection.

If d is the g.c.d. of the integers a and b, then it is also the g.c.d. of $-a$ and b, of a and $-b$, and of $-a$ and $-b$. Accordingly, without loss of generality, we now assume that a and b are positive integers. By the Division Algorithm, we may write

$$a = qb + r, \qquad\qquad 0 \leq r < b.$$

If $r \neq 0$, we now divide b by r, getting

$$b = q_1r + r_1, \qquad\qquad 0 \leq r_1 < r.$$

If $r_1 \neq 0$, we divide r by r_1, and obtain

$$r = q_2r_1 + r_2, \qquad\qquad 0 \leq r_2 < r_1,$$

and repeat this process. Since $r > r_1 > r_2 > \cdots$, and all these remainders are nonnegative integers, we must eventually get a zero remainder. If r_{k+1} is the first zero remainder, we then have the following system of equations:

4.14

$$
\begin{aligned}
a &= qb + r, & 0 &< r < b, \\
b &= q_1r + r_1, & 0 &< r_1 < r, \\
r &= q_2r_1 + r_2, & 0 &< r_2 < r_1, \\
r_1 &= q_3r_2 + r_3, & 0 &< r_3 < r_2, \\
&\cdot\ \cdot\ \cdot\ \cdot\ \cdot & &\cdot\ \cdot\ \cdot\ \cdot\ \cdot \\
r_{k-2} &= q_kr_{k-1} + r_k, & 0 &< r_k < r_{k-1}, \\
r_{k-1} &= q_{k+1}r_k.
\end{aligned}
$$

We now assert that r_k (the last nonzero remainder) is the g.c.d. of a and b. To establish this fact, we need to verify the two properties (i) and (ii) of Definition 4.10. First, let us show that r_k is a common divisor of a and b. We do so by starting with the last of Equations 4.14 and working back to the first as follows. It is clear from the last equation that r_k is a divisor of r_{k-1}. Since now r_k is a common divisor of r_k and r_{k-1}, the next-to-last equation shows that it is also a divisor of r_{k-2}. Proceeding in this way, when we get to the second equation we will know that r_k is a common divisor of r_1 and r, and hence is also a divisor of b. The first equation then shows that r_k is also a divisor of a. Hence, r_k is a common divisor of a and b, and 4.10(i) is established. To establish 4.10(ii), let c be any common divisor of a and b. We now use Equations 4.14 in the other order. The first equation shows that c is a divisor of r, the next that it is a divisor of r_1, and so on. Eventually, we find that it is a divisor of r_k, and the proof is completed.

Let us now give a numerical example. Suppose that we desire to compute the g.c.d. of the integers 26 and 382. By ordinary division we find that Equations 4.14 take the following form:

$$382 = 14 \cdot 26 + 18,$$
$$26 = 1 \cdot 18 + 8,$$
$$18 = 2 \cdot 8 + 2,$$
$$8 = 4 \cdot 2.$$

In this case, 2 is the g.c.d. since it is the last nonzero remainder.

Not only is the Euclidean Algorithm useful in computing the g.c.d. of two integers, but it is also useful in expressing the g.c.d. of two integers as a linear combination of these integers. Actually, *each* of the remainders in Equations 4.14 can be expressed, in turn, as a linear combination of a and b. From the first of Equations 4.14, we see that

4.15
$$r = a - qb,$$

and hence r is a linear combination of a and b. Substituting this expression for r in the second equation, and solving for r_1, we get

4.16
$$r_1 = b - q_1(a - qb) = (1 + q_1q)b - q_1a,$$

and hence r_1 is a linear combination of a and b. Now substituting from 4.15 and 4.16 into the third of Equations 4.14, we obtain

$$r_2 = r - q_2r_1 = (a - qb) - q_2[(1 + q_1q)b - q_1a]$$
$$= (1 + q_2q_1)a - (q + q_2 + q_2q_1q)b,$$

so that r_2 is a linear combination of a and b. By continuing in this way (induction is involved here) we see that each remainder and, in particular, the g.c.d. r_k is expressible as a linear combination of a and b. We are not here interested in general formulas which express these remainders as linear combinations of a and b since, in a numerical case, it is easy to compute, in turn, each of these linear combinations.

As an example, let us carry out the calculations for the case in which $a = 382$ and $b = 26$. The Euclidean Algorithm has been applied above to these two integers to find that their g.c.d. is 2. Let us now use the equations previously exhibited to express each of the remainders as a linear combination of 382 and 26. For simplicity, we shall write a in place of 382 and b in place of 26. The calculations are as follows:

$$18 = a - 14b,$$
$$8 = b - 18 = b - (a - 14b) = 15b - a,$$
$$2 = 18 - 2 \cdot 8 = a - 14b - 2(15b - a)$$
$$= 3a - 44b.$$

Hence,

$$2 = 3(382) - 44(26),$$

and we have expressed the g.c.d. of 382 and 26 as a linear combination of these two integers.

We shall sometimes find it convenient to let (a, b) designate the g.c.d. of a and b. Thus, for example, we have that $(382, 26) = 2$. There can be no possible confusion with other uses of the number pair notation since the context will make it clear that we are considering the g.c.d. of two integers and not, for example, the coordinates of a point in the plane.

We shall frequently need to refer to a pair of integers with 1 as their g.c.d. Accordingly, it is convenient to make the following definition.

4.17 Definition. The integers a and b are said to be *relatively prime* if their g.c.d. is 1; that is, if $(a, b) = 1$.

_____ E X E R C I S E S

Unless otherwise specified, the letters represent arbitrary nonzero integers.

1. Find the g.c.d. of each of the following pairs of integers and express it as a linear combination of the two integers:

   (*i*) 52 and 38, (*ii*) 81 and 110, (*iii*) 320 and 112, (*iv*) 7469 and 2387, (*v*) 10,672 and -4147.

2. Show that a and b are relatively prime if and only if 1 is expressible as a linear combination of a and b.

3. If $d = (a, b)$ and $a = da_1$, $b = db_1$, show that $(a_1, b_1) = 1$.

4. If m is a positive integer, show that $(ma, mb) = m(a, b)$.

5. Show each of the following:

   (*i*) If p is a positive prime and a is a nonzero integer, then either $(a, p) = 1$ or $(a, p) = p$.

   (*ii*) If p and q are distinct positive primes, then 1 is expressible as a linear combination of p and q.

6. If $x = yz + t$, show that $(x, z) = (z, t)$.

7. (*i*) Define the g.c.d. of *three* nonzero integers.

(*ii*) Establish the existence of the g.c.d. of three integers by proving a result analogous to Theorem 4.12.

(*iii*) If d is the g.c.d. of a, b, and c, show that $d = ((a, b) . c) = ((a, c), b) = (a, (b, c))$.

(*iv*) Let d be the g.c.d. of a, b, and c. If $a = a_1 d$, $b = b_1 d$, and $c = c_1 d$, show that 1 is the g.c.d. of the three integers a_1, b_1, and c_1.

4.4 THE FUNDAMENTAL THEOREM

The principal theorem to be proved in this section has to do with the factorizations of an integer into a product of primes. The following result will be needed in the proof.

4.18 Lemma. *If a and b are nonzero integers such that ab is divisible by the prime p, then a is divisible by p or b is divisible by p.*

To prove this lemma, let us suppose that a is not d'visible by p, and show that b is divisible by p. Since p is a prime which is not a divisor of a, the definition of a prime implies that $(a, p) = 1$. Then Theorem 4.12 shows that there exist integers x and y such that $1 = ax + py$. Multiplying by b, we obtain

$$b = abx + bpy.$$

Since we are given that p is a divisor of ab, clearly p is a divisor of the right member of this equation, and therefore a divisor of b.

It is almost obvious that the preceding lemma can be generalized to apply to a product of more than two integers. For future reference we now state this more general result.

4.19 Lemma. *If m is any positive integer and a_1, a_2, $\cdots$, a_m are nonzero integers such that the product $a_1 a_2 \cdots a_m$ is divisible by the prime p, then some integer a_i is divisible by p.*

This lemma is easily established by induction, and the proof will be left as an exercise. The case in which $m = 2$ is covered by the preceding lemma.

It is easy to verify, for example, that $60 = 2 \cdot 2 \cdot 3 \cdot 5$, and hence that 60 can be expressed as a product of positive primes. We could also write $60 = 2 \cdot 5 \cdot 3 \cdot 2$, but we shall not consider these two factorizations as essentially different since they differ only in the order in which the prime factors are written down. With this understanding, it is true that

60 has only one factorization into a product of positive primes. This is a special case of the following important theorem.

4.20 Fundamental Theorem of Arithmetic. *Every positive integer $a > 1$ can be expressed as a product of positive primes in one and only one way (except for the order of the factors).*

In the statement of the theorem it is to be understood that, as a special case, a "product" of primes may consist of a single prime. This agreement is to take care of the case in which a is itself a prime.

First, we shall show that every positive integer $a > 1$ can be expressed, in at least one way, as a product of positive primes. Let K be the set of all integers greater than one that can *not* be so expressed. If K is not the empty set, there is a least integer c in K, and clearly c is not a prime. Hence, $c = c_1 c_2$, where $1 < c_1 < c$ and $1 < c_2 < c$. Since c is the least element of K, we have $c_1 \notin K$ and $c_2 \notin K$. This implies that both c_1 and c_2 can be expressed as products of primes, and since $c = c_1 c_2$ it is clear that c can also be so expressed. However, this contradicts the fact that $c \in K$, and therefore K must be the empty set. In other words, every integer $a > 1$ can be expressed as a product of positive primes. To complete the proof of the theorem, we shall now show by induction that every such integer can be expressed as a product of positive primes *in only one way.*

Let S_n be the statement, "If a positive integer can be expressed as a product of n positive primes, then there is only one way in which it can be expressed as a product of positive primes." By the definition of a prime, it is clear that S_1 is true. Now let k be a positive integer such that S_k is true, and let us prove that S_{k+1} is true also. Accordingly, let b be a positive integer which can be expressed in the form

4.21
$$b = p_1 p_2 \cdots p_{k+1},$$

where the p's are positive primes, and suppose that b can also be expressed in the form

4.22
$$b = q_1 q_2 \cdots q_m,$$

where the q's are positive primes. It is easy to see that we must have $m > 1$ since there are at least two prime factors in 4.21 and b is therefore not itself a prime. Now from 4.21 and 4.22, it follows that

4.23
$$p_1 p_2 \cdots p_{k+1} = q_1 q_2 \cdots q_m.$$

The prime p_1 is therefore a divisor of the product $q_1 q_2 \cdots q_m$, and Lemma 4.19 assures us that it must be a divisor of some q_i. For convenience of notation, let us suppose that p_1 is a divisor of q_1. Then, since these are positive primes, we must have $p_1 = q_1$. By canceling this factor from both sides of Equation 4.23, we obtain

24
$$p_2 p_3 \cdots p_{k+1} = q_2 q_3 \cdots q_m.$$

But the left side is now a positive integer expressed as a product of k positive primes, and by the assumption that S_k is true it follows that $m = k + 1$ and the primes $p_2, p_3, \cdots, p_{k+1}$ must coincide with the primes $q_2, q_3, \cdots, q_m$ in some order. In turn, since $p_1 = q_1$, we conclude that the two expressions 4.21 and 4.22 are identical except possibly for the order of the factors. We have now shown that S_{k+1} is true, and therefore S_n is true for every positive integer n. The theorem is therefore established.

Of course, the primes occurring in a factorization of an integer into prime factors need not all be distinct. By combining the equal primes, we see that every integer $a > 1$ can be expressed uniquely in the form

25
$$a = p_1^{n_1} p_2^{n_2} \cdots p_k^{n_k},$$

where the p's are primes such that $1 < p_1 < p_2 < \cdots < p_k$, and each of $n_1, n_2, \cdots, n_k$ is a positive integer. The right side of 4.25 may conveniently be called the *standard form* of the integer a. As an example, $2^2 \cdot 3 \cdot 5$ is the standard form of the integer 60.

Throughout this section we have considered positive integers only. However, this is no essential restriction as we can see as follows. If $a < -1$, then $-a > 1$ and the Fundamental Theorem shows that $-a$ can be expressed uniquely as a product of positive primes. It follows that a itself is then expressible uniquely as -1 times a product of positive primes. For example, $-60 = (-1) \cdot 2^2 \cdot 3 \cdot 5$.

4.5 SOME APPLICATIONS OF THE FUNDAMENTAL THEOREM

If a and c are positive integers and c is a divisor of a, then $a = cd$ for some positive integer d. If c and d are expressed as products of prime factors, then clearly a is a product of all prime factors of c times all prime factors of d. Moreover, the Fundamental Theorem then states that this gives the unique factorization of a as a product of prime factors. It follows that the only possible prime factors of c (or of d) are the primes that are factors of a. If then a is expressed in the standard form 4.25, any divisor c of a is necessarily of the form

$$c = p_1^{m_1} p_2^{m_2} \cdots p_k^{m_k},$$

where $0 \leq m_i \leq n_i$ ($i = 1, 2, \cdots, k$). Conversely, any integer c of this form is clearly a divisor of a.

It is now easy to obtain the g.c.d. (a, b) of two integers a and b if both a and b are expressed in standard form. Clearly, (a, b) is the product of those primes which are factors of both a and b, each such prime occurring to the smaller of the two powers to which it occurs in a and in b. For example, $60 = 2^2 \cdot 3 \cdot 5$ and $252 = 2^2 \cdot 3^2 \cdot 7$. It follows that $(60, 252) = 2^2 \cdot 3$.

We have previously had a method for computing the g.c.d. of two integers by the use of Euclid's algorithm—a method which does not involve finding any prime factors of the given integers. From a computational point of view, the previous method may involve much less work than the present one since it may be exceedingly difficult to find the prime factors of fairly large numbers, and therefore difficult to express them in standard form.

We shall not have much occasion to use the concept we now define, but we include it here for the sake of completeness.

4.26 Definition. The *least common multiple* (l.c.m.) of two nonzero integers a and b is the positive integer m with the following two properties:

(i) m is a multiple of both a and b,
(ii)   Every multiple of both a and b is a multiple of m.

It is easy to verify the *uniqueness* of the l.c.m., and its existence may be established in various ways. (See Exercises 3 and 5 below.)

We conclude this section with a special, but fairly important, result. We shall show that there do not exist integers a and b such that

4.27 $$a^2 = 2b^2.$$

Let us suppose, on the contrary, that there do exist such integers, which we may obviously assume to be positive. If $d = (a, b)$, by Exercise 3 of the preceding set we have $a = da_1$, $b = db_1$, where $(a_1, b_1) = 1$. Substituting in 4.27, and dividing by d^2, we find that

4.28 $$a_1^2 = 2b_1^2.$$

This equation implies that a_1^2 is divisible by 2 and Lemma 4.18 (or the Fundamental Theorem) shows that a_1 must have 2 as a divisor. But then a_1^2 is divisible by 4 and therefore $2b_1^2$ is divisible by 4 and b_1^2 is divisible by 2. This requires that b_1 be divisible by 2, and we have shown that 2 is a common divisor of a_1 and b_1. We have therefore obtained a contradiction of the fact that $(a_1, b_1) = 1$, and hence there can be no integers satisfying 4.27. The proof is therefore completed.

Another, perhaps more familiar, way of stating the result just proved is to say that $\sqrt{2}$ is not a rational number; that is, it is not expressible in the form a/b, where a and b are integers.

1. Express 120 and 4851 in standard form, and find their g.c.d. and their l.c.m.

2. Do the same for 970 and 3201.

3. Explain how one can find the l.c.m. of any two integers if their standard forms are known.

4. (*i*) Using a method similar to that used in the proof of Lemma 4.18, show that if a is a divisor of bc and $(a, b) = 1$, then a is a divisor of c.
   (*ii*) Prove the same result by use of the Fundamental Theorem.

5. If $a = a_1 d$ and $b = b_1 d$, where $d = (a, b)$, show that the l.c.m. of a and b is $a_1 b_1 d$.

6. Show that a positive integer $a > 1$ is a perfect square (that is, is the square of an integer) if and only if in the standard form of a all the exponents are even integers.

7. Show that if b and c are positive integers such that bc is a perfect square and $(b, c) = 1$, then both b and c are perfect squares.

8. Prove that there do not exist integers a and b such that $a^2 = 3b^2$.

9. If n is a positive integer which is not a perfect square, prove that there do not exist integers a and b such that $a^2 = nb^2$.

10. For each positive integer n, show that there are more than n positive primes. [Hint: Use the result of Exercise 4, Section 4.1.]

11. Prove Lemma 4.19.

4.6 PYTHAGOREAN TRIPLES (OPTIONAL)

If x, y, and z are *positive* integers such that

4.29
$$x^2 + y^2 = z^2,$$

we shall call the ordered triple (x, y, z) a *Pythagorean triple*. Clearly, (x, y, z) is a Pythagorean triple if and only if there exist right triangles whose sides have respective lengths x, y, and z units. Well-known examples of Pythagorean triples are (3, 4, 5), (6, 8, 10), and (5, 12, 13). In this section we shall determine all Pythagorean triples.

First, we observe that we can limit our problem somewhat. If (x, y, z) is a Pythagorean triple, then so is (kx, ky, kz) for every positive integer k. Conversely, let (x, y, z) be a Pythagorean triple and suppose that d is a common divisor of x, y, and z. If we write $x = x_1 d$, $y = y_1 d$, and $z = z_1 d$, we can cancel d^2 from each term of the equation

$$(x_1 d)^2 + (y_1 d)^2 = (z_1 d)^2,$$

and find that (x_1, y_1, z_1) is also a Pythagorean triple. If it happens that d is the g.c.d. of the *three* integers x, y, and z (see Exercise 7, Section 4.3), then x_1, y_1, and z_1 have 1 as their g.c.d. Let us say that a Pythagorean triple (a, b, c) is a *primitive* Pythagorean triple if a, b, and c have 1 as their g.c.d. Then the observations that we have just made assure us that *every* Pythagorean triple is of the form (ra, rb, rc), where (a, b, c) is a primitive Pythagorean triple and r is a positive integer. Our general problem is therefore reduced to the problem of finding all primitive Pythagorean triples.

Now let (x, y, z) be a primitive Pythagorean triple. It is easy to see that *each pair* of the numbers x, y, and z must be relatively prime. If, on the contrary, two of these numbers were not relatively prime, they would have a common prime factor p. Then Equation 4.29 would show that p is also a factor of the third, which would contradict the assumption that (x, y, z) is primitive. As a special case of what we have just proved, we see that x and y cannot both be even. We next show that, also, x and y cannot both be odd. If they were both odd, we could write $x = 2m + 1$ and $y = 2n + 1$, where m and n are properly chosen integers. But then we would have

$$z^2 = x^2 + y^2 = (2m + 1)^2 + (2n + 1)^2$$
$$= 2(2m^2 + 2n^2 + 2m + 2n + 1).$$

Since the second factor in this last expression is odd, we see that z^2 would be divisible by 2 but not by 4, and this is clearly impossible. It follows that x and y cannot both be odd. We have therefore proved that one of the integers x and y must be even and the other odd. It is trivial that (a, b, c) is a primitive Pythagorean triple if and only if (b, a, c) is also, and there will be no real loss of generality if we now limit ourselves to the study of primitive Pythagorean triples (x, y, z) in which x is even, and therefore y is odd.

We are now ready to prove the following theorem.

4.30 Theorem. *If (x, y, z) is a primitive Pythagorean triple in which x is even, then*

31 $$x = 2uv, \quad y = u^2 - v^2, \quad z = u^2 + v^2,$$

where u and v are positive integers satisfying the following three conditions:

(i)   *u and v are relatively prime,*
(ii) $u > v$,
(iii)   *One of u, v is even and the other is odd.*

Conversely, if u and v are any positive integers satisfying these three conditions and x, y, and z are determined by Formulas 4.31, then (x, y, z) is a primitive Pythagorean triple in which x is even.

To prove the first part of the theorem, let (x, y, z) be a primitive Pythagorean triple in which x is even. We have proved that no two of x, y, and z can be even; hence y and z are both odd. This implies that $z + y$ and $z - y$ are both even; that is, that there exist positive integers r and s such that

.32 $$z + y = 2r, \quad z - y = 2s.$$

From these, it is easy to verify that

.33 $$z = r + s, \quad y = r - s.$$

Now r and s must be relatively prime since any common factor of r and s would be a common factor of the relatively prime integers z and y. Moreover, since

$$x^2 = z^2 - y^2 = (z + y)(z - y),$$

it follows from Equations 4.32 that

.34 $$x^2 = 4rs.$$

Since x is even, $x = 2t$ for some integer t, and the preceding equation shows that

.35 $$t^2 = rs.$$

Since r and s are relatively prime, Exercise 7 of the preceding set implies that both r and s are perfect squares. That is, there exist positive integers u and v such that

.36 $$r = u^2, \quad s = v^2.$$

Then Equations 4.34 and 4.33 show that

.37 $$x = 2uv, \quad y = u^2 - v^2, \quad z = u^2 + v^2,$$

and Formulas 4.31 are satisfied. There remains only to prove that u and v have the required properties. Since r and s are relatively prime, it follows from 4.36 that u and v are relatively prime. Next, we see that $u > v$ since $y > 0$. We already know that u and v cannot both be even inasmuch as they are relatively prime. Finally, from 4.37 it follows that they cannot both be odd since otherwise y (and z also) would be even, whereas we know that it is odd. This completes the proof of the first part of the theorem.

To prove the second part, suppose that u and v are any positive integers satisfying conditions (i), (ii), and (iii); and let x, y, and z be defined by Formulas 4.31. Clearly x, y, and z are all positive, and it is easy to verify that

$$(2uv)^2 + (u^2 - v^2)^2 = (u^2 + v^2)^2,$$

and hence that (x, y, z) is a Pythagorean triple. We shall prove that it is necessarily primitive by showing that y and z are relatively prime. By condition (iii), $u^2 - v^2$ and $u^2 + v^2$ are both odd, that is, y and z are both odd. If y and z were not relatively prime, they would have a common prime factor $p \neq 2$. But since $z + y = 2u^2$ and $z - y = 2v^2$, it would follow that p is also a common factor of u and v. However, it is given that u and v are relatively prime, and therefore y and z can have no common prime factor. Hence, (x, y, z) is a primitive Pythagorean triple. It is obvious that x is even, and the proof is therefore completed.

It follows from the theorem that there are infinitely many primitive Pythagorean triples. The triple $(4, 3, 5)$ is obtained by setting $u = 2$, $v = 1$ in 4.31; the triple $(12, 5, 13)$ by choosing $u = 3$, $v = 2$; the triple $(8, 15, 17)$ by choosing $u = 4$, $v = 1$; and so on.

4.7 THE RING OF INTEGERS MODULO n

In this section we shall make use of the concepts of equivalence relation and equivalence set, which were defined in Chapter 1. First, we make the following definition.

4.38 Definition. Let n be a fixed integer greater than 1. If a and b are integers such that $a - b$ is divisible by n, we say that "a is congruent to b modulo n," and indicate this by writing $a \equiv b \pmod{n}$.

As an illustration of the use of this notation, let $n = 5$. Then we have $18 \equiv 3 \pmod 5$ since $18 - 3$ is divisible by 5. In like manner, $-2 \equiv 8 \pmod 5$, $4 \equiv 4 \pmod 5$, $1342 \equiv 2 \pmod 5$, and so on.

We leave it to the reader to verify that congruence modulo n is an equivalence relation on the set I of all integers. By this we mean, of course, that the three properties of Definition 1.7 of an equivalence relation are satisfied. We may emphasize that throughout this section n will always be a positive integer greater than 1.

Now that we have an equivalence relation on the set I, we can consider equivalence sets as introduced in Definition 1.8. We may point out that, relative to the equivalence relation of congruence modulo n, an equivalence set $[k]$ is defined as follows:

$$[k] = \{x; \; x \in I, \, x \equiv k \pmod{n}\}.$$

For convenience, we shall refer to $[k]$ as an "equivalence set modulo n." If $[k]$ and $[l]$ are equivalence sets modulo n, then 1.10 (ii) shows that $[k] = [l]$ if and only if $k \equiv l \pmod{n}$.

Next, let us observe that if $a \in I$ and r is the remainder in the division of a by n, then necessarily $a \equiv r \pmod{n}$. This follows from the observation that if $a = qn + r$, then $a - r = qn$ and hence $a \equiv r \pmod{n}$. Since we have $0 \leq r < n$, it follows that every integer is congruent modulo n to some one of the n integers 0, 1, 2, $\cdots$, $n - 1$. Moreover, since each of these integers is less than n, no two of them can be congruent to each other modulo n. Since $[k] = [l]$ if and only if $k \equiv l \pmod{n}$, we have shown that there are precisely n different equivalence sets modulo n, namely, the sets [0], [1], [2], $\cdots$, [$n - 1$].

As an example, let us take $n = 5$. It is easy to verify that the five equivalence sets modulo 5 are the following:

$$[0] = \{\cdots, -15, -10, -5, 0, 5, 10, 15, \cdots\},$$
$$[1] = \{\cdots, -14, -9, -4, 1, 6, 11, 16, \cdots\},$$
$$[2] = \{\cdots, -13, -8, -3, 2, 7, 12, 17, \cdots\},$$
$$[3] = \{\cdots, -12, -7, -2, 3, 8, 13, 18, \cdots\},$$
$$[4] = \{\cdots, -11, -6, -1, 4, 9, 14, 19, \cdots\}.$$

.39

A special case of 1.10 (i) shows, for example, that if $a \in [2]$, then necessarily $[a] = [2]$. Hence, $[2] = [-3] = [17]$, and so on. In view of the observation made above, we see that $[2]$ consists of all those integers a such that the remainder in the division of a by 5 is 2. Otherwise expressed, the equivalence set $[2]$ consists of the set of all integers of the form $5q + 2$, $q \in I$. Similar remarks hold for the other equivalence sets modulo 5, as well as for equivalence sets modulo n.

Still considering the special case of congruence modulo 5, let us give a description of the procedure, which we shall justify in detail below, by which we propose to construct a new ring. Let $U = \{[0], [1], [2], [3], [4]\}$, and hence an element of the set U is just one of the equivalence sets 4.39. We propose to make U into a ring by suitable definitions of addition and multiplication of its elements. What shall we mean, for example, by $[2] + [4]$? By examining 4.39, it appears that the sum of an element of [2] and an element of [4] always gives an element of [6]. Hence, it is natural to define $[2] + [4] = [6]$. Of course, $[6] = [1]$, so we could equally well say that $[2] + [4] = [1]$. Similarly, the product of an element of [2] and an element of [4] is always an element of [8], and we therefore define $[2] \cdot [4] = [8]$. Again, since $[8] = [3]$, this is the same as saying that $[2] \cdot [4] = [3]$. In a similar way we could define the sum or the product of any two elements of U, always obtaining an element of U. The importance of all this is that with respect to these operations of addition and multiplication on U, it can be shown that U is a ring. This ring we shall call the "ring of integers modulo 5," and denote it by $I/(5)$. The ring $I/(5)$ therefore has five elements, each element being one of the equivalence sets 4.39.

We now proceed to justify these statements, and to generalize them to the case of congruence modulo n. The following properties of congruence modulo n are fundamental for our purpose.

4.40 Theorem. *If $a \equiv b$ (mod n) and $c \equiv d$ (mod n), then*

(i) $a + c \equiv b + d$ (mod n),

and

(ii) $ac \equiv bd$ (mod n).

To prove these properties, we observe that $a \equiv b$ (mod n) means that there is an integer k such that $a = b + kn$. Similarly, we have $c = d + ln$ for some integer l. It follows that

$$a + c = b + d + (k + l)n;$$

that is, that $a + c \equiv b + d$ (mod n), and (i) is established. The second part follows easily by observing that

$$ac = (b + kn)(d + ln)$$
$$= bd + (bl + kd + kln)n,$$

and hence $ac \equiv bd$ (mod n), as required.

For the moment, let us denote by T the set of all equivalence sets modulo n. We proceed to define operations of addition and multiplication on T as follows. If $[r], [s] \in T$, we define

4.41 $[r] + [s] = [r + s]$,

and

4.42 $[r] \cdot [s] = [rs]$.

Now in order to show that these, in fact, do define addition and multiplication on the set T, we must show that the sum and product of the equivalence sets $[r]$ and $[s]$ do not depend upon the particular notation used to designate these sets, but only upon the sets themselves. This is sometimes expressed by saying that we must show that addition and multiplication are *well-defined* by 4.41 and 4.42. The preceding theorem is just what we need to establish this fact. For, suppose that $[x] = [r]$ and that $[y] = [s]$. These imply that $x \equiv r \pmod{n}$ and that $y \equiv s \pmod{n}$. The theorem then asserts that $x + y \equiv r + s \pmod{n}$ and that $xy \equiv rs \pmod{n}$, that is, that $[x + y] = [r + s]$ and that $[xy] = [rs]$. Hence, addition and multiplication of elements of T are well-defined by 4.41 and 4.42.

It is now quite easy to establish the following result.

43 Theorem. *With respect to the definitions 4.41 and 4.42 of addition and multiplication, the set of all equivalence sets of I modulo n is a commutative ring with unity. This ring is called "the ring of integers modulo n," and denoted by $I/(n)$.*

Let us prove, for example, the associative law of addition for elements of $I/(n)$. If $[r]$, $[s]$, and $[t]$ are elements of $I/(n)$, we wish therefore to prove that

44
$$([r] + [s]) + [t] = [r] + ([s] + [t]).$$

Now, by 4.41, $[r] + [s] = [r + s]$, and again applying 4.41, we see that the left side of 4.44 is the element $[(r + s) + t]$ of $I/(n)$. A similar calculation shows that the right side of 4.44 is equal to $[r + (s + t)]$. However, by the associative law of addition *for the integers*, we know that $(r + s) + t = r + (s + t)$, and it follows that 4.44 must hold.

In a similar way, each of the other properties of $I/(n)$ which need to be verified in order to establish the theorem follows from the corresponding property of the ring I. The proofs of these will be left as exercises. In particular, it is almost obvious that $[0]$ is the zero of the ring $I/(n)$, and that $[1]$ is its unity.

As an illustration, let us again consider the special case in which $n = 5$. As pointed out above, the five elements of this ring are $[0]$, $[1]$, $[2]$, $[3]$, and $[4]$. The reader may verify the following addition and multiplication tables for this ring. For convenience, we have omitted the brackets and written "k" in place of "$[k]$". This is often done when the context makes the meaning clear.

(+)	0	1	2	3	4
0	0	1	2	3	4
1	1	2	3	4	0
2	2	3	4	0	1
3	3	4	0	1	2
4	4	0	1	2	3

(·)	0	1	2	3	4
0	0	0	0	0	0
1	0	1	2	3	4
2	0	2	4	1	3
3	0	3	1	4	2
4	0	4	3	2	1

THE RING $I/(5)$

By examining the multiplication table for this ring we see that a product of elements is zero only if one of the factors is zero, and hence that the ring is an integral domain. The following theorem tells us for just what integers n the ring $I/(n)$ is an integral domain.

4.45 Theorem.   *The ring $I/(n)$ is an integral domain if and only if n is a prime.*

First, suppose that n is a prime p, and that $[r]$ and $[s]$ are elements of $I/(p)$ such that $[r] \cdot [s] = [0]$. Then $rs \equiv 0 \pmod{p}$, which implies that rs is divisible by p. Now since p is a prime, it follows that r is divisible by p or s is divisible by p, that is, that $r \equiv 0 \pmod{p}$ or $s \equiv 0 \pmod{p}$. Hence, $[r] = [0]$ or $[s] = [0]$, and $I/(p)$ is an integral domain by Definition 3.1.

Now, suppose that n is not prime. It follows that there exist integers n_1 and n_2 such that $n = n_1 n_2$, $1 < n_1 < n$, $1 < n_2 < n$. Hence, in $I/(n)$, we have $[n_1] \cdot [n_2] = [0]$, with $[n_1] \neq [0]$ and $[n_2] \neq [0]$. This shows that the ring $I/(n)$ is not an integral domain.

——————————————— **E X E R C I S E S**

1. Prove that congruence modulo n is an equivalence relation.

2. Complete the proof of Theorem 4.43.

3. Make addition and multiplication tables for each of the following rings: $I/(2)$, $I/(3)$, $I/(4)$, $I/(6)$, and $I/(7)$. By examining the multiplication tables, determine which of these rings are integral domains and compare with Theorem 4.45.

4. Show that the ring $I/(2)$ is isomorphic to the ring of Example 5, Section 2.3.

5. Is the ring $I/(4)$ isomorphic to either of the rings of Examples 6 or 7, Section 2.3?

6. Verify that the elements $[0]$, $[3]$, $[6]$, and $[9]$ of the ring $I/(12)$ are the elements of a subring of $I/(12)$. Make an addition and a multiplication table for this subring, and verify that it is isomorphic to the ring $I/(4)$.

7. Show that, for any positive prime p, the integral domain $I/(p)$ cannot be an ordered integral domain. [Hint: *Cf.* Exercises 9, 10; Section 3.2.]

8. Prove that the nonzero element $[a]$ of the ring $I/(n)$ has a multiplicative inverse if and only if a and n are relatively prime.

9. Show that any positive integer is congruent modulo 9 to the sum of its digits, it being assumed that the integer is written with the usual base 10. [This is the basis of the arithmetical check called, "casting out nines."]

10. Let S be the set of all positive integers n such that $n > 1$. If a, $b \in S$, let us define $a \sim b$ to mean that a and b have the same number of positive prime factors (distinct or identical). Show that "$\sim$" is an equivalence relation defined on S. If $[a]$ is the equivalence set (relative to this equivalence relation) which contains the integer a, and we set $[a] + [b] = [a + b]$, verify that we do *not* have a well-defined addition of equivalence sets.

5

Fields and the
Rational Numbers

The ring I of integers has the property, which is not true of the natural numbers (positive integers) alone, that every equation of the form $a + x = b$, where $a, b \in I$, has a solution x in I. In fact, one of the principal reasons for the introduction of the negative integers and zero is to assure us that every such equation is solvable. However, in I, an equation of the form $ax = b$ is solvable if and only if a is a divisor of b. Clearly, in order that an equation of this form, where $a, b \in I$ and $a \neq 0$, always have a solution we need to have available the rational numbers as well as the integers. Later on in this chapter we shall show how to extend the ring I of integers to the larger system of rational numbers. In this process we shall not use any previous knowledge of the rational number system, except perhaps to motivate the procedure used, but shall carry out the construction using only the properties of the integers which have already been given. Before presenting this construction we shall introduce and discuss the important concept of a *field*.

In a final optional section we shall briefly indicate how the ring of integers can be constructed from the system of natural numbers. This material is presented here because the method closely parallels that by which the rational numbers are constructed from the integers.

5.1 FIELDS

Let us make the following definition.

5.1 Definition. A commutative ring F with more than one element and having a unity is said to be a *field* if it has the following additional property:

P_{10}: Every nonzero element of F has a multiplicative inverse in F.

In view of Theorem 2.9, we know that each nonzero element of a field has a *unique* multiplicative inverse. As indicated in Section 2.5, we may denote the multiplicative inverse of a nonzero element r of a field F by "r^{-1}". If 1 is the unity of F, r^{-1} is therefore the unique element of F such that

5.2
$$r \cdot r^{-1} = r^{-1} \cdot r = 1.$$

However, the commutative law of multiplication is required to hold in a field, and we shall henceforth use it without explicit mention. In particular, we may consider that r^{-1} is defined by the single equation $r \cdot r^{-1} = 1$.

We shall now prove the following result.

5.3 Theorem. *A field is necessarily an integral domain.*

In view of the definition (3.1) of an integral domain, we only need to show that Property P_9 holds in a field. Suppose that r and s are elements of a field F such that $rs = 0$. If $r \neq 0$, r has a multiplicative inverse r^{-1} in F and it follows that

$$r^{-1}(rs) = (r^{-1}r)s = 1 \cdot s = s.$$

But also,

$$r^{-1}(rs) = r^{-1} \cdot 0 = 0.$$

Hence $s = 0$, and we have shown that $r = 0$ or $s = 0$. This establishes Property P_9, and F is therefore an integral domain.

By Theorem 3.2, we now know that the cancellation law of multiplication (Property P_9') always holds in a field.

Although in the definition of a field we only required the existence of the multiplicative inverse of each nonzero element r, that is, the solvability of each equation of the form $rx = 1$, we can easily establish the following more general result.

5.4 Theorem. *If r and s are elements of a field F and $r \neq 0$, there exists a unique element y of F such that $ry = s$. Moreover, $y = r^{-1} \cdot s$.*

It is clear that $r^{-1} \cdot s$ *is* a solution of this equation since

$$r(r^{-1} \cdot s) = (r \cdot r^{-1})s = 1 \cdot s = s.$$

To obtain the *uniqueness* of the solution, suppose that $ry_1 = s$ and $ry_2 = s$. Then $ry_1 = ry_2$ and, since $r \neq 0$, the cancellation law of multiplication shows that $y_1 = y_2$.

Let us now give a few examples of fields. It is to be understood that the usual definitions of addition and multiplication are implied.

Example 1. The set of all rational numbers; that is, all numbers of the form a/b, where $a, b \in I$ with $b \neq 0$.

Example 2. The set of all real numbers of the form $x + y\sqrt{2}$, where x and y are rational numbers. What is the multiplicative inverse of each nonzero element?

Example 3. The set of all real numbers of the form $u + v\sqrt{3}$, where u and v are elements of the field of the preceding example. It is true that every nonzero element has a multiplicative inverse in this set, but we shall not here write out a proof of this fact.

The following theorem gives some other examples of fields of quite a different type.

5.5 Theorem. *If p is a prime, the ring $I/(p)$ of integers modulo p is a field.*

This theorem is implied by the result of Exercise 8 of the preceding set of exercises. However, we now give a detailed proof of this important theorem.

We already know that $I/(p)$ is a commutative ring with unity and, using the notation of Section 4.7, the unity is $[1]$. Let $[r]$ be any nonzero element of $I/(p)$. In order to show that we have a field, we need to show that there exists an element $[x]$ of $I/(p)$ such that $[r] \cdot [x] = [1]$. The fact that $[r] \neq [0]$ implies that $r \not\equiv 0 \pmod{p}$, that is, that r is not divisible by p. Since p is a prime, it follows that r and p are relatively prime and Theorem 4.12 then assures us that there exist integers x, y such that $rx + py = 1$. This implies that $rx \equiv 1 \pmod{p}$, and hence that $[r] \cdot [x] = [1]$, as required.

We may remark that if n is not prime, we know by Theorem 4.45 that the ring $I/(n)$ is not even an integral domain, and certainly then is not a field.

A field $I/(p)$ differs from the usual fields of elementary algebra in that it has only a finite number of elements. However, in this as in any field we can always perform the so-called rational operations of addition, multiplication, subtraction, and division (except by zero). We are here using the familiar word "subtraction" to mean addition of the additive inverse, and "division" to mean multiplication by the multiplicative inverse. We may emphasize that division by zero is not defined in any field F since $0 \cdot x \neq 1$ for every x in F, and therefore 0 cannot have a multiplicative inverse.

We have required that a field contain at least two elements, and we may now observe that there does exist a field having exactly two elements, namely, the field $I/(2)$.

In view of Theorems 4.45 and 5.5, we know that if the ring $I/(n)$ is an integral domain, it is actually a field. On the other hand, the ring I of integers is an integral domain which is not a field. In this connection, the following theorem may be of some interest.

6 Theorem. *An integral domain S with a finite number of elements is necessarily a field.*

Suppose that S has the n distinct nonzero elements a_1, a_2, $\cdots$, a_n; and let A denote the set of these elements, that is, $A = \{a_1, a_2, \cdots, a_n\}$. Let a_k be any fixed element of A, and consider the set $B = \{a_k a_1, a_k a_2, \cdots, a_k a_n\}$ consisting of the products of elements of A by the element a_k. Since S is an integral domain, all elements of B are different from zero and hence $B \subseteq A$. Moreover, the elements of B are distinct, for $a_k a_i = a_k a_j$ would imply that $a_i = a_j$ by the cancellation law of multiplication. Hence the subset B of A has n distinct elements. Since A also has n elements, B cannot be a proper subset of A, and we must therefore have $B = A$. Now the unity 1 of S is an element of A, and hence also of B. Accordingly, we must have $a_k a_l = 1$ for some l, $1 \leq l \leq n$. Since a_k was an arbitrary nonzero element of S, we have shown that every such element has a multiplicative inverse and therefore S is a field.

Incidentally, the proof of this theorem furnishes an alternate proof of Theorem 5.5 since we already know by Theorem 4.45 that $I/(p)$ is an integral domain if p is a prime.

--------------------------------- **E X E R C I S E S**

1. Find the multiplicative inverse of each nonzero element of (i) the field $I/(5)$, (ii) the field $I/(11)$, and (iii) the field $I/(17)$.

2. Find the multiplicative inverse of each of the following elements of the field $I/(1847)$: $[12]$, $[30]$, $[100]$, $[431]$.

3. Show that not every finite field is of the form $I/(p)$ for some prime p. [Hint: Consider Example 7 of Section 2.3.]

4. Prove: If R is a commutative ring with more than one element and with the property that for a, $b \in R$, $a \neq 0$, there exists $x \in R$ such that $ax = b$, then R is a field. [Hint: First, prove that R has

Property P_9. Then let c and d be nonzero elements of R, so that there exist elements s and t of R such that $cs = c$ and $dt = d$. Prove that necessarily $s = t$; hence that R has s as a unity.]

5. Let P be the set of all positive real numbers, and q a fixed positive real number not equal to 1. If a, $b \in P$, we define operations of addition "$\oplus$" and multiplication "$\odot$" on P as follows:

$$a \oplus b = ab \text{ (ordinary multiplication)}, \quad a \odot b = a^{\log_q b}.$$

Show that with respect to these new definitions of addition and multiplication, P is a field.

5.2 THE CHARACTERISTIC

Although we are now primarily interested in fields, the concept to be introduced in this section applies to any ring and we therefore give the definition in its general form. We recall that if a is an element of a ring and n is a positive integer, we have given in Section 2.6 a recursive definition of na. We now make the following definition.

5.7 Definition. Let R be a ring. If there exists a positive integer n such that $na = 0$ for every element a of R, the smallest such positive integer n is called the *characteristic* of R. If no such positive integer exists, R is said to have *characteristic zero*.

All the familiar number systems of elementary algebra certainly have characteristic zero. However, let us consider, for example, the ring $I/(4)$ of integers modulo 4. If $[r]$ is any element of this ring, then $2[r] = [r] + [r] = [2r]$ and, generally, if k is a positive integer, $k[r] = [kr]$. The smallest positive integer k such that $[kr] = [0]$ for every element $[r]$ of $I/(4)$ is clearly 4, so $I/(4)$ has characteristic 4. In general, the ring $I/(n)$ has characteristic n.

We know that the ring $I/(n)$ is a field if and only if n is a prime. Hence the characteristic of every field that has been mentioned so far is either zero or a prime. In fact, we shall now prove that this is always true for every integral domain and certainly then for every field.

5.8 Theorem. *Every integral domain D has characteristic zero or a prime.*

To prove this theorem, suppose that D has characteristic $n > 0$, and that n is *not* a prime. Then $n = n_1 n_2$, where $1 < n_1 < n$, $1 < n_2 < n$. If e is the unity of D, we have $ne = 0$ and therefore $(n_1 n_2)e = 0$. However, this implies that $(n_1 e)(n_2 e) = 0$ and, by the definition of an integral domain, it follows that $n_1 e = 0$ or $n_2 e = 0$. Suppose that $n_1 e = 0$. If

$a \in D$, then, by 2.28 (iv), $n_1 a = n_1(ea) = (n_1 e)a = 0$. Hence, $n_1 a = 0$ for every element a of D. Since $1 < n_1 < n$ and D has characteristic n, this is impossible. Therefore n must be a prime, and the proof is completed.

The theory of fields is an important branch of modern algebra, and the literature on this subject is extensive. In much of this work the concept of the characteristic of a field plays an essential role. It frequently happens, for example, that although a theorem may be true for every field, different proofs have to be given for the case in which the characteristic is zero and that in which it is a prime. Later on in this book we shall present additional examples of fields.

5.3   SOME FAMILIAR NOTATION

Let F be a field with unity 1, and t a nonzero element of F. We have introduced the symbol "t^{-1}" to designate the multiplicative inverse of t, and have found that if $s \in F$, the unique element x of F such that $tx = s$ is given by $x = t^{-1}s$. In accordance with familiar usage, we shall also designate this element $t^{-1}s$ by $\dfrac{s}{t}$ or by s/t. In particular, we have $t^{-1} = 1/t$.

Suppose, now, that v is also a nonzero element of F. Since $(tv)(v^{-1}t^{-1}) = 1$, the multiplicative inverse of tv is $v^{-1}t^{-1}$, that is,

5.9
$$(tv)^{-1} = v^{-1}t^{-1}.$$

It is now easy to see that

5.10
$$\frac{sv}{tv} = \frac{s}{t}.$$

This follows by the following calculation, making use of 5.9:

$$\frac{sv}{tv} = (tv)^{-1}(sv) = v^{-1}t^{-1}sv = t^{-1}s = \frac{s}{t}.$$

As a generalization of 5.10, let s and u be arbitrary elements of F, and t and v arbitrary nonzero elements of F. Then we assert that

5.11
$$\frac{s}{t} = \frac{u}{v} \quad \text{if and only if} \quad sv = tu.$$

Suppose, first, that $s/t = u/v$, that is, that $t^{-1}s = v^{-1}u$. Multiplication by tv yields $sv = tu$. Conversely, if $sv = tu$, multiplication by $t^{-1}v^{-1}$ shows that $t^{-1}s = v^{-1}u$ or, otherwise expressed, that $s/t = u/v$.

The following are also easy to establish and will be left as exercises:

5.12
(i)
$$\frac{s}{t} + \frac{u}{v} = \frac{sv + tu}{tv},$$

(ii)
$$\frac{s}{t} \cdot \frac{u}{v} = \frac{su}{tv}.$$

Now a few remarks about exponents. If t is a nonzero element of F, we have a definition of t^{-1}; and if n is any positive integer, we now define t^{-n} to be $(t^{-1})^n$; also we define $t^0 = 1$. Under these definitions, the following laws of exponents hold for every choice of m and n as arbitrary integers (positive, negative, or zero), it being understood that t and v are arbitrary nonzero elements of F:

5.13
$$t^m \cdot t^n = t^{m+n},$$
$$\frac{t^m}{t^n} = t^{m-n},$$
$$(t^m)^n = t^{mn},$$
$$(tv)^m = t^m \cdot v^m,$$
$$\left(\frac{t}{v}\right)^m = \frac{t^m}{v^m}.$$

Of course, these are generalizations of the laws 2.26, 2.27, which hold for a commutative ring. Complete proofs of 5.13 can be given by mathematical induction.

_____ **E X E R C I S E S**

1. Let R be a ring with a finite number of elements, and r a nonzero element of R.

(i) Show that there must exist a positive integer m such that $mr = 0$.

(ii) Show that R cannot have characteristic zero.

2. Let a be a fixed nonzero element of an integral domain D such that $ma = 0$ for some positive integer m. Prove that the smallest such positive integer is the characteristic of D (that is, it is independent of the particular nonzero element a which is chosen). Show, by an example, that this result is not necessarily true for a *ring*.

3. Prove 5.12 (i), (ii).

4. If s, t, u, and v are elements of a field F, prove (without using the laws of exponents) each of the following in which it is assumed that the necessary elements are different from zero:

(i) $\qquad$ $(t^{-1})^{-1} = t,$

(ii) $\qquad$ $(-t)^{-1} = -(t^{-1}),$

(iii) $\qquad$ $\left(\dfrac{s}{t}\right)^{-1} = \dfrac{t}{s},$

(iv) $\qquad$ $\dfrac{\dfrac{s}{t}}{\dfrac{u}{v}} = \dfrac{vs}{ut},$

(v) $\qquad$ $-\dfrac{s}{t} = \dfrac{(-s)}{t} = \dfrac{s}{(-t)},$

(vi) $\qquad$ $\dfrac{s}{t} + \dfrac{u}{t} = \dfrac{s+u}{t},$

(vii) $\qquad$ $\dfrac{s}{t} - \dfrac{u}{v} = \dfrac{sv - tu}{tv}.$

5.4 THE FIELD OF RATIONAL NUMBERS

We now change our point of view as follows. Instead of studying properties of a given field, let us see how we can start with the integral domain I of the integers and *construct* a field which contains I. This is our first example of an important algebraic problem which may be stated in a general way as follows. Given an algebraic system U which does not have some specified property, to construct a larger system V which contains U and which does have the property in question. Naturally, this is not always possible, but it is in a number of interesting cases. At present, we start with the integral domain I in which not every nonzero element has a multiplicative inverse, and shall construct a larger system — the field of rational numbers — which contains I and in which every nonzero element necessarily has a multiplicative inverse. In this construction, our previous knowledge of the rational numbers will certainly be useful in suggesting procedure, but will be used in no other way.

Let S denote the set of all ordered pairs (a, b), where $a, b \in I$ and $b \neq 0$, that is,

$$S = \{(a, b); \ a, b \in I, b \neq 0\}.$$

What we are going to do will be *suggested* by thinking of (a, b) as the familiar a/b, but we use an unfamiliar notation in order to clarify the logical procedure and to avoid using any property until we have actually proved it. If (a, b) and (c, d) are elements of S, we define $(a, b) \sim (c, d)$ to mean that $ad = bc$. Actually, "$\sim$" is an equivalence relation defined on S. The reflexive and symmetric properties are obviously true, and we now prove the transitive property. Suppose that $(a, b) \sim (c, d)$ and $(c, d) \sim (e, f)$, and let us show that $(a, b) \sim (e, f)$. Since $(a, b) \sim (c, d)$, we have $ad = bc$; and, similarly, we have $cf = de$. Multiplication of these equations by f and by b, respectively, yields $adf = bcf$ and $bcf = bde$. Hence $adf = bde$ and, since $d \neq 0$, it follows that $af = be$, that is, that $(a, b) \sim (e, f)$.

Now that we have an equivalence relation "$\sim$" defined on S, we follow a procedure somewhat like that previously used in obtaining the ring of integers modulo n. That is, we shall consider equivalence sets relative to "$\sim$", and give appropriate definitions of addition and multiplication of these sets.

If $(a, b) \in S$, according to our previous usage the equivalence set containing (a, b) would be designated by "$[(a, b)]$." However, we shall now use the simpler notation "$[a, b]$" to designate this equivalence set. In the sequel it is important to keep in mind that $[a, b] = [a_1, b_1]$ if and only if $(a, b) \sim (a_1, b_1)$, that is, if and only if $ab_1 = ba_1$. Of course, this is just the general property 1.10 (ii) of equivalence sets as applied in this particular case. The equivalence set $[a, b]$ may therefore be expressed as follows:

5.14 $$[a, b] = \{(x, y); \ (x, y) \in S, \ xb = ya\}.$$

We now define addition and multiplication of equivalence sets as follows:

5.15 $$[a, b] + [c, d] = [ad + bc, bd],$$
and
5.16 $$[a, b] \cdot [c, d] = [ac, bd].$$

First, we observe that since (a, b) and (c, d) are elements of S, we have $b \neq 0$ and $d \neq 0$. Hence, $bd \neq 0$, so that in fact $(ad + bc, bd)$ and (ac, bd) are elements of S and the right sides of 5.15 and 5.16 are equivalence sets.

Now, just as in the case of integers modulo n, we must show that addition and multiplication of equivalence sets are well-defined by 5.15 and 5.16. Suppose, then, that

5.17 $$[a, b] = [a_1, b_1] \quad \text{and} \quad [c, d] = [c_1, d_1].$$

In order to show that addition of equivalence sets is well-defined by 5.15, we must show that necessarily

$$[a, b] + [c, d] = [a_1, b_1] + [c_1, d_1];$$
that is, that

.18 $$[ad + bc, bd] = [a_1d_1 + b_1c_1, b_1d_1].$$

From 5.17, we have that $ab_1 = ba_1$, and that $cd_1 = dc_1$. If we multiply the first of these equations by dd_1, the second by bb_1, and add the corresponding members, it follows that

$$(ad + bc)b_1d_1 = bd(a_1d_1 + b_1c_1).$$

However, this implies 5.18, and therefore addition of equivalence sets is well-defined by 5.15. The proof that multiplication is well-defined by 5.16 will be left as an exercise.

We may now state the following theorem.

.19   Theorem.   *Let R denote the set of all equivalence sets of S relative to the equivalence relation "$\sim$". Then with respect to the operations of addition and multiplication on R defined by 5.15 and 5.16, R is a field. Moreover, the set of all elements of R of the form $[a, 1]$, $a \in I$, is a subring I' of R; and the mapping*

$$[a, 1] \to a \qquad\qquad a \in I,$$

is an isomorphism of I' onto I.

The commutative laws of addition and multiplication, as well as the associative law of multiplication, are almost obvious, and we omit the details. The associative law of addition may be verified by the following straightforward calculation. Let $[a, b]$, $[c, d]$, and $[e, f]$ be elements of R. Then

$$([a, b] + [c, d]) + [e, f] = [ad + bc, bd] + [e, f]$$
$$= [adf + bcf + bde, bdf],$$

and

$$[a, b] + ([c, d] + [e, f]) = [a, b] + [cf + de, df]$$
$$= [adf + bcf + bde, bdf],$$

and we therefore have

$$([a, b] + [c, d]) + [e, f] = [a, b] + ([c, d] + [e, f]).$$

Since $[0, 1] + [a, b] = [a, b]$, and $[1, 1] \cdot [a, b] = [a, b]$, it follows that $[0, 1]$ is the zero and $[1, 1]$ the unity of R. However, if d is a nonzero integer, we have $[d, d] = [1, 1]$ and, similarly, $[0, 1] = [0, d]$. Hence the unity is $[d, d]$ and the zero is $[0, d]$ for *any* nonzero integer d. We may also observe that $[a, b] = [0, 1]$ if and only if $a = 0$, and to say, therefore, that $[a, b]$ is a nonzero element of R is to say that $a \neq 0$.

Since $[a, b] + [-a, b] = [0, b^2]$, and $[0, b^2]$ is the zero of R, it follows that the additive inverse of $[a, b]$ is $[-a, b]$, that is, we have $-[a, b] = [-a, b]$, and each element of R has an additive inverse.

One of the distributive laws is a consequence of the following calculations in which, at one point, we make use of the fact that $[b, b]$ is the unity of R:

$$[a, b]([c, d] + [e, f]) = [a, b] \cdot [cf + de, df]$$
$$= [acf + ade, bdf],$$
$$[a, b] \cdot [c, d] + [a, b] \cdot [e, f] = [ac, bd] + [ae, bf]$$
$$= [acbf + bdae, b^2df]$$
$$= [acf + ade, bdf] \cdot [b, b]$$
$$= [acf + ade, bdf].$$

The other distributive law is an immediate consequence of this one since multiplication is commutative.

Up to this point we have proved that R is a commutative ring with unity. To prove that R is a field, there remains only to show that every nonzero element of R has a multiplicative inverse in R. If $[a, b]$ is a nonzero element of R, then $a \neq 0$ as well as $b \neq 0$, and it is clear that $[b, a] \in R$. Moreover,

$$[a, b] \cdot [b, a] = [ab, ab] = [1, 1],$$

and the multiplicative inverse of $[a, b]$ is $[b, a]$. That is, if $[a, b]$ is a nonzero element of R, then $[a, b]^{-1} = [b, a]$. This completes the proof that R is a field.

We now let I' be the set of all elements of R of the form $[a, 1]$, $a \in I$, and consider the mapping $[a, 1] \rightarrow a$ of I' onto I. Since $[a, 1] = [b, 1]$ if and only if $a = b$, this is a one-one mapping of I' onto I. Moreover,

$$[a, 1] + [b, 1] = [a + b, 1] \rightarrow a + b,$$

and

$$[a, 1] \cdot [b, 1] = [ab, 1] \rightarrow ab,$$

so that the operations of addition and multiplication are preserved under this mapping. We therefore have an isomorphism of I' onto I. Since I' is a subring of the field R, we have shown that R contains a subring isomorphic to I. As a matter of notation, we shall henceforth find it convenient to identify I' with I and write simply "a" to designate the element $[a, 1]$ of R. We may then consider that the field R actually contains the ring I of integers.

As a further simplification of notation, let us observe that

$$[a, b] = [a, 1] \cdot [1, b] = [a, 1] \cdot [b, 1]^{-1},$$

and hence we are justified in writing $a \cdot b^{-1}$ or a/b for the element $[a, b]$ of R. Now that we have justified our familiar notation, we shall henceforth call an element of R a *rational number* and the field R the *field of rational numbers*. All of the notation of the preceding section naturally applies to the field R.

In the notation which we have finally introduced, the field R of rational numbers consists of all numbers of the form a/b, where a and b are integers with $b \neq 0$, addition and multiplication being defined in the usual way (5.15, 5.16).

Let us emphasize the meaning of the notation we have introduced by considering, for example, the rational number $1/2$. We are writing $1/2$ for the equivalence set $[1, 2]$ used above. Now $[1, 2] = [c, d]$ if and only if $d = 2c$, so we see that $1/2$ represents the equivalence set consisting of all ordered pairs of the form $(c, 2c)$, where c is a nonzero integer. Moreover, for example, $1/2 = 3/6$ simply because, by our definition of equivalence, $(1, 2) \sim (3, 6)$ and therefore $[1, 2] = [3, 6]$.

Since $(-a)/b = a/(-b)$, we see that every rational number can be written in the form c/d, where $d > 0$. Moreover, if the integers c and d have a common nonzero factor k, so that $c = c_1 k$ and $d = d_1 k$, then $c/d = c_1/d_1$. It follows that every rational number r can be written uniquely in the form a/b, where a and b are relatively prime integers with $b > 0$. If r is expressed in this form, it is sometimes said that r is expressed *in lowest terms*.

5.5 A FEW PROPERTIES OF THE FIELD OF RATIONAL NUMBERS

We have defined in Section 3.2 what we mean by an ordered integral domain. Since a field is necessarily an integral domain, by an *ordered field* we shall naturally mean a field which is an ordered integral domain. We shall now prove the following result.

5.20 Theorem. *Let R_p denote the set of all rational numbers a/b, where a and b are integers such that $ab > 0$. Then R_p has the Properties 3.3 which define an ordered integral domain, and therefore the field R is an ordered field whose positive elements are the elements of R_p.*

We may point out that when we write $ab > 0$, we mean that ab is a positive *integer* and we are only making use of the fact that I is an ordered integral domain.

First, we need to show that the definition of an element of R_p does not depend upon the particular representation of a rational number. That is, we need to show that if $a/b = c/d$ and $ab > 0$, then also $cd > 0$. This follows from the observation that $a/b = c/d$ means that $ad = bc$, and $ab > 0$ implies that either a and b are both positive or they are both negative. The same must therefore be true of c and d; hence also $cd > 0$.

Now let us show (3.3 (i)) that the set R_p is closed under addition. Let a/b and c/d be elements of R_p, and therefore $ab > 0$ and $cd > 0$. Then

$$\frac{a}{b} + \frac{c}{d} = \frac{ad + bc}{bd},$$

and we wish to show that

$$(ad + bc)bd = abd^2 + cdb^2 > 0.$$

However, this inequality follows easily from the following known inequalities: $ab > 0$, $cd > 0$, $b^2 > 0$, and $d^2 > 0$.

It is trivial that R_p is closed under multiplication (3.3 (ii)). Moreover, if a/b is a nonzero rational number, then either $ab > 0$ or $ab < 0$. It follows that for every rational number a/b, exactly one of the following holds (3.3 (iii)):

$$\frac{a}{b} = 0, \qquad \frac{a}{b} > 0, \qquad -\frac{a}{b} > 0.$$

Hence R_p has the three required properties, and the field R of rational numbers is ordered.

It will be observed that what we have done is to make use of the known ordering of the integers to establish an ordering of the rational numbers. Inasmuch as we have identified the integer a with the rational number $a/1$, it is clear that a is a positive integer if and only if a is a positive rational number. In other words, our ordering of the rational numbers is an *extension* of the previous ordering of the integers.

In view of Theorem 5.20, we can introduce inequalities involving rational numbers in the usual way. That is, if r, $s \in R$, we write $r > s$ (or $s < r$) to mean that $r - s \in R_p$, and so on. We now have available all the usual properties (3.5) of inequalities for rational numbers. In the future we shall make use of these properties without specific reference. In the next chapter we shall find that inequalities involving rational numbers play an important role in establishing the properties of the *real* numbers.

The following is a significant property of the rational numbers.

5.21 Theorem. *Between any two distinct rational numbers there is another rational number.*

Suppose that r, $s \in R$ with $r < s$. The theorem will be established by showing that

$$r < \frac{r + s}{2} < s,$$

and hence $(r + s)/2$ is a rational number between r and s. Since $r < s$, we have $r + r < r + s$, or $2r < r + s$. Now multiplying this last inequality by the positive rational number $1/2$, we obtain $r < (r + s)/2$. In a similar manner, it can be shown that $(r + s)/2 < s$, and we omit the details.

The property of the rational numbers stated in the preceding theorem is often expressed by saying that the rational numbers are *dense*. We shall now prove in the following theorem another simple, but important, property of the rational numbers.

5.22 Theorem. (Archimedean Property) *If r and s are any positive rational numbers, there exists a positive integer n such that $nr > s$.*

Let $r = a/b$, $s = c/d$, where a, b, c, and d are positive integers. If n is a positive integer, then $n(a/b) > c/d$ if and only if $n(ad) > bc$. We now assert that this last inequality is necessarily satisfied if we choose $n = 2bc$. For $ad \geq 1$, and therefore $2ad > 1$. Multiplying this inequality by the positive integer bc shows that $2adbc > bc$. Hence, $n = 2bc$ certainly satisfies our requirement. Of course, we do not mean to imply that this is necessarily the smallest possible choice of n.

——————————————————————————— **E X E R C I S E S**

1. Prove that multiplication of equivalence sets is well-defined by 5.16.

2. Complete the proof of Theorem 5.21, and state what properties of inequalities have been used.

3. If u and v are positive rational numbers with $u < v$, show that $1/u > 1/v$.

4. If $r, s \in R$ with $r < s$, and $u, v \in R_p$, show that

$$r < \frac{ur + vs}{u + v} < s.$$

5. If $r, s \in R$ with $r < s$, and n is an arbitrary positive integer, show that there exist rational numbers $t_1, t_2, \cdots, t_n$ such that

$$r < t_1 < t_2 < \cdots < t_n < s.$$

5.6 THE QUOTIENT FIELD OF AN INTEGRAL DOMAIN

In our construction of the rational numbers in Section 5.4, *no* properties of the integers were used except those which imply that the set of all integers is an integral domain. Accordingly, by exactly the same construction we could start with any integral domain D and construct a field F of "quotients" a/b of elements of D, which contains D as a subring. This field F is called the *quotient field* of D. Hence, the field of rational numbers is the quotient field of the integral domain of integers.

—————————————————————— *EXERCISES*

1. Go through the proof of Theorem 5.19 and verify that all the steps could be carried out if any integral domain D were used in place of I.

2. In the proof of Theorem 5.19 why could we not use an arbitrary commutative ring with unity in place of I?

3. If D is an ordered integral domain, verify that the quotient field of D is an ordered field.

5.7 CONSTRUCTION OF THE INTEGERS FROM THE NATURAL NUMBERS (OPTIONAL)

We indicated in Section 3.5 how all the familiar properties of the natural numbers, that is, the positive integers, can be obtained from a few simple axioms. Let N be the system of all natural numbers. In this system we have operations of addition and multiplication, and all the properties of an integral domain hold except that there is no zero, and elements do not have additive inverses. In this section we shall outline a procedure by which we can start with N and *construct* the ring I of all integers. The method closely parallels that by which we have constructed the rational numbers from the ring of integers. We may emphasize that we now assume as known only the properties of the natural numbers.

Let T be the set of all ordered pairs (a, b) of elements of N. Our procedure will be *suggested* by thinking of (a, b) as meaning $a - b$, but we must so formulate our statements that only natural numbers are involved. If (a, b) and (c, d) are elements of T, we shall write $(a, b) \sim (c, d)$ to mean that $a + d = b + c$. It is easy to verify that "$\sim$" is an equivalence relation on T. One way to characterize the equivalence set $[a, b]$ which contains (a, b) is as follows:

$$[a, b] = \{(x, y); \ x, y \in N, \ x + b = y + a\}.$$

Now let I be the set of all such equivalence sets, and let us make the following definitions:

5.23
$$[a, b] + [c, d] = [a + c, b + d],$$

and

5.24
$$[a, b] \cdot [c, d] = [ac + bd, ad + bc].$$

It can be shown that addition and multiplication are well-defined, and hence that we have operations of addition and multiplication defined on I. The following theorem can now be established.

5.25 Theorem. *With respect to the Definitions 5.23 and 5.24 of addition and multiplication, I is an integral domain and, by a suitable change of notation, we may consider that I contains the set N of natural numbers. If we now define the set I_p of positive elements of I to be the set N, then I is an ordered integral domain in which the set of positive elements is well-ordered.*

We shall make a few remarks about the proof of this theorem, but shall not write out all the details. The zero of I is $[c, c]$ for an arbitrary natural number c. The additive inverse of $[a, b]$ is $[b, a]$, that is, $-[a, b] = [b, a]$.

Let N' be the set of all elements of I of the form $[x + 1, 1]$, $x \in N$. Then the mapping

$$x \to [x + 1, 1] \qquad\qquad x \in N,$$

is a one-one mapping of N onto N' and, moreover, addition and multiplication are preserved under this mapping. Hence, as a matter of notation, let us identify N' with N; that is, let us write x in place of $[x + 1, 1]$ so that I now actually contains N. If $[a, b] \in I$, it is easy to verify that

$$[a, b] = [a + 1, 1] + [1, b + 1]$$
$$= [a + 1, 1] - [b + 1, 1]$$
$$= a - b.$$

We have therefore justified writing $a - b$ in place of $[a, b]$.

If $c, d \in N$, we defined $c > d$ in Section 3.5 to mean that there exists a natural number e such that $c = d + e$. Since $[a, b] = a - b$, we see that $[a, b]$ is an element of N if $a > b$, and that $-[a, b]$ is an element of N if $b > a$. The elements of I therefore consist of the natural numbers, the additive inverses of the natural numbers, and zero. Of course, the integral domain I is called the *ring of integers*.

If we set $I_p = N$, then I_p has the properties (3.3) which make I an ordered integral domain. Finally, then, since the set N is well-ordered, we have that I is an ordered integral domain in which the set of positive elements is well-ordered. Our viewpoint in this book has been to *assume* that the ring of integers has all the properties implied in this statement. However, we have now indicated how this result can be proved by starting only with the Peano Axioms for the natural numbers.

6

The Field of Real
Numbers

In this chapter we shall extend the field of rational numbers to the larger field of real numbers, and then establish a few properties of the real numbers. It will be found that the procedure involves somewhat lengthy calculations with inequalities in the ordered field of rational numbers. However, in view of the importance of the system of real numbers in mathematical analysis, we shall carry out these calculations in some detail. A substantial part of the proof of the principal theorem is postponed until the last section of the chapter and is marked "optional." This section and, for that matter, some of the other proofs may be omitted on a first reading if it seems desirable to do so.

6.1 INTRODUCTION

The rational numbers are sufficient for use in all simple applications of mathematics. For example, measurements are usually given to a certain number of decimal places, and any finite decimal is a rational number. However, from a theoretical point of view, the system of rational numbers is entirely inadequate. The Pythagoreans made this discovery about 500 B.C. and were profoundly shocked by it. Consider, for example, an isosceles right triangle whose legs are 1 unit in length. Then, by the Pythagorean theorem, the hypotenuse has length $\sqrt{2}$; and from this geometrical consideration it appears that there must exist a "number" $\sqrt{2}$, although we have shown in Section 4.5 that it cannot be a rational number.

As a matter of fact, the Greeks did not assign a number as the length of a segment, but they were interested in considering ratios of segments in connection with such concepts as similarity of triangles. Two segments a and b are *commensurable* if there exists some segment c such that for properly chosen positive integers m and n, $a = mc$ and $b = nc$. The argument given above shows that a side of an isosceles right triangle and its hypotenuse are not commensurable, since $\sqrt{2}$ is not a rational number. In the earliest proofs that the ratios of corresponding sides of similar triangles are equal it was tacitly assumed that the segments whose ratios were being considered were commensurable. When it was discovered that this is not necessarily always the case, entirely new methods had to be developed. In fact, it was not even clear what might be meant by *equal* ratios of incommensurable segments. In the fourth century B.C., Eudoxus gave what proved to be a satisfactory definition of equality of two ratios of any segments. If a, b, c, and d are segments, without going into any explanation of the meaning of a ratio of segments, let us designate by "$a : b$" the ratio of a to b, and by "$c : d$" the ratio of c to d. Now Eudoxus defined $a : b = c : d$ to mean that both of the following are true:

(1) For every choice of m and n as positive integers such that $ma < nb$, then also $mc < nd$,

(2) For every choice of m and n as positive integers such that $ma > nb$, then also $mc > nd$.

Now if we think of $a : b$ as a number, these conditions say that if $n/m > a : b$, then $n/m > c : d$; and if $n/m < a : b$, then $n/m < c : d$. In other words, the "number" $a : b$ is equal to the "number" $c : d$ if the *rational* numbers that are greater than $a : b$ are also greater than $c : d$, and the *rational* numbers that are less than $a : b$ are also less than $c : d$.

This definition of Eudoxus was remarkably clever, and led to a satisfactory geometric theory of equality of ratios of incommensurable segments—a theory that was included in Euclid's famous treatise of about 300 B.C.

Since the theory of the Greeks was geometric in nature and they did not associate a number with the length of a segment, it is perhaps not surprising that they did not proceed to develop the system of real numbers as we know it. It is, however, somewhat surprising that this system was not developed in a satisfactory way until the latter half of the

19th century. Although other men made contributions to the theory, it is usually attributed to the German mathematicians Cantor (1845–1918) and Dedekind (1831–1916). The method of Dedekind is strongly suggested by the work of Eudoxus, and it is his approach which we shall now present.

6.2 DEFINITION AND EXAMPLES OF DEDEKIND CUTS

In order to motivate the definition to be given presently, we begin with a suggestive, but not very precise, geometric description of the concept which will play a central role in our development of the system of real numbers. Let us think of the rational numbers marked off in the usual way as coordinates of points on a line, as suggested by Figure 4,

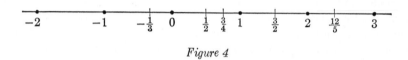

Figure 4

and let us consider the effect of cutting the line into two parts. Since we are at present interested only in the points with rational coordinates, we shall vaguely think of the line as consisting only of these points. With this understanding, let us consider, for example, the effect of cutting the line at the point with coordinate 2, and let us designate the left-hand part of the line by $\mathcal{L}$ and the right-hand part by $\mathcal{R}$. All the points with coordinates less than 2 are therefore in $\mathcal{L}$, and all those points with coordinates greater than 2 are in $\mathcal{R}$. The point with coordinate 2, at which the cut was made, could be considered to be in either $\mathcal{L}$ or $\mathcal{R}$, or left out entirely for that matter. However, we shall find it convenient to assume that it is in $\mathcal{R}$. Since every point is now in either $\mathcal{L}$ or $\mathcal{R}$, it is clear that instead of describing a cut by considering both $\mathcal{L}$ and $\mathcal{R}$, we might describe it by specifying, say $\mathcal{L}$, and then $\mathcal{R}$ would be automatically determined as the points of the line *not* in $\mathcal{L}$.

Instead of speaking vaguely of cutting a *line*, we proceed to express precisely what we mean in terms of certain sets of rational numbers. Throughout this chapter we shall designate by "R" the field of rational numbers.

6.1 Definition. A subset A of R is called a *Dedekind cut*, or simply a *cut*, if it has the following three properties:

(i) A is not the empty set, and also $A \neq R$,

(ii) If $a \in A$ and b is an arbitrary element of R such that $b < a$, then $b \in A$,

(iii) If $a \in A$, there exists $c \in A$ such that $c > a$.

As an example of a cut, let A be the set of all rational numbers that, in the example described above, are coordinates of points in $\mathcal{L}$. That is, $A = \{a; \, a \in R, \, a < 2\}$. Since $1 \in A$ and $3 \notin A$, Property (i) is satisfied. Also Property (ii) is obviously satisfied since if $a < 2$ and $b < a$, then also $b < 2$. Property (iii) is not quite as obvious but it follows from the fact (Theorem 5.21) that if $a < 2$, then there exists a rational number c such that $a < c < 2$. Hence, if $a \in A$, there exists $c \in A$ such that $c > a$. Since all the requirements are met, A is a cut. This cut we shall call the *cut at* 2.

In like manner, if r is an arbitrary rational number, the set of all rational numbers less than r is a cut, which we call the *cut at* r. This cut we shall designate by "C_r"; that is,

$$C_r = \{a; \, a \in R, \, a < r\}.$$

The cut at 2 given in the example above is, in the present notation, the cut C_2.

If A is a cut, it will often be convenient to designate the set of all rational numbers which are *not* in A by "A'". Thus, for example,

$$C_r' = \{a; \, a \in R, \, a \geq r\}.$$

Property (iii) states that in a cut A there can be no largest rational number. However, it may happen that there exists a smallest rational number not in A, that is, in A'. This is certainly the case for any cut of the form C_r, for obviously r is the smallest rational number in C_r'.

Now it is a significant fact that there exist cuts other than cuts at rational numbers, that is, other than those of the form C_r for some rational number r. We shall establish this fact by exhibiting a cut D with the property that in D' there is no smallest rational number. The cut D can then not be a cut at a rational number.

Let us define D to be the set of all negative rational numbers and zero, together with all positive rational numbers a such that $a^2 < 2$. We now verify in turn the three properties 6.1 (i)–(iii), which will show that D is indeed a cut.

(i)   Evidently, $1 \in D$ and $2 \notin D$.

(ii) Let $a \in D$ and $b < a$. If either a or b is zero or negative, it is trivial that $b \in D$. Suppose that $a > 0$ and $b > 0$. Then $b < a$ implies that $b^2 < ab < a^2$, and hence $b^2 < 2$ since $a^2 < 2$. Therefore $b \in D$, as required.

(iii)   Let $a \in D$, and again we may suppose that $a > 0$. Since $a^2 < 2$, we have $2 - a^2 > 0$ and, by the Archimedean Property of the rational numbers (Theorem 5.22), there exists a positive integer n such that $n(2 - a^2) > 2a + 1$. From this inequality it follows that $(2a + 1)/n < 2 - a^2$; moreover, since $n \geq 1$, we have $1/n^2 \leq 1/n$. Using these, we find that

$$\left(a + \frac{1}{n}\right)^2 = a^2 + \frac{2a}{n} + \frac{1}{n^2}$$
$$\leq a^2 + \frac{2a + 1}{n}$$
$$< a^2 + 2 - a^2 = 2.$$

Hence, $a + 1/n$ is an element of D. Since $a + 1/n > a$, this third property has been established.

We have now verified all the required properties, and therefore D is a cut. Next we show that among the rational numbers in D' (that is, not in D) there is no smallest. We proved in Section 4.5 that 2 is not the square of a rational number, and hence we have

$$D' = \{r;\ r \in R, r > 0, r^2 > 2\}.$$

Now suppose that $r \in D'$ and let us prove that there exists a smaller element of D'. Since $r^2 > 2$, the Archimedean Property of the rational numbers assures us that there exists a positive integer m such that $m(r^2 - 2) > 2r$. From this inequality, it follows that $2r/m < r^2 - 2$, and therefore $-2r/m > 2 - r^2$. Hence, we conclude that

$$\left(r - \frac{1}{m}\right)^2 = r^2 - \frac{2r}{m} + \frac{1}{m^2}$$
$$> r^2 - \frac{2r}{m}$$
$$> r^2 + 2 - r^2 = 2.$$

Moreover, since $r > 1$ and $m \geq 1$, we see that $r - 1/m > 0$. We have therefore verified that $r - 1/m$ is an element of D'. Since $r - 1/m < r$, we have shown that given an arbitrary element r of D' there exists a smaller element of D'. The cut D can therefore not be a cut at a rational number. Naturally, we would like to associate the cut D in some way with a "number" $\sqrt{2}$. How this is done will be indicated later in this chapter.

At the beginning of this section we gave a geometric motivation for the definition of a cut. The geometric interpretation, if not the formal definition itself, should make it clear that if A is a cut, there must exist in A rational numbers that are quite close to some numbers in A'. Let us now give the following precise formulation of this fact, which will be useful in later proofs.

.2 Lemma. *If A is a cut and r an arbitrary positive rational number, there exists an element a of A such that $a + r \in A'$.*

We shall prove this result for the case in which A contains some *positive* rational numbers. It is easy to modify the proof so that it will apply to any cut. One method of doing so will be suggested in Exercise 7 below.

If $r \in A'$, then $0 + r \in A'$ and since $0 \in A$ (why?), there is nothing more to prove. Suppose, now, that $r \notin A'$ and hence that $r \in A$; and let b be a fixed element of A'. By the Archimedean property of the rational numbers, there exists a positive integer n such that $nr > b$, and hence $nr \in A'$ (since $nr \in A$ would imply that $b \in A$, which is false). The set of all positive integers n such that $nr \in A'$ is therefore not empty and must contain a least element, say m. Moreover, $m > 1$ inasmuch as $r \notin A'$ and, by definition of m, we must have $(m - 1)r \in A$. Since $(m - 1)r + r \in A'$, the desired result has been obtained with $a = (m - 1)r$.

_____ **E X E R C I S E S**

1. If A is a cut and A' the set of all rational numbers not in A, verify each of the following:

   (*i*) Every element of A' is greater than every element of A,

   (*ii*) A' is not the empty set, and also $A' \neq R$,

   (*iii*) If $a \in A'$ and $b > a$, then $b \in A'$.

2. Write out a proof that if r is a rational number and $C_r = \{a; \ a \in R, \ a < r\}$, then C_r is a cut.

3. If $r, s \in R$, show that $C_r \subset C_s$ if and only if $r < s$.

4. If A and B are cuts with $A \neq B$, prove that either $A \subset B$ or $B \subset A$.

5. Let k be a positive integer which is not a perfect square, and let D be the set of all negative rational numbers and zero, together with all positive rational numbers a such that $a^2 < k$. Prove that D is a cut and that there is no smallest rational number in D'.

6. Prove that if A is a cut and $t \in R$, then $E = \{t + a; \ a \in A\}$ is a cut and that $E' = \{t + a'; \ a' \in A'\}$.

7. Use the result of the preceding exercise to show that Lemma 6 2 holds even if A contains no positive rational numbers.

6.3 ADDITION OF CUTS

Throughout the rest of this chapter we shall let K denote the set of all cuts of the rational numbers. Hence $A \in K$ is merely another way of stating that A is a cut. Our general program is to define operations of addition and multiplication on K in such a way that K will be a field with respect to these operations, and eventually we shall call this field the field of real numbers. In the present section we shall define addition on K and prove that it has all the required properties. Our definition of addition, as well as the later definition of multiplication, is suggested by a consideration of cuts at rational numbers. For example, if C_2 and C_3 are the cuts at 2 and 3, respectively, we would like to define addition in such a way that $C_2 + C_3$ will be the cut C_5. However, since there exist cuts other than those of the form C_r for $r \in R$, we must so formulate our definition that it will apply to arbitrary cuts. Accordingly, we introduce the following definition.

6.3 Definition. If $A, B \in K$, then

$$A + B = \{a + b;\ a \in A, b \in B\}.$$

Now $A + B$ is clearly a *set* of rational numbers; namely, the set of all rational numbers of the form $a + b$, with $a \in A$ and $b \in B$. However, in order for 6.3 to define an operation of addition on K, it is essential that the set $A + B$ be a *cut*, and therefore an element of K. We proceed to show that $A + B$ is a cut by verifying in turn the three defining properties (6.1(i), (ii), (iii)) of a cut.

(i)   Since A and B are cuts, neither is the empty set and therefore $A + B$ is not the empty set. Also $A \neq R$ and $B \neq R$ imply that there exist $a_1, b_1 \in R$ such that $a_1 \notin A$ and $b_1 \notin B$. It follows that $a_1 + b_1$ is greater than every element of $A + B$, and hence that $a_1 + b_1 \notin A + B$. Therefore $A + B \neq R$.

(ii)   Suppose that $a + b \in A + B$, with $a \in A$ and $b \in B$; and that $c \in R$ such that $c < a + b$. Since $c - a < b$ and $b \in B$, we know that $c - a \in B$. But then $c = a + (c - a)$ and therefore $c \in A + B$.

(iii)   Again, suppose that $a + b \in A + B$, with $a \in A$ and $b \in B$. Since A is a cut, there exists $d \in A$ such that $d > a$. Then $d + b > a + b$ and $d + b \in A + B$.

We have shown that if $A, B \in K$, then also $A + B \in K$, and hence 6.3 actually defines an operation of addition on the set K.

Let us now verify, for example, that $C_2 + C_3 = C_5$. In order to show that $C_2 + C_3 \subseteq C_5$, let $a + b \in C_2 + C_3$, $a \in C_2$, $b \in C_3$. Hence, $a < 2$ and $b < 3$, and these certainly imply that $a + b < 5$; therefore that $a + b \in C_5$. This shows that $C_2 + C_3 \subseteq C_5$. On the other hand, if $c \in C_5$, so that $c < 5$, then $5 - c = d$, where d is a positive rational number. It follows that $c = (2 - d/2) + (3 - d/2)$, and since $2 - d/2 < 2$ and $3 - d/2 < 3$, we see that $2 - d/2 \in C_2$ and $3 - d/2 \in C_3$. Hence $c \in C_2 + C_3$, and therefore $C_5 \subseteq C_2 + C_3$. Since we have proved inclusion both ways, we must have $C_2 + C_3 = C_5$. A trivial modification of this argument shows that if $r, s \in R$, then

.4
$$C_r + C_s = C_{r+s}.$$

We now proceed to verify the properties of addition that are required in the definition of a ring. The commutative and associative laws of addition in K follow at once from Definition 6.3 and the fact that these laws are known to hold in R. We shall now show that C_0 is the zero, that is, that $A + C_0 = A$ for every element A of K. By C_0, we mean the cut at the rational number zero, that is, C_0 is the set of all *negative* rational numbers. By Definition 6.3, we have

$$A + C_0 = \{a + r; \; a \in A, r \in R, r < 0\}.$$

Since $a + r < a$ and $a \in A$, it follows that $a + r \in A$ and hence $A + C_0 \subseteq A$. Conversely, if $a \in A$, there exists $a_1 \in A$ such that $a < a_1$ and therefore $a - a_1 < 0$. Since $a = a_1 + (a - a_1)$, with $a_1 \in A$ and $a - a_1 \in C_0$, it follows that $a \in A + C_0$. Hence, $A \subseteq A + C_0$, and we conclude that $A + C_0 = A$. We have therefore shown that C_0 plays the required role of the zero. For the time being, we shall continue to designate this zero by "C_0" to emphasize that it is the cut at the rational number zero.

There remains to prove that each element of K has an additive inverse. It follows immediately from 6.4 that each element of K of the form C_r, $r \in R$, has C_{-r} as its additive inverse since $C_r + C_{-r} = C_0$. However, since there are elements of K not of the form C_r, we shall proceed as follows. If $A \in K$, we shall define a *set* of elements of R which we shall designate by "$- A$", then we shall prove that $- A$ is necessarily a cut, and finally that $A + (- A) = C_0$.

.5 Definition. If $A \in K$, let A' be the set of elements of R that are not in A. We then define

$$- A = \{x; \; x \in R, x < - a' \text{ for some } a' \in A'\}.$$

Before proving that $- A$ is a cut, let us clarify the definition by considering, for example, $- C_2$. Clearly, $C_2' = \{r; \; r \in R, r \geq 2\}$, and 2 is the smallest element of C_2'. Since $s > 2$ implies that $- s < - 2$, the elements of $- C_2$, according to Definition 6.5, are precisely those rational numbers which are less than $- 2$. That is, $- C_2 = C_{-2}$, and it follows that $- C_2$ is indeed the additive inverse of C_2.

Now let us verify the three properties required to show that $-A$, as defined in 6.5, is a cut and therefore an element of K.

(i) Since $A \in K$, A' is not the empty set, and hence $-A$ is not the empty set. Moreover, A is not the empty set, and hence there exists $a \in A$. Then $-a \notin -A$ since otherwise we would have $-a < -a'$ for some element a' of A' and this would imply that $a' < a$, whereas every element of A' is greater than every element of A. Since $-a \notin -A$, $-A \neq R$.

(ii) This property is obvious.

(iii) If $x \in -A$, then $x < -a'$ for some element a' of A'. Now $x < \dfrac{x - a'}{2} < -a'$, and therefore $\dfrac{x - a'}{2} \in -A$. This shows that there is no largest element of $-A$.

We have proved that $-A$ is a cut, and we proceed to justify the notation "$-A$" by showing that $-A$ is the additive inverse of A; that is, that $A + (-A) = C_0$. Let $a + x \in A + (-A)$, with $a \in A$ and $x \in -A$. Suppose that $x < -a'$, where $a' \in A'$. Then $a + x < a - a'$, and $a - a' < 0$ since necessarily $a < a'$. It follows that $a + x < 0$, that is, that $a + x \in C_0$; and we conclude that $A + (-A) \subseteq C_0$. Conversely, suppose that $z \in C_0$, and hence that $z < 0$. Let z_1 be an element of C_0 greater than z; for example, we could choose $z_1 = z/2$ if we wished. At any rate, $z_1 - z > 0$. By Lemma 6.2, there exist $a \in A$ and $a' \in A'$ such that $a + (z_1 - z) = a'$. Hence, $z = a + (z_1 - a')$, and $z_1 - a' < -a'$ since $z_1 < 0$. It follows that $z_1 - a' \in -A$ and hence that $z \in A + (-A)$. This shows that $C_0 \subseteq A + (-A)$, and completes the proof that $A + (-A) = C_0$.

We have now shown that the Properties $P_1 - P_4$ of addition in a ring are satisfied in K with addition as we have defined it in 6.3. It follows that all the properties of addition established in Section 2.4 must hold. In particular, the zero C_0 is unique, as is also the additive inverse $-A$ of each element A of K. We adopt all the usual notations of a ring. For example, instead of writing $A + (-B)$, we shall write $A - B$, and so on. Also, $-(-A) = A$, and the other familiar properties (2.5) of "$-$" which do not involve multiplication must hold in K, and we henceforth use them without hesitation.

6.4   THE FIELD OF REAL NUMBERS

In this section we shall define an operation of multiplication on K in such a way that K will become a field with respect to our definitions of addition and multiplication. Actually, K will be shown to be an ordered field in accordance with Definition 3.3. Before giving the definition of multiplication, we shall find it convenient to define the set K_p of positive elements of K required for K to satisfy Definition 3.3 for an ordered integral domain.

6 Definition. We define the set K_p of *positive* elements of K as follows:

$$K_p = \{A; \ A \in K, \ A \text{ contains positive rationals}\}.$$

That is, the cut A is a *positive* cut if A contains some positive rational numbers.

We may observe that a cut cannot contain just *one* positive rational number. For if $a \in A$ with $a > 0$, then any positive rational less than a (for example $a/2$) is also an element of A.

It is clear from Definition 6.3 of addition that if $A, B \in K_p$, then $A + B \in K_p$. The corresponding property for the product will also be obvious as soon as multiplication is defined below. However, to justify calling K_p the set of *positive* elements of K, we do need to prove Property 3.3 (iii), which in our present notation states that if $A \in K$, exactly one of the following holds:

7 $$A = C_0, \qquad A \in K_p, \qquad -A \in K_p.$$

It is trivial that $C_0 \notin K_p$ and, since $-C_0 = C_0$, that also $-C_0 \notin K_p$. Next, let us assume that $A \neq C_0$ and $A \notin K_p$, and prove that $-A \in K_p$. Since $A \notin K_p$, A contains no positive rationals and, since $A \neq C_0$, A does not consist of the set of all negative rational numbers. Hence, there exists a negative rational number a' not in A; that is, in A'. Since $a' < 0$, we have $a' < a'/2 < 0$ and therefore $0 < -a'/2 < -a'$. By Definition 6.5, we see that $-a'/2 \in -A$ and hence that $-A \in K_p$. To complete the proof of Property 3.3 (iii), let us now assume that $A \in K_p$ and show that $-A \notin K_p$. Since $A \in K_p$, A' consists entirely of positive rationals, and Definition 6.5 shows that all elements of $-A$ are negative. Hence, $-A \notin K_p$, and the proof is completed.

Since C_0 is the zero in our present notation, we shall write $A > C_0$ to indicate that $A \in K_p$; that is, that A is a positive cut. Similarly, $A < C_0$ will mean that $-A \in K_p$, or that A is a negative cut. It should be observed that if $A = C_r$, the cut at the rational number r, then $A > C_0$ if and only if $r > 0$; and $A < C_0$ if and only if $r < 0$. If $A, B \in K$, we shall use the general notation of inequalities and write, for example, $A > B$ (or $B < A$) to mean that $A - B > C_0$. What this means concerning the *sets* A and B will be clarified by the following theorem.

8 Theorem. *If $A, B \in K$, then $A > B$ if and only if $B \subset A$, that is, if and only if B is a proper subset of A.*

First, suppose that $B \subset A$, so that every element of B is also an element of A and, moreover, there exists $a \in A$ such that $a \in B'$. Let a_1 and a_2 be elements of A such that $a < a_1 < a_2$. Since $a \in B'$ and $-a_1 < -a$, we see that $-a_1 \in -B$. Hence, $a_2 - a_1$ is a positive rational number in the cut $A - B$, and therefore $A - B \in K_p$. This shows that $A - B > C_0$ or that $A > B$.

Conversely, suppose that $A > B$ and that $A - B$ contains the positive rational number $a + r$, $a \in A$, $r < -b'$ for some $b' \in B'$. Since $a + r > 0$ and $r < -b'$, we have $a > -r > b'$, so $a \notin B$ and therefore $A \neq B$ since $a \in A$. Moreover, for every $b \in B$, we have $b < b'$ and hence $b < a$. It follows that $b \in A$, and we therefore have $B \subset A$. The proof is therefore completed.

Now if $A \in K$, we recall the Definition 3.6 of the absolute value of A:

$$\text{If} \quad A \geq C_0, \quad \text{then} \quad |A| = A,$$
$$\text{If} \quad A < C_0, \quad \text{then} \quad |A| = -A.$$

It follows that $|A| \in K$ and that if $A \neq C_0$, then $|A| > C_0$.

If $A \in K_p$, that is, if $A > C_0$, we shall find it convenient to designate the set of all positive rational numbers in A by A_p. If, then, $A \in K_p$, we know that A_p is not the empty set. Moreover, it is clear that the cut A consists precisely of the rational numbers that are in the set A_p together with zero and all the negative rational numbers. It follows that the element A of K_p is completely determined as soon as the set A_p of *positive* rationals in A is specified.

We are now ready to define the operation of multiplication on K as follows.

6.9 Definition. If $A, B \in K$, we define AB as follows:

(1) If $A > C_0$ and $B > C_0$, then AB is the cut whose positive elements are given by $(AB)_p = \{ab; \ a \in A_p, b \in B_p\}$.

(2) If $A > C_0$ and $B < C_0$ or if $A < C_0$ and $B > C_0$, then $AB = -(|A| \cdot |B|)$.

(3) If $A < C_0$ and $B < C_0$, then $AB = |A| \cdot |B|$.

(4) $AC_0 = C_0A = C_0$ for every $A \in K$.

In order for us to have an operation on the set K, we need to show that AB is, in fact, a cut. We shall establish this result in case (1), and it will follow at once that the same is true in every case. Suppose, then, that $A > C_0$ and $B > C_0$. We verify in turn the three defining properties of a cut.

(i)   Since $A > C_0$ and $B > C_0$, neither A_p nor B_p is the empty set, and hence $(AB)_p$ is not the empty set. Certainly, then, AB is not the empty set. Moreover, since A is a cut, there exists $a' \notin A$ and clearly then $a < a'$ for every element a of A_p. Similarly, there exists $b' \notin B$ and $b < b'$ for every element b of B_p. Hence, $ab < a'b'$ for every $a \in A_p$, $b \in B_p$. This shows that $a'b'$ is a positive rational number not an element of $(AB)_p$ and hence $AB \neq R$.

(ii)   Let $ab \in (AB)_p$ with $a \in A_p$ and $b \in B_p$. If c is a rational number such that $0 < c < ab$, we want to show that $c \in (AB)_p$. Since $c/a < b$, we know that $c/a \in B_p$ and, since $c = a(c/a)$, it follows at once that $c \in (AB)_p$.

(iii)   Let $ab \in (AB)_p$ with $a \in A_p$ and $b \in B_p$. Since B is a cut, there exists $b_1 \in B_p$ such that $b_1 > b$. It follows that $ab_1 \in (AB)_p$ and $ab_1 > ab$. This shows that in $(AB)_p$, and therefore in AB, there exists no largest rational number.

We have now shown that 6.9 actually defines multiplication in K, and we can therefore state the following fundamental theorem.

10   Theorem.   *With respect to the Definitions 6.3 and 6.9 of addition and multiplication, K is a field with zero C_0 and unity C_1. Moreover, using Definition 6.6 of the positive elements, K is an ordered field.*

An element of K will be called a *real number*, and K the *field of real numbers*.

Since, by Definition 6.9 (1), the product of two elements of K_p is an element of K_p, we have shown that K_p has all the required properties for the positive elements of a field. Hence, when we have proved that K is a field, we will know that it is an *ordered* field.

We have already proved that C_0 is the zero of K. The proof that K is a field with unity C_1 is fairly tedious, and we therefore postpone it until the last section of this chapter. However, for the present we shall assume the truth of this fact and proceed to discuss some properties of the field K.

The following property of the field K will enable us to consider that the field of real numbers is an extension of the field R of rational numbers.

11   Theorem.   *Let R' be the set of all elements of K of the form C_r, $r \in R$. Then the mapping $r \rightarrow C_r$ is a one-one mapping of R onto R'. Moreover, R' is a field and this mapping is an isomorphism of R onto R'.*

It is easy to verify (*cf.* Exercise 3 of the preceding set) that $r \neq s$ implies that $C_r \neq C_s$; hence the mapping $r \rightarrow C_r$ is a one-one mapping of R onto R'. Moreover, Equation 6.4 shows that R' is closed under addition and also that this mapping preserves the operation of addition. Corresponding statements for multiplication will follow as soon as we have shown that if $r, s \in R$, then

6.12 $$C_r C_s = C_{rs}.$$

By Definition 6.9 (4), this equation is true if $r = 0$ or $s = 0$. Suppose, then, that we consider first the case in which $r > 0$ and $s > 0$. It follows that $C_r > C_0$ and $C_s > C_0$ so by Definition 6.9 (1) the positive elements of $C_r C_s$ are given by

$$(C_r C_s)_p = \{ab;\ a, b \in R,\ 0 < a < r,\ 0 < b < s\}.$$

If ab is any positive element of $C_r C_s$, then clearly $ab < rs$, so that $ab \in C_{rs}$; hence $C_r C_s \subseteq C_{rs}$. Conversely, suppose that $c \in R$ such that $0 < c < rs$. Since between any two distinct rational numbers there is another rational number, there exists $d \in R$ such that $0 < c < d < rs$. Since $d/s < r$, we have $d/s \in C_r$; and since $c/d < 1$, we have $cs/d < s$ and therefore $cs/d \in C_s$. By writing $c = (d/s)(cs/d)$, it is then apparent that $c \in C_r C_s$, and it follows that $C_{rs} \subseteq C_r C_s$. We have obtained inclusion both ways and have therefore established 6.12 for the case in which $r > 0$ and $s > 0$.

In order to establish Equation 6.12 in the other possible cases, we use the case just proved and the fact, which follows from Equation 6.4, that if $t \in R$, then

6.13 $$-C_t = C_{-t}.$$

Suppose, now, that one of r and s is positive and the other is negative, and let us choose the notation so that $r < 0$ and $s > 0$. In this case, $|C_r| = -C_r$ and $|C_s| = C_s$. The desired result is then obtained by the following calculations:

$$
\begin{aligned}
C_r C_s &= -[(-C_r)C_s] & &\text{(by Def. 6.9 (2))}, \\
&= -(C_{-r}C_s) & &\text{(by 6.13)}, \\
&= -(C_{-rs}) & &\text{(by case of 6.12 already proved)}, \\
&= C_{rs} & &\text{(by 6.13)}.
\end{aligned}
$$

We have therefore proved Equation 6.12 for the case in which one of r and s is positive and the other is negative. The remaining case, that in which they are both negative, is easily disposed of in a similar manner, and we leave the proof of this case as an exercise.

Since 6.12 holds for every choice of r and s, it follows that R' is also closed under multiplication and, moreover, if $r \neq 0$, $C_r C_{r^{-1}} = C_1$, so the multiplicative inverse of C_r is $C_{r^{-1}}$, and R' is a field. Of course, 6.12 shows that the operation of multiplication is also preserved under the mapping $r \to C_r$, and hence this mapping is an isomorphism of R onto R'. The theorem is therefore established.

Now since the field K of real numbers contains a subfield R' which is isomorphic to the field R of rational numbers, we may identify R' with

R and consider that K actually contains R. Accordingly, we shall feel free to write "r" in place of C_r whenever we wish. The context will make it clear just what is intended. For example, if A is a real number and we write $r \in A$, it is clear that we are thinking of r as a rational number which is an element of the cut A of rational numbers. On the other hand, if we write $r < A$, we must be thinking of r as a real number, that is, as the cut C_r; and we really mean that $C_r < A$. We shall frequently continue to use the notation "C_r" in proofs where we wish to emphasize that we are dealing with cuts of rational numbers.

In accordance with the notation just introduced, the zero of the ring K may be denoted by "0" as well as by the previous "C_0"; similarly, the unity may be denoted by "1" as well as by "C_1".

We should perhaps remark that our ordering of the real numbers is an *extension* of the previous ordering of the rational numbers. By this statement we mean that a rational number r is a positive *real number* if and only if it is a positive rational number. Otherwise expressed, $r \in R_p$ if and only if $C_r \in K_p$.

EXERCISES

1. Prove 6.12 for the case in which $r < 0$ and $s < 0$.

2. Prove that the cut E of Exercise 6 of Section 6.2 is actually the cut $C_t + A$.

3. Write out a proof that if $r,\ s \in R$, then $r < s$ if and only if $C_r < C_s$.

4. If $A \in K$, $r \in R$ and $r \notin A$, prove that $A \leq C_r$, and verify by an example that it is possible for equality to hold.

5. If $A \in K$ and $r \in R$, prove that $r \in A$ if and only if $C_r < A$.

6.5 SOME PROPERTIES OF THE REAL NUMBERS

Since we have agreed to identify a real number C_r with the rational number r, we observe that the rational numbers are real numbers. However, the cut D exhibited in Section 6.2 is not of the form C_r for $r \in R$, and hence there exist real numbers that are not rational numbers. A real number which is not a rational number is called an *irrational number*. The following theorem will be used a little later to show that an irrational number may be approximated by a rational number to any desired degree of accuracy.

6.14 Theorem. *Between any two distinct real numbers there is a rational number.*

Let $A, B \in K$ with $A < B$. We wish to show that there exists a real number of the form C_s, $s \in R$, such that $A < C_s < B$. Since $A < B$, there exists by Theorem 6.8 a rational number r such that $r \in B$, $r \notin A$. Since B is a cut, one of the defining properties of a cut asserts that in B there is no largest rational number. Hence, there exists $s \in B$ such that $r < s$ and it follows (cf. Exercises 4, 5 of the preceding set) that

$$A \leq C_r < C_s < B.$$

Hence, C_s has the required property.

The following is a generalization of the corresponding property (5.22) for the rational numbers.

6.15 Theorem. (Archimedean Property) *If A and B are positive real numbers, there exists a positive integer n such that $nA > B$.*

By the preceding theorem, there exists $s \in R$ such that $C_0 < C_s < A$. Moreover, it is clear that there exists $t \in R$ such that $B < C_t$. Now by the Archimedean Property of the rational numbers, there exists a positive integer n such that $ns > t$ or $C_n C_s > C_t$. It follows that

$$C_n A > C_n C_s > C_t > B,$$

and by identifying C_n with n, we have $nA > B$, as we wished to show.

Let us now return to a consideration of the cut D defined in Section 6.2, which in our later notation may be given by specifying D_p as follows:

$$D_p = \{a; \ a \in R, a > 0, a^2 < 2\}.$$

We already know that D is an irrational number and we shall now prove that $D^2 = C_2$. To establish this fact, we shall prove that it is impossible to have $D^2 > C_2$ or $D^2 < C_2$; hence, it must be true that $D^2 = C_2$.

First, let us suppose that $D^2 > C_2$. Then, by Theorem 6.14, there exists a rational number s such that $C_2 < C_s < D^2$. Hence, by Theorem 6.8, there must exist $x_1, x_2 \in D_p$ such that $x_1 x_2 \geq s$. If, for example, $x_1 \geq x_2$, then $x_1^2 \geq x_1 x_2 \geq s$, and since $s > 2$ it follows that $x_1^2 > 2$. However, this violates the assumption that $x_1 \in D_p$ and therefore we cannot have $D^2 > C_2$.

Now, let us suppose that $D^2 < C_2$. Again, Theorem 6.14 assures us that there exists $t \in R$ such that $D^2 < C_t < C_2$, and clearly $1 < t < 2$. The rational number $r = (2 - t)/5$ will play a useful role in obtaining the desired contradiction. It is clear that $0 < r < 1$; moreover, by Lemma 6.2, there exists an element d of D (necessarily positive) such that $d + r \notin D$, that is, such that $(d + r)^2 > 2$. Now $d < 2$, and $r^2 < r$ since $0 < r < 1$. Accordingly, we have

$$(d + r)^2 = d^2 + 2dr + r^2 < d^2 + 5r = d^2 + 2 - t.$$

But since $(d + r)^2 > 2$, we conclude that

$$d^2 + 2 - t > 2,$$

and finally that $d^2 > t$. However, since $d^2 \in D^2$, we have a violation of the assumption that $D^2 < C_t$. Hence, we have reached the desired contradiction, and we cannot have $D^2 < C_2$.

We have therefore shown that we must have $D^2 = C_2$. Since we have agreed to identify C_2 with the rational number 2, we have thus proved that $D^2 = 2$. Accordingly, we may conveniently denote the irrational number D by the familiar symbol "$\sqrt{2}$".

Let us now point out how Theorem 6.14 assures us that any irrational number, such as $\sqrt{2}$, for example, can be approximated arbitrarily closely by rational numbers. If a is an arbitrary positive rational number, no matter how small, the theorem assures us that there exists a rational number r such that

$$\sqrt{2} - a < r < \sqrt{2} + a.$$

Taking a in turn as $1/10$, $1/10^2$, $1/10^3$, $\cdots$, the corresponding rational numbers r give increasingly accurate approximations to $\sqrt{2}$. For example, we have

$$\sqrt{2} - 1/10 < 1.4 < \sqrt{2} + 1/10,$$
$$\sqrt{2} - 1/10^2 < 1.41 < \sqrt{2} + 1/10^2,$$
$$\sqrt{2} - 1/10^3 < 1.414 < \sqrt{2} + 1/10^3,$$

and so on.

It took considerable calculation above to prove the existence of the particular real number $\sqrt{2}$, and it is therefore apparent that more general methods would be very helpful in establishing results of this kind. Accordingly, we shall introduce a fundamental property of the field of real numbers which has not yet been mentioned. We begin by defining the necessary new terms.

For the moment we consider any ordered field F, but our only applications will be to the ordered field R of rational numbers or to the ordered field K of real numbers.

.16 Definition. Let S be a set of elements of the ordered field F. If there exists an element b of F such that $x \leq b$ for *every* element x of S, then b is called an *upper bound* of the set S in F.

For example, the set $S_1 = \{1/2, 1, 2\}$ of elements of R has an upper bound 2. Also, $5/2$ is an upper bound of this set, as is also 117, and so on. The set $S_2 = \{a; a \in R, a > 0, a^2 < 2\}$ has 2 as one upper bound. The set I_p of all positive integers has no upper bound in R (or in K) since there exists no rational number (or real number) which is as large as every positive integer.

6.17 Definition. Let S be a set of elements of the ordered field F. If there exists an upper bound c of S such that no smaller element of F is an upper bound of S, then we call c the *least upper bound* (l.u.b.) of the set S in F.

Although a set may have many upper bounds, it is easy to see that if it has a l.u.b., it is unique. The set S_1, defined above, has 2 as its l.u.b. In this case, the l.u.b. of the set S_1 is an element of S_1. The set S_2 does not have a l.u.b. in R since we have shown earlier that there is no largest rational number in S_2 and also no smallest rational number not in S_2. However, if the set S_2 of rational numbers is considered as a subset of the field K of real numbers, then in K the set S_2 does have a l.u.b., namely $\sqrt{2}$. In this case, the l.u.b. is not an element of the set S_2. The fact that there exists a real number which is the l.u.b. of the set S_2 is an illustration of the following important property of the field of real numbers.

6.18 Theorem. *Any nonempty subset S of the ordered field K of real numbers which has an upper bound in K has a l.u.b. in K.*

To prove this theorem, let $S = \{A, B, C, \cdots\}$ be a nonempty subset of K with an upper bound M. Considering the elements $A, B, C, \cdots$ of S as sets of rational numbers, let L be the *union* of all these sets, that is, L consists of the set of all rational numbers that are in one (or more) of these sets. We shall show that L is a cut of rational numbers and therefore a real number. Moreover, L is the l.u.b. of the set S of real numbers.

To show that L is a cut, we need to verify the three defining properties of a cut.

(i) Since S is not the empty set, it contains at least one element, say A. Then since A is a cut, it must contain some rational numbers; and since $A \subseteq L$, we see that L is not the empty set. Also, since it is given that M is an upper bound of S, we have that $A \leq M, B \leq M, C \leq M, \cdots$. But then Theorem 6.8 implies that, as sets of rational numbers, $A \subseteq M$, $B \subseteq M, C \subseteq M, \cdots$. Since every element of S is contained in M, the union L of these sets is contained in M. Now M is a cut and therefore $M \neq R$, and it follows that $L \neq R$.

(ii) If $a \in L$ and $b \in R$ such that $b < a$, we want to show that $b \in L$. Since $a \in L$, a is an element of some one of the cuts in S, say $a \in A$. Since A is a cut and $b < a$, we know that $b \in A$ and, since $A \subseteq L$, it follows that $b \in L$.

(iii) If $a \in L$, then a is an element of some cut, say A, in the set S. Since A is a cut there exists $c \in A$ such that $a < c$. Again, since $A \subseteq L$, it follows that $c \in L$.

We have now shown that L is a cut, and therefore L is a real number. Since, considered as sets, $A \subseteq L$ for every element A of S, it is clear that as real numbers $A \leq L$ for every such element and hence that L is an upper bound of the set S. It is now easy to prove that it is the l.u.b. of the set S. Suppose that T is an arbitrary upper bound of the set S, and hence that $A \leq T$ for every element A of S. Considered as sets of rational numbers, this means that $A \subseteq T$ for every A in S. It is then immediate that every element of the union L of elements of S is an element of T, and therefore that $L \subseteq T$. As real numbers, we then have $L \leq T$. Hence, the upper bound L is in fact the l.u.b., and the proof is completed.

It is an important fact, which we shall state without proof, that the field of real numbers is the *only* ordered field which does have the property stated in Theorem 6.18. Among all possible ordered fields, this property, then, completely characterizes the field K of real numbers; and all properties of this field can be deduced from the fact that every nonempty subset of K which has an upper bound has in K a l.u.b. In fact, this property is a starting point for many discussions of the system of real numbers. We shall conclude this section by mentioning without proof a few additional properties which can be proved by appropriate use of Theorem 6.18. The first one we state as the following theorem.

.19 Theorem. *For each positive real number A and each positive integer n, there exists exactly one positive real number X such that $X^n = A$.*

The real number X, whose existence is asserted in this theorem, may be called the *principal nth root* of A and designated by $A^{1/n}$ or by $\sqrt[n]{A}$. Now if m is an arbitrary integer, we define

$$A^{m/n} = (A^{1/n})^m,$$

so that A^r is defined for *every* rational number r.

Suppose, now, that B is an arbitrary *real* number, and let us consider how we can define A^B, where A is a positive real number. It is easy to see that B is the l.u.b. of the *rational* numbers that are less than B. Let us then consider the set of real numbers $\{A^r; \; r \in R, \, r < B\}$. If $A > 1$, it can be verified that this set has an upper bound, namely, A^s if s is a rational number such that $s > B$. Theorem 6.18 then assures us that this set has a l.u.b. and we define A^B to be this l.u.b. If $A < 1$, then $1/A > 1$ and $(1/A)^{-B}$ is therefore defined by the case just considered. We now define $A^B = (1/A)^{-B}$, and hence A^B is defined for every positive real number A and every real number B. The "laws of exponents"

(5.13) can then be shown to hold if t and v are taken to be positive real numbers, and m and n arbitrary real numbers.

Now let us make a few remarks about decimals. Any finite decimal is a rational number. For example, $3.1416 = (31,416)/10,000$. Incidentally, π is an irrational number, although the proof of this fact is difficult.

We are now interested in what precise meaning can be given to an infinite decimal. For example, what shall we mean by the symbol

6.20 .32332333233332 $\cdots$,

it being understood that one more 3 is inserted each time? To answer this question, consider the following set of finite decimals and therefore of rational numbers:

$$\{.3, .32, .323, .3233, .32332, \cdots\}.$$

This set of numbers has an upper bound, for example, .4; hence it must have a real number C as its l.u.b. We then define the infinite decimal given by 6.20 to mean this number C. In a similar way, every infinite decimal represents a real number; also every real number has a finite or infinite decimal representation. It is familiar to the reader that some infinite decimals are rational numbers and others are irrational numbers. It can be proved that an infinite decimal is a rational number if and only if it is eventually a repeating decimal. For example, $.33333\cdots$ and $.58623623623\cdots$ are rational numbers, whereas the infinite decimal C given by 6.20 must be an irrational number.

We conclude our brief discussion of the properties of the real numbers with the following observation. We have obtained the real numbers as cuts of rational numbers. One might ask whether or not it would be possible in a similar way to extend the field of real numbers to a larger field consisting of cuts of *real* numbers. The answer turns out to be in the negative since Theorem 6.18 has the effect of assuring us that every cut of real numbers would be a cut *at* some real number.

We have been using capital letters to designate real numbers in order to emphasize that they are defined as sets of rational numbers. We shall continue to do so in the next section where we complete the proof of Theorem 6.10. However, in later chapters we shall designate real numbers by lower-case letters.

--- *E X E R C I S E S*

1. Let n be an arbitrary positive integer. Show that between any two distinct real numbers there are n distinct rational numbers.

2. Prove that between any two distinct rational numbers there is an irrational number. [Hint: If a, $b \in R$ with $a < b$, show that $a < a + \dfrac{b-a}{\sqrt{2}} < b$.]

3. Prove that between any two distinct real numbers there is an irrational number.

4. Prove that $\log_{10}2$ is irrational. [Hint: Use the definition of the logarithm, assume that $\log_{10}2$ is rational, and then use the Fundamental Theorem of Arithmetic to obtain a contradiction.]

6.6 PROOF OF THEOREM 6.10 (OPTIONAL)

From the Definition 6.9 of multiplication, it is apparent that multiplication is commutative. We have shown in Section 6.3 that addition has all the required properties and hence, in particular, that "$-$" has the usual properties as long as multiplication is not involved. For example, if $A \in K$, we know that $-(-A) = A$, and so on. The following lemma shows that when we come to consider multiplication, "$-$" has another familiar property.

21 Lemma. *If A, $B \in K$, then*

$$A(-B) = (-A)B = -(AB).$$

This result is trivial if either A or B is the zero cut C_0, for then by 6.9(4) each expression is equal to C_0. If $A \neq C_0$ and $B \neq C_0$, then the desired result follows easily by consideration of different cases. For example, if $A < C_0$ and $B > C_0$, then $-B < C_0$ and Definition 6.9 (3) shows that $A(-B) = |A| \cdot |-B| = |A| \cdot |B|$. Furthermore, $(-A)B = |A| \cdot |B|$ since, in this case, $|A| = -A$ and $|B| = B$. Finally, by 6.9 (2), $AB = -(|A| \cdot |B|)$, and hence $-(AB) = |A| \cdot |B|$. We have thus verified the lemma in this case since each of $A(-B)$, $(-A)B$, and $-(AB)$ is equal to $|A| \cdot |B|$. We leave it to the reader to verify the truth of the lemma for the other possible cases as to the signs of A and B.

In view of the lemma, we are justified in writing $-AB$ since this may be interpreted either as $(-A)B$ or as $-(AB)$.

We may point out that when we established in 2.11 (i), (ii), the properties of a ring similar to those of the above lemma, we made use of the distributive laws. Since we have not yet proved the distributive laws for K, we have had to use a different approach. In fact, we shall find the above lemma useful in establishing the distributive laws in K.

Let us next consider the associative law of multiplication. If A, B, $C \in K$, we wish therefore to show that

6.22 $$(AB)C = A(BC).$$

If A, B, and C are all positive, this follows easily from Definition 6.9 (1). For then the positive elements of $(AB)C$ are of the form $(ab)c$, where $a \in A_p$, $b \in B_p$, and $c \in C_p$. However, by the associative law of multiplication in the field of rational numbers, $(ab)c = a(bc)$, and $a(bc)$ is a positive element of $A(BC)$. This argument works both ways, and we conclude that 6.22 holds in this case. By use of Lemma 6.21, the argument is easily extended to the case in which not all of A, B, and C are positive. Suppose, for example, that $A > C_0$, $B > C_0$, and $C < C_0$. Then $-C > C_0$ and, by the case just established, we know that

$$(AB)(-C) = A[B(-C)].$$

However, Lemma 6.21 shows that $(AB)(-C) = -[(AB)C]$ and also that $A[B(-C)] = A[-(BC)] = -[A(BC)]$. Hence, we have $-[(AB)C] = -[A(BC)]$ and 6.22 follows at once. The other possible cases are similarly disposed of without difficulty, and the associative law therefore holds in general.

In order to show that K is a commutative ring, there remains only to prove the distributive laws. If A, B, $C \in K$, we proceed to prove that

6.23 $$A(B + C) = AB + AC.$$

The other distributive law will follow at once from this one.

We shall prove 6.23 by a consideration of several different cases. First, we observe that it is certainly true if any one of A, B, and C is the zero cut C_0. Henceforth, we assume that $A \neq C_0$, $B \neq C_0$, and $C \neq C_0$.

Case 1. $A > C_0$, $B > C_0$, $C > C_0$.

First, we need to show that every *positive* element of $B + C$ is necessarily expressible in the form $r + s$, where $r \in B_p$ and $s \in C_p$. Let $b + c \in B + C$, $b + c > 0$, with $b \in B$ and $c \in C$. Then at least one of b, c must be positive, so let us assume that $b > 0$. If also $c > 0$, there is nothing to prove since $b + c$ would then be of the desired form. Suppose, then, that $c \leq 0$. Since $C > C_0$, there exists $c_1 \in C_p$, that is, $c_1 > 0$ and $c_1 \in C$. Choose c_2 as a positive rational number such that $c_2 < c_1$ and also $c_2 < b + c$. It follows that $c_2 \in C_p$ since $c_1 \in C_p$. Now

6.24 $$b + c = (b + c - c_2) + c_2.$$

Moreover, $b + c - c_2 > 0$ and also $b + c - c_2 < b$ since $c \leq 0$ and $c_2 > 0$. Therefore $b + c - c_2 \in B_p$ and 6.24 shows that $b + c$ is expressible in the desired form.

From what we have just proved and the Definition 6.9 (1) of the product of two positive cuts, it follows that every positive element of $A(B+C)$ can be expressed in the form $a(b+c)$, where $a \in A_p$, $b \in B_p$, and $c \in C_p$. But, by the distributive law for the rational numbers, we have $a(b+c) = ab + ac$, and therefore every positive element of $A(B+C)$ is a positive element of $AB + AC$. We have therefore verified that

$$A(B+C) \subseteq AB + AC.$$

Conversely, let p be a positive element of $AB + AC$. By the argument used above, applied to AB and AC, we know that $p = r + s$, where $r \in (AB)_p$ and $s \in (AC)_p$. Hence $r = ab$, $s = a_1 c$, where a, $a_1 \in A_p$, $b \in B_p$, and $c \in C_p$. Let us suppose for convenience of notation that $a_1 \le a$. It follows that $a_1 c \le ac$, and hence that

$$p = ab + a_1 c \le ab + ac = a(b+c).$$

But $a(b+c) \in A(B+C)$, and so we must have $p \in A(B+C)$. This shows that every positive element of $AB + AC$ is also an element of $A(B+C)$; hence that

$$AB + AC \subseteq A(B+C).$$

We have now obtained inclusion both ways, and hence 6.23 has been established in this case.

Case 2. $A > C_0$, $\quad B > C_0$, $\quad C < C_0$.

If it happens that $B + C = C_0$, so that $C = -B$, then $A(B+C) = AC_0 = C_0$. But then also $AB + AC = AB + A(-B) = AB - AB = C_0$, by use of Lemma 6.21. Hence, 6.23 holds under this condition.

If $B + C > C_0$, then since $-C > C_0$, we can proceed as follows:

$$\begin{aligned} AB &= A[(B+C) + (-C)] \\ &= A(B+C) + A(-C) \quad &\text{(by Case 1)} \\ &= A(B+C) - AC \quad &\text{(by Lemma 6.21)}. \end{aligned}$$

Hence $A(B+C) = AB + AC$, as required.

If $B + C < C_0$, the desired result follows by the following calculation:

$$\begin{aligned} -(AC) &= A(-C) \quad &\text{(by Lemma 6.21)} \\ &= A[B + (-(B+C))] \\ &= AB + A[-(B+C)] \quad &\text{(by Case 1)} \\ &= AB - A(B+C) \quad &\text{(by Lemma 6.21)}. \end{aligned}$$

Again, it follows that $A(B+C) = AB + AC$.

We have exhausted all possibilities, and therefore the proof is completed for this case.

Case 3. $A > C_0$, $B < C_0$, $C > C_0$.

We omit the proof as it follows immediately from the preceding case by interchanging the roles of B and C.

Case 4. $A > C_0$, $B < C_0$, $C < C_0$.

In this case, we proceed as follows:

$$
\begin{aligned}
-A(B+C) &= A[-(B+C)] && \text{(by Lemma 6.21)}\\
&= A[-B+(-C)]\\
&= A(-B)+A(-C) && \text{(by Case 1)}\\
&= -AB-AC && \text{(by Lemma 6.21).}
\end{aligned}
$$

Again, it follows that $A(B+C) = AB + AC$, as required.

We have now proved the distributive law 6.23 for every choice of B and C provided that $A \geq C_0$.

Case 5. $A < C_0$, B and C arbitrary.

This case is easily disposed of by the following calculation:

$$
\begin{aligned}
-[A(B+C)] &= (-A)(B+C) && \text{(by Lemma 6.21)}\\
&= (-A)B+(-A)C && \text{(by the cases already}\\
& && \text{proved since } -A > C_0)\\
&= -AB-AC && \text{(by Lemma 6.21).}
\end{aligned}
$$

The proof of the distributive law 6.23 has finally been completed.

We now know that K is a commutative ring, and we next prove that the cut C_1 at the rational number 1 is the unity of K. That is, we shall show that if $A \in K$, then

6.25 $$AC_1 = A.$$

This is obviously true if $A = C_0$. Suppose, now, that $A > C_0$. Then by Definition 6.9 (1), we see that

$$(AC_1)_p = \{ax;\ a \in A_p, x \in R, 0 < x < 1\}.$$

If ax is a positive element of AC_1, clearly $ax < a$ since $0 < x < 1$. It follows that $ax \in A_p$; hence, that $(AC_1)_p \subseteq A_p$. Conversely, if $a_1 \in A_p$, there exists $a_2 \in A_p$ such that $a_2 > a_1$. It follows that $a_1 = a_2(a_1/a_2)$, where $0 < a_1/a_2 < 1$. In view of the definition of $(AC_1)_p$, we see at once that $a_1 \in (AC_1)_p$, and therefore we have $A_p \subseteq (AC_1)_p$. This completes the proof that $(AC_1)_p = A_p$, and therefore that $AC_1 = A$. If $A < C_0$, we can use as follows the case we have just established, since now $-A > C_0$:

$$AC_1 = -[(-A)C_1] = -(-A) = A.$$

Hence, 6.25 holds for every $A \in K$, and therefore C_1 is the unity.

To show that K is a field, there remains only to prove that every nonzero element A of K has a multiplicative inverse in K. Suppose, first, that $A > C_0$, and let us define the set B as follows:

$$B = \{x; \ x \in R, \ x < 1/a' \text{ for some } a' \in A'\}.$$

We first show that B is a cut, and therefore an element of K, by verifying the three defining properties of a cut.

(i)   If $a' \in A'$, then $1/(2a') < 1/a'$, so $1/(2a') \in B$ and B is not empty. Moreover, if $a \in A_p$, then $a < a'$ for every element a' of A'; hence $1/a > 1/a'$ for every such a', and it follows that $1/a \notin B$, and therefore $B \neq R$.

(ii)   If $x \in B$ and $y < x$, it is trivial that $y \in B$.

(iii)   Suppose that $x \in B$, $x < 1/a'$ for some $a' \in A'$. Then, by Theorem 5.21, there exists a rational number r such that $x < r < 1/a'$, and therefore also $r \in B$. Hence, there is no largest element of B.

We now know that B is a cut, and clearly $B > C_0$. We shall now prove that $AB = C_1$. If $a \in A_p$ and $b \in B_p$, then $b < 1/a'$ for some $a' \in A'$. Hence, $0 < ab < a/a' < 1$, so that $ab \in C_1$. It follows that $(AB)_p \subseteq C_1$ and hence that $AB \subseteq C_1$.

Now let y be an arbitrary positive element of C_1, so that $0 < y < 1$, and let $a \in A_p$. Since $(1 - y)a > 0$, we apply Lemma 6.2 to show that there must exist $a_1 \in A$ such that $a_1 + (1 - y)a = a'$ for some $a' \in A'$; and clearly we may assume that $a_1 > 0$. Since $a < a'$, $a_1 < a'$, and $1 - y > 0$, we see that

$$0 < a' - a_1 = (1 - y)a < (1 - y)a'.$$

Accordingly,

$$a' - a_1 + ya' < (1 - y)a' + ya' = a',$$

and this implies that $ya' < a_1$. It follows that $a' < a_1/y$, from which we obtain $y/a_1 < 1/a'$, and therefore $y/a_1 \in B_p$. Hence, $y = a_1 b$ for some $b \in B_p$, and this implies that $y \in (AB)_p$. Since y was an arbitrary positive element of C_1, we see that $C_1 \subseteq AB$.

We have now obtained inclusion both ways, and have therefore shown that $AB = C_1$, and hence that B is the multiplicative inverse of A.

So far we have assumed that $A > C_0$, but if $A < C_0$, it follows from what we have just proved that $-A$ has a multiplicative inverse, say D, in K. But then Lemma 6.21 shows that $-D$ is the multiplicative inverse of A, so that every nonzero element of K has a multiplicative inverse. We have therefore completed the proof of the theorem.

7

The Field of
Complex Numbers

In the preceding chapter we extended the field of rational numbers to the larger field of real numbers. In this chapter we shall complete our program of the development of the number systems of elementary algebra by extending the field of real numbers to the still larger field of complex numbers. In contrast to the complicated procedure required to get the real numbers from the rational numbers, the complex numbers are obtained quite easily from the real numbers.

After we have constructed the field of complex numbers we shall proceed to establish a few of their elementary properties. However, additional properties will be presented at appropriate points in the following chapter.

7.1 THE COMPLEX NUMBERS

Henceforth we shall let K (rather than the boldface K) denote the field of real numbers. Moreover, in the future we shall designate real numbers by lower-case letters.

In order to construct the field of complex numbers, we begin by considering ordered pairs (a, b) of *real* numbers. Our definitions of addition and multiplication will be motivated by the formal properties of expressions of the form $a + bi$, where $i^2 = -1$. However, we are not justified in assuming that there *is* a "number" whose square is -1 until we have constructed a field which has an element with this property. Accordingly, as in the case of the construction of the rational numbers, we begin with an unfamiliar notation in order to avoid using any property until we have established it. We may remind the reader that the equal sign "$=$" is being used in the sense of identity, that is, $(a, b) = (c, d)$ means that $a = c$ and $b = d$.

We proceed to prove the following theorem, which establishes the existence of the field we shall presently call the field of complex numbers.

7.1 Theorem. *Let C be the set of all ordered pairs (a, b) of elements of the field K of real numbers, and let us define operations of addition and multiplication on C as follows:*

7.2
$$(a, b) + (c, d) = (a + c, b + d),$$

and

7.3
$$(a, b)(c, d) = (ac - bd, ad + bc).$$

Then C is a field with respect to these definitions of addition and multiplication. Moreover, the set of all elements of C of the form $(a, 0)$, $a \in K$, is a subfield of C which is isomorphic to the field K.

The required properties of addition are almost obvious. From 7.2, it follows that addition is commutative and associative, that $(0, 0)$ is the zero of C, and that the additive inverse of (a, b) is $(-a, -b)$.

The associative law of multiplication is a consequence of the following straightforward calculations:

$$((a, b)(c, d))(e, f) = (ac - bd, ad + bc)(e, f)$$
$$= (ace - bde - adf - bcf, acf - bdf + ade + bce),$$
$$(a, b)((c, d)(e, f)) = (a, b)(ce - df, cf + de)$$
$$= (ace - adf - bcf - bde, acf + ade + bce - bdf),$$

and these turn out to be equal elements of C.

Next, let us verify one of the distributive laws as follows:

$$(a, b)((c, d) + (e, f)) = (a, b)(c + e, d + f)$$
$$= (ac + ae - bd - bf, ad + af + bc + be),$$
$$(a, b)(c, d) + (a, b)(e, f) = (ac - bd, ad + bc) + (ae - bf, af + be)$$
$$= (ac - bd + ae - bf, ad + bc + af + be),$$

and again we have equal elements of C. The other distributive law follows from this one as soon as we show that multiplication is commutative, and the commutativity of multiplication follows easily from 7.3. For, by interchanging (a, b) and (c, d) in 7.3, we see that

$$(c, d)(a, b) = (ca - db, cb + da),$$

and the right side of this equation is equal to the right side of 7.3. Hence,

$$(a, b)(c, d) = (c, d)(a, b).$$

We have now proved that C is a commutative ring, and it is easily verified that it has the unity $(1, 0)$. To show that C is a field, we need only show that each nonzero element (a, b) of C has a multiplicative inverse in C. Since the zero is $(0, 0)$, to say that (a, b) is not the zero of C is to say that a and b are not both equal to zero. Since a is an element of the ordered field K, we know that if $a \neq 0$, then $a^2 > 0$. Similarly, if $b \neq 0$, we have $b^2 > 0$. It follows that if (a, b) is not the zero of C, then necessarily $a^2 + b^2 > 0$ and, in particular, $a^2 + b^2 \neq 0$. Hence,

$$\left(\frac{a}{a^2 + b^2}, \frac{-b}{a^2 + b^2} \right)$$

is an element of C and it may be verified by direct calculation (using 7.3) that

7.4 $$(a, b) \left(\frac{a}{a^2 + b^2}, \frac{-b}{a^2 + b^2} \right) = (1, 0).$$

We have therefore shown that every nonzero element of C has a multiplicative inverse in C, and hence we have proved that C is a field.

To complete the proof of the theorem, let K' be the set of all elements of C of the form $(a, 0)$, $a \in K$. Then the mapping $(a, 0) \to a$ is a one-one mapping of K' onto K. Moreover,

$$(a, 0) + (b, 0) = (a + b, 0) \to a + b,$$

and

$$(a, 0)(b, 0) = (ab, 0) \to ab.$$

Hence, the operations of addition and multiplication are preserved under this mapping, and the mapping therefore defines an isomorphism of K' onto K. This completes the proof of the theorem.

An element of the field C which we have constructed is called a *complex number*, and C is called the *field of complex numbers*.

We shall henceforth adopt a more familiar notation by identifying K' with K, that is, we shall write "a" in place of "$(a, 0)$," and consider that the field C of complex numbers actually contains the field K of real numbers. Also, for simplicity of notation, as well as for historical reasons, we shall use the symbol "i" to designate the particular element $(0, 1)$ of C. Since $(0, 1)^2 = (-1, 0)$, in our new notation we have $i^2 = -1$. Now it is easily verified that

$$(a, 0) + (b, 0)(0, 1) = (a, b)$$

and, using the notation we have introduced, it follows that $a + bi = (a, b)$. Accordingly, in the future we shall write $a + bi$ in place of (a, b). In this notation, the product 7.3 of two elements of C may be expressed in the following form:

5
$$(a + bi)(c + di) = ac - bd + (ad + bc)i.$$

Of course, the right side of 7.5 may be obtained from the left by multiplying out with the aid of the usual distributive, associative, and commutative laws, and replacing i^2 by -1.

We have now extended the field of real numbers to the field of complex numbers. It should be pointed out, however, that one familiar property of the field of rational numbers and of the field of real numbers does not carry over to the field of complex numbers.

6 Theorem. *The field C of complex numbers is not an ordered field.*

By this statement we mean that there does not exist any set C_p of elements of C having the properties (3.3) required for C to be an ordered field. This fact is a consequence of the following observations. If C were ordered, 3.5 (v) would show that the square of every nonzero element would be positive; in particular, both i^2 and 1 would be positive. Then -1 would be negative, and we have a contradiction since $i^2 = -1$.

The fact that C is not ordered means that inequalities cannot be used between complex numbers. In other words, it is meaningless to speak of one complex number as being greater or less than another.

7.2 THE CONJUGATE OF A COMPLEX NUMBER

Let us make the following definition.

7 Definition. If $u = a + bi \in C$, we define the *conjugate* of u to be the element u^* of C given by: $u^* = a - bi$.†

As examples, we have $(1 + 7i)^* = 1 - 7i$, $(2 - 2i)^* = 2 + 2i$, $4^* = 4$, and so on.

†Historically, the usual notation for the conjugate of a complex number z is $\bar{z}$ instead of z*. The present notation has been adopted only because it makes it easier to print such expressions as the conjugate of the sum of two or more complex numbers.

Now the mapping $u \rightarrow u^*$, $u \in C$, is a one-one mapping of C *automorphism* onto itself. We proceed to show that the operations of addition and multiplication are preserved under this mapping. Let $u = a + bi$ and $v = c + di$ be elements of C. Then

$$(u + v)^* = [(a + c) + (b + d)i]^* = a + c - (b + d)i$$
$$= a - bi + c - di = u^* + v^*,$$

and

$$(uv)^* = [ac - bd + (ad + bc)i]^* = ac - bd - (ad + bc)i$$
$$= (a - bi)(c - di) = u^*v^*.$$

Since the operations of addition and multiplication are preserved under the mapping $u \rightarrow u^*$, it follows that this is an isomorphism of the field C onto the same field C.

In working with complex numbers, the concept of conjugate plays an important role. A number of simple, but significant, properties are presented in Exercise 2 below.

EXERCISES

1. Find the multiplicative inverse of (a, b), as given in 7.4, by assuming that r and s are real numbers such that $(a, b)(r, s) = (1, 0)$, and solving for r and s.

2. Prove each of the following:
   (i) If $u \in C$, then $uu^* \in K$ and $u + u^* \in K$; moreover, if $u \neq 0$, then $uu^* > 0$,
   (ii) If $u \in C$, then $(u^*)^* = u$,
   (iii) If $u \in C$ and $u \neq 0$, then $(u^{-1})^* = (u^*)^{-1}$,
   (iv) If $u \in C$, then $u = u^*$ if and only if $u \in K$,
   (v) If $u \in C$ and n is a positive integer, then $(u^n)^* = (u^*)^n$.

3. Let S be an arbitrary ring and T the set of all ordered pairs (a, b) of elements of S. If addition and multiplication are defined by 7.2 and 7.3, respectively, verify each of the following:
   (i) T is a ring,
   (ii) T is a commutative ring if and only if S is a commutative ring,
   (iii) T has a unity if and only if S has a unity.

4. In the notation of the preceding exercise, let S be the ring $I/(2)$ of integers modulo 2. Exhibit addition and multiplication tables for the corresponding ring T. Is T a field in this case? Is it an integral domain? Is it isomorphic to any of the rings with four elements given in Chapter 2?

7.3 GEOMETRIC REPRESENTATION AND TRIGONOMETRIC FORM

It is implicit in our construction of the complex numbers that the mapping $a + bi \rightarrow (a, b)$ is a one-one mapping of the set C of all complex numbers onto the set of all ordered pairs of real numbers. Now in ordinary plane analytic geometry we represent points in the plane by their coordinates, that is, by ordered pairs of real numbers. Accordingly, we may represent a point in the plane by a single complex number. In other words, we shall sometimes find it convenient to associate with the complex number $a + bi$ the point with rectangular coordinates (a, b), and to say that this point has *coordinate* $a + bi$. A number of examples are given in Figure 5. It will be observed that a real number; that is,

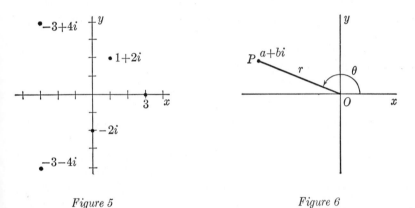

Figure 5   Figure 6

a complex number of the form $a + 0i$, is the coordinate of a point on the x-axis. A number of the form $0 + bi$, sometimes called a *pure imaginary*, is the coordinate of a point on the y-axis. We may also observe that a complex number $a + bi$ and its conjugate $a - bi$ are coordinates of points that are symmetrically located with respect to the x-axis.

Instead of specifying points in a plane by means of rectangular coordinates, we may of course use polar coordinates. If P is the point with nonzero coordinate $a + bi$, the distance of P from the origin O of coordinates is the positive real number $r = \sqrt{a^2 + b^2}$. If θ is an angle in standard position with terminal side OP, as in Figure 6, then by the definition of the trigonometric functions we have

$$a = r \cos \theta, \qquad b = r \sin \theta.$$

It follows that the complex number $a + bi$ can be expressed in the form

7.8 $$a + bi = r(\cos \theta + i \sin \theta).$$

We have been assuming that $a + bi \neq 0$. If $a + bi = 0$, then $r = 0$ in 7.8, and θ may be a completely arbitrary angle.

We now introduce some appropriate terms in the following definition.

7.9 Definition. The expression on the right side of 7.8 is called the *trigonometric form* of the complex number $a + bi$. The nonnegative real number $r = \sqrt{a^2 + b^2}$ is called the *absolute value* of the complex number $a + bi$, and may be designated by "$| a + bi |$." The angle θ occurring in 7.8 is called *an angle* of $a + bi$.

Clearly, the nonnegative real number r occurring in the trigonometric form of $a + bi$ is uniquely determined. However, the angle θ is not unique, but if $r \neq 0$ and θ_1 and θ_2 are any two possible angles of $a + bi$, then elementary properties of the sine and cosine functions show that $\theta_1 = \theta_2 + n \cdot 360°$ for some integer n.

As a consequence of these observations, let us point out that if r and s are positive real numbers and we know that

$$r(\cos \theta + i \sin \theta) = s(\cos \phi + i \sin \phi),$$

then necessarily $r = s$ and $\theta = \phi + n \cdot 360°$ for some integer n.

We have previously defined (3.6) absolute values for an ordered integral domain, and we know that the field of complex numbers is not ordered. However, the present definition of absolute value is an extension of the concept for real numbers. For if a is a real number, we may consider it to be the complex number $a + 0i$ and, by 7.9, we have $| a | = \sqrt{a^2}$. But if c is a positive real number, by $\sqrt{c}$ we mean the *positive* square root of c. It follows that $\sqrt{a^2} = a$ if $a \geq 0$, whereas $\sqrt{a^2} = -a$ if $a < 0$. Hence, for a *real* number a, the present meaning of $| a |$ coincides with its meaning according to Definition 3.6.

Let us now illustrate the trigonometric form of a complex number by some examples. First, let us consider the number $-2 + 2i$. As indicated in Figure 7, $| -2 + 2i | = 2\sqrt{2}$, and an angle of $-2 + 2i$ is $135°$. Hence, 7.8 takes the form

$$-2 + 2i = 2\sqrt{2}(\cos 135° + i \sin 135°),$$

which is easily verified by direct calculation. Other examples, which the reader may check, are the following:

$$1 + \sqrt{3}\, i = 2(\cos 60° + i \sin 60°),$$
$$4 = 4(\cos 0° + i \sin 0°),$$
$$-i = 1(\cos 270° + i \sin 270°),$$
$$-2(\cos 40° + i \sin 40°) = 2(\cos 220° + i \sin 220°).$$

It is clear that only in special cases can we find in degrees an angle of a given complex number. Naturally, an approximation may be obtained by use of trigonometric tables, or an angle may be merely indicated as in the following example. Let us attempt to express $1 + 3i$ in trigonometric form. Clearly, $|\,1 + 3i\,| = \sqrt{10}$, but we cannot exactly express its angle in degrees. However, if θ_1 is the positive acute angle such that $\tan \theta_1 = 3$, as indicated in Figure 8, we may write

$$1 + 3i = \sqrt{10}\,(\cos \theta_1 + i \sin \theta_1)$$

as the trigonometric form of $1 + 3i$.

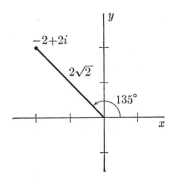

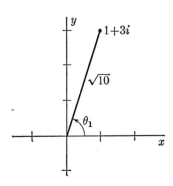

Figure 7   Figure 8

The fact that every complex number can be expressed in trigonometric form is of considerable significance largely because of the following remarkable theorem.

7.10 Theorem. *If u and v are complex numbers such that in trigonometric form,*

$$u = r(\cos \theta + i \sin \theta),$$

and

$$v = s(\cos \phi + i \sin \phi),$$

then the trigonometric form of uv is given by

7.11 $$uv = rs(\cos(\theta + \phi) + i \sin(\theta + \phi)).$$

Otherwise expressed, $|\,uv\,| = |\,u\,| \cdot |\,v\,|$, and an angle of uv is the sum of an angle of u and an angle of v.

To establish this result we need only multiply together the trigonometric forms of u and v and then use the simple addition formulas of trigonometry. Thus we have

$$uv = rs(\cos \theta + i \sin \theta)(\cos \phi + i \sin \phi)$$
$$= rs[(\cos \theta \cos \phi - \sin \theta \sin \phi) + i (\cos \theta \sin \phi + \sin \theta \cos \phi)]$$
$$= rs[\cos (\theta + \phi) + i \sin (\theta + \phi)],$$

and the desired result follows immediately.

The special case of the preceding theorem in which $u = v$ shows at once that

$$u^2 = r^2(\cos 2\theta + i \sin 2\theta).$$

The following generalization of this result is of great importance.

7.12 De Moivre's Theorem. *If n is an arbitrary positive integer and*

$$u = r(\cos \theta + i \sin \theta),$$

then

7.13 $$u^n = r^n(\cos n\theta + i \sin n\theta).$$

Let us prove this theorem by mathematical induction, and let S_n be the statement that 7.13 is true. Then S_1 is true, and we have also just verified that S_2 is true. Suppose that we know that S_k is true, and hence that

$$u^k = r^k(\cos k\theta + i \sin k\theta).$$

Then we see that

$$u^{k+1} = [r^k(\cos k\theta + i \sin k\theta)][r(\cos \theta + i \sin \theta)],$$

and, applying Theorem 7.10, it follows at once that

$$u^{k+1} = r^{k+1}[\cos (k + 1)\theta + i \sin (k + 1)\theta],$$

and hence that S_{k+1} is true. The Induction Principle now shows that S_n is true for every positive integer n, and the proof of the theorem is completed.

One application of this theorem will be given in the next section. However, let us point out here how certain trigonometric identities can be obtained in an easy way by use of this theorem. By letting $r = 1$ and, as an example, taking $n = 3$, we see that

$$(\cos \theta + i \sin \theta)^3 = \cos 3\theta + i \sin 3\theta.$$

However, by actually multiplying out the left side, we find that

$$(\cos \theta + i \sin \theta)^3 = \cos^3 \theta - 3 \cos \theta \sin^2 \theta + i (3 \cos^2 \theta \sin \theta - \sin^3 \theta),$$

and it follows that

$$\cos 3\theta + i \sin 3\theta = \cos^3 \theta - 3 \cos \theta \sin^2 \theta + i(3 \cos^2 \theta \sin \theta - \sin^3 \theta).$$

From this equation we get at once the two following trigonometric identities:

$$\cos 3\theta = \cos^3 \theta - 3 \cos \theta \sin^2 \theta,$$

and

$$\sin 3\theta = 3 \cos^2 \theta \sin \theta - \sin^3 \theta.$$

_____ **E X E R C I S E S**

1. Express each of the following complex numbers in trigonometric form and indicate the points in a coordinate plane that have these numbers as coordinates:

   (a) $-1 - i$,   (b) $-\sqrt{3} + i$,
   (c) $\sqrt{3} + i$,   (d) $-1 + \sqrt{3}i$,
   (e) -4,   (f) $3 - 2i$,
   (g) $2 - 2i$,   (h) $\cos 26° - i \sin 26°$.

2. Express each of the following complex numbers in the form $a + bi$:

   (a) $4(\cos 45° + i \sin 45°)$,
   (b) $2(\cos 120° + i \sin 120°)$,
   (c) $3(\cos 180° + i \sin 180°)$,
   (d) $3(\cos 270° + i \sin 270°)$,
   (e) $(1/2)(\cos 300° + i \sin 300°)$,
   (f) $12(\cos 0° + i \sin 0°)$,
   (g) $11(\cos 90° + i \sin 90°)$,
   (h) $(\cos 117° + i \sin 117°)(\cos 123° + i \sin 123°)$.

3. Use De Moivre's Theorem to compute each of the following, and then express your answers in algebraic form by evaluating the necessary trigonometric functions:

   (a) $(-1 - i)^5$,   (b) $(\sqrt{3} - i)^8$,
   (c) $(-i)^{12}$,   (d) $\left(\dfrac{1}{\sqrt{2}} + \dfrac{i}{\sqrt{2}}\right)^{100}$,
   (e) $\left(-\dfrac{1}{2} - \dfrac{\sqrt{3}\,i}{2}\right)^6$,   (f) $(-1 + i)^{10}$,
   (g) $(1 - \sqrt{3}\,i)^{11}$,   (h) $(\cos 18° + i \sin 18°)^{10}$.

4. Verify that the points with coordinates

   $$(\cos 60° + i \sin 60°)^n, \quad (n = 1, 2, 3, 4, 5, 6),$$

   are the vertices of a regular hexagon inscribed in a circle of radius 1.

5. If u^* is the conjugate of the complex number u, verify each of the following:

(a) $|u^*| = |u|$,

(b) $uu^* = |u|^2$,

(c) $u^{-1} = \dfrac{u^*}{|u|^2}$, if $u \neq 0$.

6. Show that if $u \neq 0$, De Moivre's Theorem also holds for every *negative* integer n.

7. Let $u, v \in C$, and let P and Q be the points in a coordinate plane having respective coordinates u and v. Let R be the point with coordinate $u + v$. If O is the origin, show that OR is a diagonal of the parallelogram having OP and OQ as adjacent sides.

8. Show that if $u, v \in C$, then $|u + v| \leq |u| + |v|$.

9. Use De Moivre's Theorem to find trigonometric identities for $\cos 4\theta$ and $\sin 4\theta$.

10. If $u = a + bi$, we have defined $|u| = \sqrt{a^2 + b^2}$. Use this definition to prove directly that if $u, v \in C$, then $|uv| = |u| \cdot |v|$.

11. If $u, v \in C$ with $v \neq 0$, prove that $\left|\dfrac{u}{v}\right| = \dfrac{|u|}{|v|}$.

7.4 THE nth ROOTS OF A COMPLEX NUMBER

In this section we give an important application of the use of the trigonometric form of a complex number. First, we give the following familiar definition.

7.14 Definition. Let n be a positive integer greater than 1. If $u, v \in C$ such that $v^n = u$, we say that v is an nth *root* of u.

We shall now prove the following theorem.

7.15 Theorem. *If n is a positive integer greater than 1, and*

$$u = r(\cos \theta + i \sin \theta)$$

is a nonzero complex number in trigonometric form, there exist exactly n nth roots of u, namely,

7.16 $\quad r^{1/n}\left(\cos \dfrac{\theta + k \cdot 360°}{n} + i \sin \dfrac{\theta + k \cdot 360°}{n}\right), \quad (k = 0, 1, \cdots, n-1).$

Here $r^{1/n}$ represents the principal nth root of the positive real number r; that is, the positive real nth root of r whose existence is asserted in Theorem 6.19.

Suppose that $v = s(\cos \phi + i \sin \phi)$ is an nth root of u. Then $v^n = u$ and De Moivre's Theorem assures us that

$$s^n(\cos n\phi + i \sin n\phi) = r(\cos \theta + i \sin \theta).$$

It follows that the absolute values of the two members of this equation are equal, and an angle of one must be equal to an angle of the other. Hence, $s^n = r$, so that $s = r^{1/n}$. Moreover, $n\phi = \theta + k \cdot 360°$ for some integer k, and it follows that $\phi = (\theta + k \cdot 360°)/n$. We have therefore shown that every nth root v of u must be of the form

17
$$v = r^{1/n}\left(\cos \frac{\theta + k \cdot 360°}{n} + i \sin \frac{\theta + k \cdot 360°}{n}\right)$$

for some integer k. Conversely, it is readily verified by De Moivre's Theorem that if v is given by 7.17, then $v^n = u$ for *every* choice of the integer k. The number of distinct nth roots of u is therefore the number of ways in which the integer k can be chosen in 7.17 so as to give distinct values of v. The angles obtained by letting k take the values $0, 1, \cdots, n-1$ have distinct terminal sides, and this fact makes it almost obvious that these n values of k yield distinct values of v. Moreover, if s is an arbitrary integer, the Division Algorithm asserts that there exist integers q and r with $0 \le r < n$ such that $s = qn + r$, and therefore

$$\frac{\theta + s \cdot 360°}{n} = \frac{\theta + r \cdot 360°}{n} + q \cdot 360°.$$

It is then clear that the angle $(\theta + s \cdot 360°)/n$ has the same terminal side as the angle $(\theta + r \cdot 360°)/n$. Since $0 \le r < n$, we see that all possible different values of v are obtained if in 7.17 we let k take the values $0, 1, \cdots, n-1$. This completes the proof of the theorem.

As an example of the use of this theorem, let us find the fifth roots of the complex number $-2 + 2i$. First, we express this number in trigonometric form as follows:

$$-2 + 2i = 2^{3/2}(\cos 135° + i \sin 135°).$$

In the notation of the theorem, we have $r = 2^{3/2}$, $\theta = 135°$, and $n = 5$. Accordingly, the fifth roots of $-2 + 2i$ are the following:

$$2^{3/10}(\cos 27° + i \sin 27°),$$
$$2^{3/10}(\cos 99° + i \sin 99°),$$
$$2^{3/10}(\cos 171° + i \sin 171°),$$
$$2^{3/10}(\cos 243° + i \sin 243°),$$
$$2^{3/10}(\cos 315° + i \sin 315°).$$

An interesting special case of Theorem 7.15 arises if we choose $u = 1$; hence $r = 1$ and $\theta = 0°$. We state this case as follows.

7.18 Corollary. *The distinct nth roots of 1 are the complex numbers*

7.19 $$\cos \frac{k \cdot 360°}{n} + i \sin \frac{k \cdot 360°}{n}, \qquad (k = 0, 1, \cdots, n - 1).$$

By De Moivre's Theorem, we have

$$\left(\cos \frac{360°}{n} + i \sin \frac{360°}{n} \right)^k = \cos \frac{k \cdot 360°}{n} + i \sin \frac{k \cdot 360°}{n}.$$

Hence, the n distinct nth roots of 1, as given in 7.19, may all be expressed as powers of a certain nth root of 1. We have then the following alternate form of the preceding corollary.

7.20 Corollary. *Let us set*

7.21 $$w = \cos \frac{360°}{n} + i \sin \frac{360°}{n},$$

so that w is the nth root of 1 having the smallest positive angle. Then the nth roots of 1 are the numbers

7.22 $$w, w^2, w^3, \cdots, w^n = 1.$$

Since all nth roots of 1 have absolute value 1, they are coordinates of points on the circle with radius 1 and center the origin. Moreover, it is clear from 7.19 that they are the vertices of a regular polygon of n sides inscribed in this circle, with one vertex at the real number 1. This fact is of considerable importance in the study of the constructability of regular polygons with ruler and compass.

_____ **E X E R C I S E S**

1. Find the cube roots of 1 and express the answers in algebraic form. Draw a figure showing that these numbers are the coordinates of the vertices of a regular polygon of three sides (equilateral triangle).

2. Do the corresponding thing for the fourth roots of 1.

3. Do the corresponding thing for the eighth roots of 1.

4. Show that the sixth roots of 1 are the cube roots of 1 and their negatives.

5. Find the required roots and express the answers in algebraic form:
   (a) The cube roots of $-2 + 2i$,
   (b) The cube roots of $-8i$,

(c) The fourth roots of -4,

(d) The sixth roots of $-i$,

(e) The fourth roots of $-1 - \sqrt{3}\, i$,

(f) The square roots of $-1 + \sqrt{3}\, i$.

6. In each of the following, express the required roots in trigonometric form:

(a) The fifth roots of 1,

(b) The fourth roots of $-1 + i$,

(c) The fourth roots of $\dfrac{1}{2} + \dfrac{\sqrt{3}\, i}{2}$,

(d) The sixth roots of $1 - i$,

(e) The square roots of $1 + 2i$,

(f) The fourth roots of $16(\cos 12° + i \sin 12°)$.

7. Show that if v is any one of the nth roots of the nonzero complex number u, and w is given by 7.21, then $v, wv, w^2v, \cdots, w^{n-1}v$ are all the nth roots of u.

8. Show that the multiplicative inverse of an nth root of 1 is also an nth root of 1.

9. If $t \subset C$ such that $t^n = 1$ but $t^m \neq 1$ for $0 < m < n$, t is called a *primitive nth root* of 1. Show each of the following:

(i) The number w, defined in 7.21, is a primitive nth root of 1.

(ii) If t is a primitive nth root of 1, then $1, t, t^2, \cdots, t^{n-1}$ are distinct and are all of the nth roots of 1.

(iii) If t is a primitive nth root of 1, then t^l is also a primitive nth root of 1 if and only if l and n are relatively prime.

8

Polynomials

In elementary algebra an important role is played by polynomials in a symbol "x" with coefficients that are real or complex numbers. In the next section we shall introduce polynomials with coefficients in a commutative ring S with unity, and show that under suitable definitions of addition and multiplication the set of all such polynomials is a ring. Actually, we could just as well start by letting S be an entirely arbitrary ring, but in most of the chapter it is essential that it be commutative and so we simplify matters by making this assumption from the beginning. The restriction that S have a unity is not very important but it does serve to simplify the notation somewhat.

The purpose of this chapter is to introduce polynomials with coefficients in a commutative ring S with unity, and to establish a number of properties of such polynomials. We shall frequently find it necessary or desirable to make additional restrictions on the ring S. In particular, we shall sometimes require that it be a field or a specified one of the fields that have already been studied in detail in previous chapters.

It will be found that a ring of polynomials with coefficients in a *field* has a considerable number of properties in common with the ring I of integers. Accordingly, several of the sections of this chapter will closely parallel corresponding material of Chapter 4. In one such section we shall present an analogue of the concept of the ring of integers modulo n, and obtain some new examples of rings and fields.

8.1 POLYNOMIAL RINGS

Let S be a commutative ring with unity. Heretofore we have used letters to denote sets or elements of sets, but we now use the letter "x" in a different way. It is not an element of S, but is just a symbol which we shall use in an entirely formal way. It is customary to call such a symbol an *indeterminate*. It is our purpose in this section to construct a ring which contains S and also has x as an element. This goal will motivate the definitions which we proceed to give.

Let x be an indeterminate and let us consider expressions of the form

1
$$a_0x^0 + a_1x^1 + a_2x^2 + \cdots + a_nx^n,$$

where n is some nonnegative integer and $a_i \in S$ ($i = 0, 1, \cdots, n$). Such an expression is called "a *polynomial* in x with coefficients in S" or simply, "a polynomial in x over S." If i is an integer such that $0 \leq i \leq n$, we say that a_i is the *coefficient* of x^i in the polynomial 8.1; also we say that a_ix^i is a *term* of the polynomial 8.1 with coefficient a_i.

At this stage we are to think of 8.1 as a purely formal expression. That is, the "$+$" signs are not to be considered as representing addition in a ring, and neither is x^i to be considered as a product $x \cdot x \cdots x$ with i factors. Later on, when we show the existence of a ring which contains S as well as x, we shall see that in this larger ring we can make these familiar interpretations and thus justify the notation we are using. At the present time, we could logically use some such symbol as $(a_0, a_1, a_2, \cdots, a_n)$ to designate the polynomial 8.1, but the definitions of addition and multiplication of polynomials to be given below will seem more natural with the familiar notation used in 8.1.

For the moment, let S be the ring I of integers. Then the following are examples of polynomials in x over I:

(i) $2x^0 + (-3)x^1 + 4x^2$, (ii) $3x^0$, (iii) $0x^0 + 0x^1 + 4x^2$, (iv) $0x^0 + 2x^1 + (-1)x^2 + 0x^3$.

In order to avoid writing so many terms with zero coefficients, we could agree in the third of these examples to write merely $4x^2$ with the understanding that x^0 and x^1 are assumed to have zero coefficients. Also, it would certainly agree with usual practice if we omitted the terms with zero coefficients in the fourth example and wrote $2x^1 + (-1)x^2$ to designate this polynomial. These simplifications will be possible under general agreements which we now make.

Let us designate the polynomial 8.1 over S by the symbol $f(x)$, and let $g(x)$ be the following polynomial over S:

8.2
$$b_0x^0 + b_1x^1 + \cdots + b_mx^m,$$

where $m \geq 0$ and $b_i \in S$ $(i = 0, 1, \cdots, m)$. By the *equality* of $f(x)$ and $g(x)$, written in the usual way as $f(x) = g(x)$, we shall mean that the expressions 8.1 and 8.2 are identical except for terms with zero coefficients. We therefore consider a polynomial as being unchanged by the insertion, or omission, of any number of terms with zero coefficients. In particular, with reference to the above examples, we may write

$$0x^0 + 0x^1 + 4x^2 = 4x^2,$$
and
$$0x^0 + 2x^1 + (-1)x^2 + 0x^3 = 2x^1 + (-1)x^2.$$

Also, if we wish, we could write

$$3x^0 = 3x^0 + 0x^1 + 0x^2 + 0x^3,$$

and so on.

With this understanding about zero coefficients, if $f(x)$ is a polynomial over S and i is an *arbitrary* positive integer, we may speak of the coefficient of x^i in $f(x)$. For example, in the polynomial $1x^0 + 2x^1 + 3x^2$ over I, the coefficient of x^{10} is zero. This language often helps to simplify statements about polynomials. As an illustration, we may state again our definition of equality of two polynomials as follows. If $f(x)$ and $g(x)$ are polynomials over S, by $f(x) = g(x)$ we mean that for *every* nonnegative integer i, the coefficients of x^i in $f(x)$ and in $g(x)$ are equal elements of S.

Now let $S[x]$ denote the set of all polynomials in the indeterminate x over S. We proceed to define operations of addition and multiplication on the set $S[x]$. Let

8.3
$$f(x) = a_0x^0 + a_1x^1 + \cdots + a_nx^n,$$

and

8.4
$$g(x) = b_0x^0 + b_1x^1 + \cdots + b_mx^m,$$

be elements of $S[x]$. We define

8.5
$$f(x) + g(x) = (a_0 + b_0)x^0 + (a_1 + b_1)x^1 + (a_2 + b_2)x^2 + \cdots;$$

in other words, for every nonnegative integer i the coefficient of x^i in $f(x) + g(x)$ is the sum of the coefficients of x^i in $f(x)$ and in $g(x)$.

Multiplication of polynomials is defined as follows:

8.6 $f(x)g(x) = (a_0b_0)x^0 + (a_0b_1 + a_1b_0)x^1 + (a_0b_2 + a_1b_1 + a_2b_0)x^2$
$$+ \cdots + (a_nb_m)x^{n+m}.$$

More explicitly, if i is an arbitrary nonnegative integer, the coefficient of x^i in this product is

$$a_0 b_i + a_1 b_{i-1} + \cdots + a_i b_0,$$

with the understanding that $a_k = 0$ if $k > n$ and $b_k = 0$ if $k > m$. Another way of expressing this fact is to say that the coefficient of x^i in $f(x)g(x)$ is the sum of all products of the form $a_r b_s$, where r and s are nonnegative integers such that $r + s = i$.

We are now ready to state the following theorem.

7 Theorem. *Let $S[x]$ be the set of all polynomials in the indeterminate x over the commutative ring S with unity. If operations of addition and multiplication are defined on $S[x]$ by 8.5 and 8.6, respectively, then*

(i) *$S[x]$ is a commutative ring with unity,*
(ii) *$S[x]$ contains a subring isomorphic to S,*
(iii) *$S[x]$ is an integral domain if and only if S is an integral domain.*

The commutative and associative laws for addition in $S[x]$ follow from 8.5 since these laws hold in the ring S. Moreover, the polynomial $0x^0$ (which is equal to the polynomial with *all* coefficients zero) is the zero of $S[x]$ since, by 8.5,

$$f(x) + 0x^0 = (a_0 + 0)x^0 + a_1 x^1 + \cdots + a_n x^n = f(x)$$

for every element $f(x)$ of $S[x]$. Moreover, since

$$a_0 x^0 + a_1 x^1 + \cdots + a_n x^n + [(-a_0)x^0 + (-a_1)x^1 + \cdots + (-a_n)x^n] = 0x^0,$$

the additive inverse of $a_0 x^0 + a_1 x^1 + \cdots + a_n x^n$ is the polynomial $(-a_0)x^0 + (-a_1)x^1 + \cdots + (-a_n)x^n$. Hence, every element of $S[x]$ has an additive inverse.

To establish that multiplication is commutative, we observe that if $f(x)$ and $g(x)$ are given by 8.3 and 8.4, respectively, then the coefficient of x^i in $g(x)f(x)$ is

$$b_0 a_i + b_1 a_{i-1} + \cdots + b_i a_0,$$

and since S is assumed to be commutative, this is equal to the coefficient

$$a_0 b_i + a_1 b_{i-1} + \cdots + a_i b_0$$

of x^i in $f(x)g(x)$. Inasmuch as this statement is true for every nonnegative integer i, it follows that $f(x)g(x) = g(x)f(x)$, and hence that multiplication in $S[x]$ is commutative.

If $f(x)$ and $g(x)$ are given by 8.3 and 8.4, respectively, and

8.8
$$h(x) = c_0 x^0 + c_1 x^1 + \cdots + c_p x^p$$

is also an element of $S[x]$, the coefficient of x^i in the product $(f(x)g(x))h(x)$ is found to be the sum of all products of the form $(a_r b_s)c_t$, where r, s, and t are nonnegative integers such that $r + s + t = i$. Similarly, the coefficient of x^i in the product $f(x)(g(x)h(x))$ is the sum of all products of the form $a_r(b_s c_t)$, with the same restriction on r, s, and t. However, since $(a_r b_s)c_t = a_r(b_s c_t)$ by the associative law of multiplication in S, it follows that

$$(f(x)g(x))h(x) = f(x)(g(x)h(x)),$$

that is, that multiplication is associative in $S[x]$.

We leave as exercises the proof of the distributive laws, and that if 1 is the unity of S, then $1x^0$ is the unity of $S[x]$. It follows then that $S[x]$ is a commutative ring with unity.

To establish part (ii) of the theorem, let S' denote the set of elements of $S[x]$ of the form ax^0, $a \in S$. Then the mapping $ax^0 \to a$ is a one-one mapping of S' onto S. Moreover,

$$ax^0 + bx^0 = (a + b)x^0 \to a + b,$$

and

$$(ax^0)(bx^0) = (ab)x^0 \to ab,$$

so that the operations of addition and multiplication are preserved under this mapping. This shows that S' is isomorphic to S and hence that $S[x]$ contains a subring S' isomorphic to S.

Before proceeding to the proof of part (iii) of the theorem, let us introduce some simplifications of our notation as follows. We shall henceforth identify S' with S, and therefore write simply a in place of ax^0; that is, we shall omit x^0 in writing polynomials. In particular, the zero polynomial will then be designated by the familiar symbol 0. We shall also write x in place of x^1, x^i in place of $1x^i$, and $-ax^i$ in place of $(-a)x^i$. We may now observe that x is itself an element of the ring $S[x]$. If $a \in S$, then also $a \in S[x]$, and ax^i can be interpreted as the product (in the ring $S[x]$) of a times x to the power i. Also, since each individual term of a polynomial 8.1 is itself equal to a polynomial, the "$+$" signs occurring in 8.1 can be correctly interpreted as addition in the ring $S[x]$. In other words, we have finally justified the use of the notation appearing in 8.1. Of course, addition is commutative in $S[x]$ and we can write the polynomial 8.1 with the terms in any order. For example, we could just as well write the polynomial 8.1 in the form

$$a_n x^n + a_{n-1} x^{n-1} + \cdots + a_1 x + a_0.$$

In this case, it is customary to say that it is written in *decreasing* powers of x. As given in 8.1, it is written in *increasing* powers of x.

The following familiar concepts are of such great importance that we give a formal definition.

.9 Definition. Let $f(x)$ be a nonzero element of the ring $S[x]$. If n is the largest nonnegative integer such that x^n has a nonzero coefficient in $f(x)$, we say that $f(x)$ has *degree n*. If $f(x)$ has degree n, the nonzero coefficient of x^n is sometimes called the *leading coefficient* of $f(x)$. The zero polynomial has no degree and therefore also no leading coefficient. The coefficient of x^0 in a polynomial; that is, as now written, the term that does not involve x, is sometimes referred to as the *constant term* of the polynomial.

It will be observed that the nonzero elements of S, considered as elements of $S[x]$, are just the polynomials of degree zero. The degree of a polynomial $f(x)$ may be conveniently designated by "deg $f(x)$."

If S is the ring I of integers, the polynomials $2 + 3x - x^2$, $4x$, 3, and $x^4 - 2x$ have respective degrees $2, 1, 0,$ and 4; and respective leading coefficients $-1, 4, 3,$ and 1. The constant terms are, respectively, $2, 0, 3,$ and 0.

The third part of Theorem 8.7 will follow immediately from the following lemma.

10 Lemma. *Let S be an integral domain and let $f(x)$ and $g(x)$ be nonzero elements of $S[x]$. Then*

.11
$$deg \ (f(x)g(x)) = deg \ f(x) + deg \ g(x).$$

Since $f(x)$ and $g(x)$ are not zero, they have degrees, and let us suppose that deg $f(x) = n$ and deg $g(x) = m$. Then $f(x)$ can be written in the form 8.3 with $a_n \neq 0$, and $g(x)$ in the form 8.4 with $b_m \neq 0$. It now follows by the definition of multiplication (8.6) that $f(x)g(x)$ cannot have degree greater than $n + m$. Moreover, since S is an integral domain and we know that $a_n \neq 0$ and $b_m \neq 0$, it follows that the coefficient $a_n b_m$ of x^{n+m} is not zero, and 8.11 follows at once.

Lemma 8.10 assures us that if $f(x)$ and $g(x)$ are nonzero elements of $S[x]$, with S an integral domain, then the element $f(x)g(x)$ of $S[x]$ has a degree and therefore is not zero. Hence, $S[x]$ is also an integral domain. Since $S \subset S[x]$, it is trivial that if $S[x]$ is an integral domain, then S must be an integral domain. The proof of Theorem 8.7 is thus completed.

The familiar property 8.11 is not necessarily true if S is not an integral domain since, in the above proof, $a_n b_m$ might be zero without either factor being zero. For example, let $S = I/(6)$. If $f(x) = [1] + [2]x$, and $g(x) = [2] + [4]x + [3]x^2$, then deg $f(x) = 1$ and deg $g(x) = 2$. However, $f(x)g(x) = [2] + [2]x + [5]x^2$, and deg $f(x)g(x) = 2$. In this case,

$$deg \ (f(x)g(x)) < deg \ f(x) + deg \ g(x).$$

In this section we have introduced polynomials in *one* indeterminate x. However, this procedure can easily be generalized as follows. If S is a commutative ring with unity, then the polynomial ring $S[x]$ is a commutative ring with unity. If now y is another indeterminate, we may as above construct a ring $(S[x])[y]$ consisting of polynomials in y with coefficients in the ring $S[x]$. It is easy to verify that the elements of this new ring can also be expressed as polynomials in x with coefficients in the ring $S[y]$; in other words, that the rings $(S[x])[y]$ and $(S[y])[x]$ are identical. Accordingly, we may denote this ring by $S[x, y]$ and call its elements polynomials in the indeterminates x and y. A double application of Theorem 8.7 (iii) then assures us that $S[x, y]$ is an integral domain if and only if S is an integral domain. These statements may be extended in an obvious way to polynomials in any finite number of indeterminates. However, for the most part we shall study polynomials in just one indeterminate.

8.2 THE SUBSTITUTION PROCESS

In defining the polynomial ring $S[x]$, where S is a commutative ring with unity, we have emphasized that x is not to be considered as an element of S. However, if $f(x) = a_0 + a_1 x + \cdots + a_n x^n$ is an element of $S[x]$ and $s \in S$, let us define

$$f(s) = a_0 + a_1 s + \cdots + a_n s^n.$$

It follows that $f(s)$ is a uniquely determined element of S associated with the polynomial $f(x)$ and the element s of S. Now the importance of this "substitution process" stems from the fact that our definitions of addition and multiplication in $S[x]$ have the same form as though x were an element of S. Let us state this fact more precisely in terms of the mapping

8.12
$$f(x) \rightarrow f(s), \qquad\qquad f(x) \in S[x],$$

of $S[x]$ onto S. We may emphasize that in this mapping we are thinking of s as being a fixed element of S. Then our definitions of addition and multiplication in $S[x]$ are such that these operations are preserved under the mapping 8.12. This means, of course, that under the mapping 8.12,

$$f(x) + g(x) \rightarrow f(s) + g(s)$$

and

$$f(x)g(x) \rightarrow f(s)g(s).$$

When we said above that addition and multiplication of polynomials were defined "as though x were an element of S," what we really meant was that the operations of addition and multiplication are preserved under the mapping 8.12 of $S[x]$ onto S.

It is easy to verify that under the mapping 8.12 different polynomials may have the same image, and hence this is not a one-one mapping. However, it certainly is a mapping *onto* S since if $a \in S$, then $a \to a$ under the mapping 8.12. Since the operations of addition and multiplication are preserved, the mapping 8.12 has all the properties of an isomorphism with the exception that it is not a one-one mapping. This situation occurs often enough that it is convenient to have an easy way to refer to such a mapping. Accordingly, we make the following definition.

13 Definition. If $t \to t'$ is a mapping of the ring U onto the ring V such that the operations of addition and multiplication are preserved, we say that the mapping is a *homomorphism* of U onto V.

An isomorphism is then the special case of a homomorphism in which the mapping is a one-one mapping.

For each element s of S, the mapping 8.12 is a homomorphism of $S[x]$ onto S. In Exercise 9 below we give another important example of a homomorphism which we have already met but without using this term to describe it.

We are frequently interested in considering elements r of S such that $f(r) = 0$, and so we make the following definition.

14 Definition. If $f(x) \in S[x]$ and $r \in S$ such that $f(r) = 0$, we say that r is a *root* of the polynomial $f(x)$.*

In later sections we shall obtain various results about roots of polynomials. However, in order to obtain results of a familiar nature, we shall find it necessary to make some additional restrictions on the ring S. In particular, we shall frequently assume that S is a *field*. As an example to show what may happen if we do not restrict the ring of coefficients, let T be the ring of all subsets of a given set (Example 10 of Section 2.3), and $T[x]$ the ring of polynomials in the indeterminate x with coefficients in T. Since $a^2 = a$ for every element a of T, it is clear that the polynomial $x^2 - x$ of $T[x]$ has as a root *every* element of T. We thus have an example of a polynomial of degree 2 that has more than two roots (if the given set has more than one element). In the next section we shall see that this cannot happen in case the ring of coefficients is restricted to be a field.

---

*In elementary algebra, r is usually said to be a root of the *equation* $f(x) = 0$, in which case x is thought of as an unknown number. However, this is not consistent with the definitions of the preceding section, and we shall continue to write $f(x) = 0$ to mean that $f(x)$ is the zero polynomial.

1. Prove the distributive laws in $S[x]$.

2. If S is a commutative ring with unity, verify that the set of all polynomials of $S[x]$ with zero constant terms is a subring of $S[x]$.

3. Verify that the set of all polynomials of $S[x]$ with the property that all odd powers of x have zero coefficients is a subring of $S[x]$. Is the same true if the word "odd" is replaced by the word "even"?

4. If I is the ring of integers and x an indeterminate, let $(I[x])_p$ be the subset of $I[x]$ consisting of those nonzero polynomials which have as leading coefficient a *positive* integer. Show that the set $(I[x])_p$ has all the properties required in 3.3, and hence that $I[x]$ is an ordered integral domain.

5. Generalize the preceding exercise by showing that if D is an ordered integral domain, then the polynomial ring $D[x]$ is also an ordered integral domain.

6. Let S be the ring $I/(6)$, and $h(x)$ the element $5x^2 - 3x + 4$ of $S[x]$. (Here we are writing 5, -3, and 4 in place of the more cumbersome $[5]$, $[-3]$, and $[4]$.) By simply trying all the elements of S, find all roots of $h(x)$.

7. If F is the ring $I/(7)$, and $g(x)$ is the element $x^7 - x$ of $F[x]$, verify that all elements of F are roots of $g(x)$.

8. Show that the first three parts of Theorem 2.33 are true if the word "isomorphism" is replaced by the word "homomorphism." Can you prove the fourth part under this modification?

9. Verify that if $k \in I$, the mapping $k \to [k]$ of I onto $I/(n)$ is a homomorphism of I onto $I/(n)$ for each positive integer n.

10. If m is a positive integer, how many polynomials are there of degree m over the ring $I/(n)$ of integers modulo n?

11. Let $a \to a'$ define a homomorphism of a ring U onto a ring V. Now if $f(x) = a_0 + a_1 x + \cdots + a_n x^n$ is a polynomial in the indeterminate x over U, let us define $f'(x) = a_0' + a_1' x + \cdots + a_n' x^n$. Verify that the mapping $f(x) \to f'(x)$ is a homomorphism of $U[x]$ onto $V[x]$.

12. If $f(x) = g(x)h(x)$, where these are elements of $I[x]$, and every coefficient of $f(x)$ is divisible by the prime p, prove that every coefficient of $g(x)$ is divisible by p or every coefficient of $h(x)$ is divisible by p. [Hint: Use Exercises 9 and 11, setting $U = I$ and $V = I/(p)$. Then consider what $f'(x) = 0$ implies about the polynomial $f(x)$.]

8.3 DIVISORS AND THE DIVISION ALGORITHM

In this and the next two sections we shall study polynomials with coefficients in an arbitrary *field F*. We then know, by Theorem 8.7, that $F[x]$ is necessarily an integral domain. The following definition is merely a restatement of Definition 4.1 as applied to the integral domain $F[x]$ instead of the integral domain I.

.15 Definition. Let $F[x]$ be the ring of polynomials in the indeterminate x over an arbitrary field F. If $f(x)$, $g(x) \in F[x]$, $g(x)$ is said to be a *divisor* (or *factor*) of $f(x)$ if there exists $h(x) \in F[x]$ such that $f(x) = g(x)h(x)$. If $g(x)$ is a divisor of $f(x)$, we say also that $f(x)$ is *divisible* by $g(x)$ or that $f(x)$ is a *multiple* of $g(x)$.

It follows immediately from this definition that if c is a nonzero element of F (that is, a polynomial of $F[x]$ of degree zero), then c is a divisor of every element $f(x)$ of $F[x]$. For, since c has a multiplicative inverse c^{-1} in F, we can write $f(x) = c(c^{-1}f(x))$, and this shows that c is a divisor of $f(x)$.

It is also important to observe that if $f(x) = g(x)h(x)$, then also $f(x) = (cg(x))(c^{-1}h(x))$, where c is any nonzero element of F. That is, if $g(x)$ is a divisor of $f(x)$, then $cg(x)$ is also a divisor of $f(x)$ for every nonzero element c of F.

The following result plays just as important a role in the study of divisibility in $F[x]$ as the corresponding result (4.3) does in establishing divisibility properties of the integers.

.16 Division Algorithm. *If $f(x)$, $g(x) \in F[x]$ with $g(x) \neq 0$, there exist unique elements $q(x)$ and $r(x)$ of $F[x]$ such that*

.17 $$f(x) = q(x)g(x) + r(x), \qquad r(x) = 0 \text{ or } \deg r(x) < \deg g(x).$$

We may recall that the zero polynomial has no degree and this fact explains the form of the condition which $r(x)$ is required to satisfy.

If $f(x)$ and $g(x)$ are given polynomials, the polynomials $q(x)$ and $r(x)$ can easily be computed by the usual process of long division. The existence of such polynomials therefore seems almost obvious. However, we shall give a detailed proof of their existence, and for the moment leave aside the question of their uniqueness. Let us first dispose of two easy cases as follows.

(A) If $f(x) = 0$ or $\deg f(x) < \deg g(x)$, then 8.17 is trivially satisfied with $q(x) = 0$ and $r(x) = f(x)$.

(B) If $\deg g(x) = 0$, so that $g(x) = c$ with c a nonzero element of F, then $f(x) = [c^{-1}f(x)]c$ and 8.17 holds with $q(x) = c^{-1}f(x)$ and $r(x) = 0$.

We are now ready to complete the proof by induction on the degree of $f(x)$. In this case, we shall use the form of the Induction Principle given in Exercise 8 of Section 3.4. If n is a positive integer, let S_n be the statement, "For every polynomial $f(x)$ of degree n and every nonzero polynomial $g(x)$, there exist polynomials $q(x)$ and $r(x)$ satisfying Equation 8.17." Let us now consider the statement S_1. By (A) and (B), we need only consider the case in which $\deg g(x) = 1$; that is, $g(x) = cx + d$, $c \neq 0$. Since $f(x) = ax + b$, $a \neq 0$, we can easily see that

8.18 $$f(x) = ac^{-1}(cx + d) + b - ac^{-1}d,$$

and 8.17 is satisfied with $q(x) = ac^{-1}$ and $r(x) = b - ac^{-1}d$. Hence, S_1 is true. Now suppose that k is a positive integer with the property that S_i is true for every positive integer $i \leq k$, and let us prove that S_{k+1} is true. Let $f(x) = ax^{k+1} + \cdots$, where $a \neq 0$, be a polynomial of degree $k + 1$ and let $g(x)$ be an entirely arbitrary polynomial. Cases (A) and (B) show that we may assume that $0 < \deg g(x) \leq k + 1$ since otherwise the existence of $q(x)$ and $r(x)$ satisfying 8.17 follows immediately. Suppose that $\deg g(x) = m$, hence that $g(x) = bx^m + \cdots$, with $b \neq 0$ and $0 < m \leq k + 1$. Now it is easily verified that

8.19 $$f(x) = b^{-1}ax^{k+1-m}g(x) + [f(x) - b^{-1}ax^{k+1-m}g(x)].$$

Perhaps we should point out that this equation is merely the result of taking one step in the usual long-division process of dividing $f(x)$ by $g(x)$. If we set $t(x) = f(x) - b^{-1}ax^{k+1-m}g(x)$, it is easy to see that the coefficient of x^{k+1} in $t(x)$ is zero; hence that $t(x) = 0$ or $\deg t(x) < k + 1$. By (A), or by the assumption that S_i is true for every positive integer $i \leq k$, we know that there exist polynomials $s(x)$ and $r(x)$, with $r(x) = 0$ or $\deg r(x) < \deg g(x)$, such that $t(x) = s(x)g(x) + r(x)$. Substituting in 8.19, we see that

$$f(x) = [b^{-1}ax^{k+1-m} + s(x)]g(x) + r(x),$$

and 8.17 is satisfied. Hence S_{k+1} is true, and it follows that S_n is true for every positive integer n. This completes the proof of the *existence* part of the Division Algorithm. The proof of the fact that $q(x)$ and $r(x)$ are *unique* will be left as an exercise. It is customary to call $q(x)$ and $r(x)$ satisfying 8.17 the *quotient* and the *remainder*, respectively, in the division of $f(x)$ by $g(x)$. Clearly, $f(x)$ is divisible by $g(x)$ if and only if the remainder in the division of $f(x)$ by $g(x)$ is zero.

A special case of the Division Algorithm that is of importance is that in which the divisor $g(x)$ is of the special form $x - c$, $c \in F$. In this case the remainder must be zero or have degree zero, that is, it is an element of F. We can thus write

$$f(x) = q(x)(x - c) + r, \qquad\qquad r \in F.$$

From this equation it is clear that $f(c) = r$, and hence that

$$f(x) = q(x)(x - c) + f(c).$$

The next two theorems then follow immediately.

8.20 Remainder Theorem. *If $f(x) \in F[x]$ and $c \in F$, the remainder in the division of $f(x)$ by $x - c$ is $f(c)$.*

8.21 Factor Theorem. *If $f(x) \in F[x]$ and $c \in F$, $f(x)$ is divisible by $x - c$ if and only if $f(c) = 0$, that is, if and only if c is a root of the polynomial $f(x)$.*

We shall now make use of the Factor Theorem to prove the following result.

8.22 Theorem. *Let F be a field and $f(x)$ an element of $F[x]$ of positive degree n and with leading coefficient a. If c_1, c_2, $\cdots$, c_n are distinct elements of F, all of which are roots of $f(x)$, then*

8.23
$$f(x) = a(x - c_1)(x - c_2) \cdots (x - c_n).$$

The proof of this theorem is by induction on the degree n of $f(x)$. If n is a positive integer, let S_n be the statement, "The statement of the theorem is true for every polynomial of degree n." We then wish to prove that S_n is true for every positive integer n. The truth of the statement S_1 follows quite easily. If $f(x)$ is of degree 1 and has leading coefficient a, then $f(x) = ax + b$, $a \ne 0$. If c_1 is a root of $f(x)$, we have $f(c_1) = 0$ or $ac_1 + b = 0$. Then $b = -ac_1$ and hence $f(x) = a(x - c_1)$, which is the desired form 8.23 in case $n = 1$.

Now let k be a positive integer such that S_k is true, and consider S_{k+1}. Accordingly, we let $f(x)$ be a polynomial of degree $k + 1$ with leading coefficient a, and let c_1, c_2, $\cdots$, c_{k+1} be distinct roots of $f(x)$. Since c_1 is a root of $f(x)$, we have $f(c_1) = 0$ and by the Factor Theorem it follows that

8.24
$$f(x) = q(x)(x - c_1).$$

Now it is clear that deg $q(x) = k$, and the leading coefficient of $q(x)$ is a since a is the coefficient of x^{k+1} in $f(x)$. If c_i $(i \ne 1)$ is any other of the given roots of $f(x)$, it follows, using 8.24 and the fact that $f(c_i) = 0$, that

$$q(c_i)(c_i - c_1) = 0.$$

Since the c's are distinct, $c_i - c_1 \ne 0$ and therefore $q(c_i) = 0$. We have therefore shown that the polynomial $q(x)$ in 8.24 is of degree k, has leading coefficient a, and has c_2, c_3, $\cdots$, c_{k+1} as distinct roots. Since S_k is assumed to be true, it follows that

$$q(x) = a(x - c_2)(x - c_3) \cdots (x - c_{k+1}).$$

Substituting this expression for $q(x)$ in 8.24, we get

$$f(x) = a(x - c_1)(x - c_2) \cdots (x - c_{k+1}).$$

Hence, S_{k+1} is true, and the Induction Principle assures us that S_n is true for every positive integer n. This completes the proof of the theorem. We next establish the following corollary.

8.25 Corollary. *A polynomial $f(x)$ of degree n over a field F cannot have more than n distinct roots in F.*

Since polynomials of degree zero have no roots, in verifying this corollary we may assume that $n \geq 1$. If c_1, c_2, $\cdots$, c_n are distinct roots of $f(x)$, then $f(x)$ can be written in the form 8.23. Now let c be an arbitrary root of $f(x)$. Since $f(c) = 0$, it follows at once from 8.23 that

$$a(c - c_1)(c - c_2) \cdots (c - c_n) = 0.$$

Since $a \neq 0$, some one of the other factors must be zero, that is, $c = c_i$ for some i. Hence, c_1, c_2, $\cdots$, c_n are the *only* roots of $f(x)$, and $f(x)$ cannot have more than n distinct roots.

The next corollary is now a simple consequence of this one.

8.26 Corollary. *Let $g(x)$ and $h(x)$ be polynomials over a field F with the property that $g(s) = h(s)$ for every element s of F. If the number of elements in F exceeds the degrees of both $g(x)$ and $h(x)$, then necessarily $g(x) = h(x)$.*

Let us set $f(x) = g(x) - h(x)$, and we then have that $f(s) = 0$ for every element s of F. If $f(x) \neq 0$, its degree can certainly not exceed the degrees of both $g(x)$ and $h(x)$, and hence $f(x)$ would have more distinct roots than its degree. Since, by the preceding corollary, this is impossible, we must have $f(x) = 0$. Hence, $g(x) = h(x)$, as required.

The following example shows that this last result is not true without the restriction on the number of elements of the field F. Let F be the field $I/(3)$, a field of three elements. If $g(x) = x^3$ and $h(x) = x$, it is easy to show by direct substitution that $g(s) = h(s)$ for every element s of F, but $g(x)$ and $h(x)$ are not equal elements of the polynomial ring $F[x]$. See also Exercise 7 of the preceding set.

8.4 GREATEST COMMON DIVISOR

It has been pointed out earlier that if c is a nonzero element of the field F, then the element $f(x)$ of $F[x]$ is divisible by the element $g(x)$ of $F[x]$ if and only if $f(x)$ is divisible by $cg(x)$. By choosing c as the multiplicative inverse of the leading coefficient of $g(x)$, the polynomial $cg(x)$ will have the unity 1 of F as its leading coefficient. Hence, we will know *all* the divisors of $f(x)$ when we have determined all those divisors that have 1 as leading coefficient. The following definition makes it easy to refer to such polynomials.

27   Definition.   A nonzero element of $F[x]$ is said to be a *monic* polynomial if its leading coefficient is the unity 1 of F.

The greatest common divisor of two elements of $F[x]$ may now be defined as follows.

28   Definition.   The monic polynomial $d(x)$ of $F[x]$ is said to be the *greatest common divisor* (g.c.d.) of the nonzero polynomials $f(x)$ and $g(x)$ of $F[x]$ if the following conditions are satisfied:

    (i) $d(x)$ is a divisor of both $f(x)$ and $g(x)$,
    (ii) Every divisor of both $f(x)$ and $g(x)$ is a divisor of $d(x)$.

As in the case of integers, it is quite easy to verify that two polynomials cannot have more than one g.c.d. We proceed to outline a proof of the existence of the g.c.d. and to develop a method for actually computing the g.c.d. of two given polynomials. Inasmuch as the procedure follows quite closely the material of Section 4.3, we shall omit most of the details.

First, we make the following definition.

29   Definition.   If $f(x)$, $g(x) \in F[x]$, we say that a polynomial of the form

$$f(x)s(x) + g(x)t(x), \qquad s(x),\, t(x) \in F[x],$$

is a *linear combination* of $f(x)$ and $g(x)$.

The following theorem can now be established by a simple modification of the proof of Theorem 4.12.

30   Theorem.   *If $f(x)$ and $g(x)$ are nonzero elements of $F[x]$, the monic polynomial of least degree which is expressible as a linear combination of $f(x)$ and $g(x)$ is the g.c.d. of $f(x)$ and $g(x)$. Hence, if $d(x)$ is the g.c.d. of $f(x)$ and $g(x)$, there exist elements $s_1(x)$ and $t_1(x)$ of $F[x]$ such that*

$$d(x) = f(x)s_1(x) + g(x)t_1(x),$$

and $d(x)$ is the monic polynomial of least degree which is expressible in this form.

In order to *compute* the g.c.d. of two nonzero polynomials $f(x)$ and $g(x)$ of $F[x]$, we use the Euclidean Algorithm as in the case of integers.

By repeated use of the Division Algorithm we obtain the following sequence of equations, it being understood that $r_k(x)$ is the last nonzero remainder:

$$
\begin{array}{ll}
f(x) = q(x)g(x) + r(x) & \deg r(x) < \deg g(x), \\
g(x) = q_1(x)r(x) + r_1(x) & \deg r_1(x) < \deg r(x), \\
r(x) = q_2(x)r_1(x) + r_2(x) & \deg r_2(x) < \deg r_1(x), \\
\end{array}
$$

8.31 $\cdots\cdots\cdots\cdots\cdots\cdots$ $\cdots\cdots\cdots\cdots\cdots\cdots$

$$
\begin{array}{ll}
r_{k-2}(x) = q_k(x)r_{k-1}(x) + r_k(x) & \deg r_k(x) < \deg r_{k-1}(x), \\
r_{k-1}(x) = q_{k+1}(x)r_k(x).
\end{array}
$$

Now from these equations it follows that $r_k(x)$ is a divisor of both $f(x)$ and $g(x)$; also that any divisor of both $f(x)$ and $g(x)$ is a divisor of $r_k(x)$. If c is the leading coefficient of $r_k(x)$, then $c^{-1}r_k(x)$ also has these same properties and, moreover, it is a *monic* polynomial. We have therefore outlined a proof of the following result.

8.32   Theorem. *Let $r_k(x)$ be the last nonzero remainder in the Euclidean Algorithm as applied to the nonzero polynomials $f(x)$ and $g(x)$ of $F[x]$. If c is the leading coefficient of $r_k(x)$, then $c^{-1}r_k(x)$ is the g.c.d. of $f(x)$ and $g(x)$.*

In a numerical case, the actual calculations may often be simplified by the following observation. If $d(x)$ is the g.c.d. of $f(x)$ and $g(x)$, then also $d(x)$ is the g.c.d. of $af(x)$ and $bg(x)$, where a and b are nonzero elements of F. Hence, instead of the first of Equations 8.31, we might use the similar equation obtained by dividing $af(x)$ by $bg(x)$. In like manner, instead of the second equation we might work with $dg(x)$ and $er(x)$, where d and e are nonzero elements of F; and so on for the other equations. This modification will not affect the validity of the arguments used to show that $c^{-1}r_k(x)$ is the g.c.d. of $f(x)$ and $g(x)$, and may greatly simplify the work involved. Let us give an illustration by finding the g.c.d. of the polynomials

$$f(x) = x^3 + \tfrac{1}{2}x^2 + \tfrac{1}{3}x + \tfrac{1}{6}$$

and

$$g(x) = x^2 - \tfrac{1}{2}x - \tfrac{1}{2}$$

over the field R of rational numbers. In order to avoid fractions, we divide $6f(x)$ by $2g(x)$, obtaining

$$6f(x) = (3x + 3)[2g(x)] + 8x + 4,$$

so that $r(x) = 8x + 4$. If we now divide $2g(x)$ by $r(x)/4$, we see that

$$2g(x) = (x - 1)[r(x)/4].$$

Since $r_1(x) = 0$, the g.c.d. of $f(x)$ and $g(x)$ is obtained from the last nonzero remainder, namely, $8x + 4$ by multiplying it by the multiplicative inverse of its leading coefficient. Hence the g.c.d. of $f(x)$ and $g(x)$ is $x + 1/2$.

It is sometimes convenient to use the following terminology, which is suggested by the corresponding definition for the integers.

33 Definition. Two nonzero elements $f(x)$ and $g(x)$ of $F[x]$ are said to be *relatively prime* if their g.c.d. is 1.

--- **E X E R C I S E S**

1. Complete the proof of the Division Algorithm by showing that the quotient and the remainder are unique.

2. If $f(x) \in F[x]$, show that $f(x)$ has as a factor a polynomial of $F[x]$ of degree one if and only if $f(x)$ has a root in F.

3. If F is the field $I/(7)$, use the result of Exercise 7 of the preceding set to show, without calculation, that in $F[x]$ we have
$$x^7 - x = x(x - 1)(x - 2)(x - 3)(x - 4)(x - 5)(x - 6).$$

4. State and prove a corresponding result with reference to each of the following fields: $I/(3)$, $I/(5)$, $I/(11)$.

5. Prove Theorem 8.30.

6. Find the g.c.d. of each of the following pairs of polynomials over the field R of rational numbers, and express it as a linear combination of the two polynomials:

   (i) $2x^3 - 4x^2 + x - 2$ and $x^3 - x^2 - x - 2$,
   (ii) $x^4 + x^3 + x^2 + x + 1$ and $x^3 - 1$,
   (iii) $x^5 + x^4 + 2x^3 - x^2 - x - 2$ and $x^4 + 2x^3 + 5x^2 + 4x + 4$,
   (iv) $x^3 - 2x^2 + x + 4$ and $x^2 + x + 1$.

7. Find the g.c.d. of each of the following pairs of polynomials over the indicated field, and express it as a linear combination of the two polynomials:

   (i) $x^3 + 2x^2 + 3x + 2$ and $x^2 + 4$; field $I/(5)$,
   (ii) $x^3 + (2i + 1)x^2 + ix + i + 1$ and $x^2 + (i - 1)x - 2i - 2$; field C of complex numbers,
   (iii) $x^2 + (1 - \sqrt{2})x - \sqrt{2}$ and $x^2 - 2$; field K of real numbers,
   (iv) $x^4 + x + 1$ and $x^2 + x + 1$; field $I/(2)$.

8. Let F and F' be fields such that $F \subset F'$, so that $F[x] \subset F'[x]$. Moreover, let $f(x)$, $g(x)$, and $h(x)$ be nonzero elements of $F'[x]$ such that $f(x) = g(x)h(x)$. Show that if any two of these polynomials are elements of $F[x]$, then so is the third.

9. Verify that the Division Algorithm (8.16) remains true if the field F is replaced by an arbitrary commutative ring S with unity, provided only that $g(x)$ is required to have as leading coefficient an element of S with a multiplicative inverse in S.

10. By using the result of the preceding exercise, verify that the Factor Theorem and the Remainder Theorem are true if the field F is replaced by a commutative ring S with unity.

11. Give an example to show that Theorem 8.22 is not necessarily true if the field F is replaced by an arbitrary commutative ring S with unity. Where does the proof break down? Verify that the proof of this theorem will remain valid if F is replaced by an integral domain.

8.5 UNIQUE FACTORIZATION IN $F[x]$

We begin this section with the following definition.

8.34 Definition. A polynomial $p(x)$ of positive degree over a field F is said to be a *prime* (or *irreducible*) polynomial over F if it cannot be expressed as the product of two polynomials of positive degree over F.

If c is a nonzero element of the field F and $f(x) \in F[x]$, then we always have $f(x) = c^{-1}(cf(x))$, so that every polynomial of the form $cf(x)$ is a divisor of $f(x)$. It is easy to verify that a polynomial $f(x)$ of positive degree over F is a prime polynomial over F if and only if the *only* elements of $F[x]$ of positive degree that are divisors of $f(x)$ are of the form $cf(x)$, $c \neq 0$.

Since the degree of the product of two polynomials over F is the sum of the degrees of the factors, it follows at once from Definition 8.34 that *every element of $F[x]$ of the first degree is necessarily prime over F.*

We may emphasize that the possible divisors of $p(x)$ that are being considered in Definition 8.34 are those which are elements of $F[x]$; that is, they must have coefficients in F. For example, consider the polynomial $x^2 - 2$ over the field R of rational numbers. Now $x^2 - 2$ cannot be factored into the product of two polynomials of the first degree in $R[x]$, and hence $x^2 - 2$ is a prime polynomial over R. However, if we should consider the same polynomial as a polynomial over the field K of real numbers, we find that it is *not* prime over K since we have the factorization $x^2 - 2 = (x - \sqrt{2})(x + \sqrt{2})$ with these factors of the first degree having coefficients in K. As this example shows, the concept of a polynomial being a prime polynomial is relative to a specified field which contains the coefficients of the given polynomial.

In later sections we shall discuss prime polynomials over each of the familiar fields of elementary algebra. As for the finite fields of the form $I/(p)$, where p is a prime integer, we may here state without proof the following fact. For each prime p and each positive integer n, there exists at least one polynomial of degree n over the field $I/(p)$, which is prime over $I/(p)$.

The prime polynomials play essentially the same role in the factorization of an element of $F[x]$ as do the prime integers in the factorization of an integer. We therefore state without proof the following lemma and theorem, which are analogous to 4.18 and 4.20, respectively.

8.35 Lemma. *If $f(x)$ and $g(x)$ are nonzero polynomials over the field F such that $f(x)g(x)$ is divisible by the prime polynomial $p(x)$ over F, then $f(x)$ is divisible by $p(x)$ or $g(x)$ is divisible by $p(x)$.*

8.36 Theorem. *If $f(x)$ is a polynomial of positive degree over the field F and a is its leading coefficient, then there exist distinct monic prime polynomials $p_1(x), \cdots, p_k(x)$ $(k \geq 1)$ over F such that*

8.37
$$f(x) = a[p_1(x)]^{n_1}[p_2(x)]^{n_2} \cdots [p_k(x)]^{n_k},$$

where the n's are positive integers. Moreover, such a factorization is unique except for the order of the factors.

We may emphasize that the prime polynomials in 8.37 are restricted to be monic polynomials, and hence the leading coefficient of the right side is just a, which is given as the leading coefficient of $f(x)$. A proof of the above theorem can be given by a simple modification of the proof of the Fundamental Theorem of Arithmetic. Although Theorem 8.36 certainly has some theoretical significance, it is not so very useful from a computational point of view. For example, from the factorizations of two polynomials in the form 8.37 it is easy to write down their g.c.d. just as in the case of two integers. However, it is often very difficult to *find* the prime factors of a given polynomial and hence to write it in the form 8.37. Accordingly, it will usually be very much easier to apply the method of Section 8.4 to find the g.c.d. of two polynomials than to make use of Theorem 8.36.

As an important special case, one or more of the monic prime polynomials occurring in a factorization 8.37 of $f(x)$ may be of the first degree. In particular, the Factor Theorem (8.21) assures us that $x - c$,

$c \in F$, is a factor of $f(x)$ if and only if $f(c) = 0$; that is, if and only if c is a root of the polynomial $f(x)$. The following definition introduces a terminology which is sometimes convenient.

8.38 Definition. The element c of F is said to be a root of *multiplicity* $m \geq 1$ of the polynomial $f(x)$ over F if $f(x)$ is divisible by $(x - c)^m$ but not by $(x - c)^{m+1}$. A root of multiplicity two is called a *double root*.

It follows that c is a root of $f(x)$ of multiplicity m if and only if in the factorization 8.37 of $f(x)$ one of the prime factors occurring is $x - c$ and, furthermore, it occurs with the exponent m.

_____ **E X E R C I S E S**

1. (*a*) Prove that a polynomial $f(x)$ of degree two or three over a field F is a prime polynomial over F if and only if the polynomial $f(x)$ has no root in F.

(*b*) Show, by means of an example, that a corresponding statement does not hold for polynomials of degree four.

2. Determine whether or not each of the following polynomials is prime over each of the given fields. If it is not prime, factor it into a product of prime factors over each given field. As usual, R is the field of rational numbers, K the field of real numbers, and C the field of complex numbers.

(*a*) $x^2 + x + 1$ over R, K, and C;
(*b*) $x^2 + 2x - 1$ over R, K, and C;
(*c*) $x^2 + 3x - 4$ over R, K, and C;
(*d*) $x^3 + 2$ over R, K, and C;
(*e*) $x^2 + x + 1$ over $I/(2)$, $I/(3)$, and $I/(5)$;
(*f*) $x^3 + x + 1$ over $I/(2)$, $I/(5)$, and $I/(11)$;
(*g*) $x^4 - 1$ over $I/(17)$;
(*h*) $x^3 + x^2 + 1$ over $I/(11)$;
(*i*) $x^2 + 15$ over K and C.

3. Find all prime polynomials of degree not more than five over the field $I/(2)$.

4. In each case the polynomial over the given field has as a root the specified element of the field. Find the multiplicity of this root and complete the factorization of the polynomial into prime factors over the given field.

(*a*) $x^4 + x^3 - 3x^2 - 5x - 2$ over R, root -1;
(*b*) $x^4 + 1$ over $I/(2)$, root 1;
(*c*) $x^4 + 2x^2 + 1$ over C, root i;
(*d*) $x^4 + 6x^3 + 3x^2 + 6x + 2$ over $I/(7)$, root 4.

8.6 RATIONAL ROOTS OF A POLYNOMIAL OVER THE RATIONAL FIELD

If $f(x)$ is a polynomial of degree $n > 0$ over a field F, then clearly $f(x)$ and $cf(x)$ have the same roots for any nonzero element c of F. If, in particular, $f(x)$ has coefficients in the field R of rational numbers and we choose c as the l.c.m. of the denominators of the coefficients of $f(x)$, $cf(x)$ will have coefficients that are integers. In studying the roots of a polynomial with rational coefficients there is therefore no loss of generality in restricting attention to polynomials that have integral coefficients. We shall now prove the following theorem.

,39 Theorem. *Let*

$$f(x) = a_n x^n + a_{n-1}x^{n-1} + \cdots + a_0, \qquad (a_n \neq 0),$$

be a polynomial of positive degree n with coefficients that are integers. If r/s is a rational number, in lowest terms, which is a root of the polynomial $f(x)$, then r is a divisor of a_0 and s is a divisor of a_n.

We may recall that by saying that r/s is in lowest terms we mean that r and s are relatively prime integers and $s > 0$. However, the requirement that s be positive plays no role in the proof of this theorem. Since r/s is assumed to be a root of $f(x)$, we have that

$$a_n \left(\frac{r}{s}\right)^n + a_{n-1}\left(\frac{r}{s}\right)^{n-1} + \cdots + a_0 = 0.$$

If we multiply throughout by the nonzero integer s^n, we obtain

,40 $$a_n r^n + a_{n-1}r^{n-1}s + \cdots + a_1 rs^{n-1} + a_0 s^n = 0.$$

By transposing the last term to the right side, this equation can be written in the form

$$(a_n r^{n-1} + a_{n-1}r^{n-2}s + \cdots + a_1 s^{n-1})r = -a_0 s^n.$$

Since all letters here represent integers, we see that the integer $a_0 s^n$ is divisible by the integer r. But we are given that r and s are relatively prime, and it therefore follows that a_0 is divisible by r.

By a similar argument, if in 8.40 we transpose $a_n r^n$ to the other side, we can see that a_n is divisible by s.

As an example of the use of this theorem, let us find all rational roots of the polynomial

$$g(x) = 4x^5 + x^3 + x^2 - 3x + 1.$$

If r/s is a rational number, in lowest terms, which is a root of this polynomial, then r must be a divisor of 1 and s a positive divisor of 4. It follows that $r = \pm 1$, $s = 1, 2$, or 4; and we see that the only possible rational roots are the following: $1, 1/2, 1/4, -1, -1/2, -1/4$. It is easy to verify by direct calculation that $g(1) \neq 0$, $g(1/2) = 0$, $g(1/4) \neq 0$, $g(-1) = 0$, $g(-1/2) \neq 0$, and $g(-1/4) \neq 0$. Hence, $1/2$ and -1 are the *only* rational roots. If we divide $g(x)$ by $x - 1/2$ and then divide the quotient by $x + 1$, we find that

$$g(x) = (x - \tfrac{1}{2})(x + 1)(4x^3 - 2x^2 + 4x - 2).$$

Any root of this third degree factor is naturally a root of $g(x)$, so its only possible rational roots are therefore $1/2$ and -1. It is easy to verify that $1/2$ is a root and if we again divide by $x - 1/2$, we can express $g(x)$ in the form

$$g(x) = (x - \tfrac{1}{2})^2(x + 1)(4x^2 + 4)$$

or

8.41
$$g(x) = 4(x - \tfrac{1}{2})^2(x + 1)(x^2 + 1).$$

We see therefore that $1/2$ is a double root of $g(x)$. Since the quadratic polynomial $x^2 + 1$ has no rational root, it is a prime polynomial over R and hence in 8.41 we have $g(x)$ expressed as a product of prime polynomials over R. For that matter, the polynomial $x^2 + 1$ is prime over the field K of real numbers and so 8.41 also gives the factorization of $g(x)$ into prime polynomials over K.

--- *E X E R C I S E S*

1. Complete the proof of Theorem 8.39 by showing that s is a divisor of a_n.

2. Prove the following corollary of Theorem 8.39. A rational root of a *monic* polynomial with coefficients that are integers is necessarily an integer which is a divisor of the constant term of the polynomial.

3. Find the factorization of the polynomial $g(x)$ of the example given above into prime factors over the field C of complex numbers.

4. Find all rational roots of each of the following polynomials over the rational field R:

  (a) $3x^3 + 5x^2 + 5x + 2$,
  (b) $2x^4 - 11x^3 + 17x^2 - 11x + 15$,
  (c) $x^5 - x^4 - x^3 - x^2 - x - 2$,
  (d) $x^3 + x^2 - 2x - 3$,
  (e) $6x^3 - 7x^2 - 35x + 6$,
  (f) $x^5 + 5x^4 + 13x^3 + 19x^2 + 18x + 8$,
  (g) $x^3 - (1/5)x^2 - 4x + 4/5$,
  (h) $x^7 + x^6 + x^5 + x^4 + x^3 + x^2 + x + 1$.

5. Find all rational roots of each of the following polynomials over the rational field R, and factor each polynomial into a product of prime polynomials over R:

(a) $9x^4 + 6x^3 + 19x^2 + 12x + 2$.
(b) $x^5 - x^4 - 3x^3 + 6x^2 - 4x + 1$,
(c) $4x^4 + 20x^3 + 33x^2 + 20x + 4$,
(d) $2x^4 + 3x^3 + 4x + 6$.

6. Show that each of the following polynomials over R has no rational root:

(a) $x^{1000} - x^{500} + x^{100} + x + 1$,
(b) $x^{12} - x^9 + x^6 - x^3 + 1$,
(c) $x^m + 2x^{m-1} - 2$, $\qquad$ (m a positive integer ≥ 2).

8.7 PRIME POLYNOMIALS OVER THE RATIONAL FIELD (OPTIONAL)

It was pointed out in Section 8.5 that every polynomial of the first degree over a field F is necessarily a prime polynomial over F. Also, the first exercise at the end of that section asserts that a polynomial of degree two or three over F is a prime polynomial over F if and only if it has no root in F. If the field F is now taken to be the field R of rational numbers, it is easy to apply Theorem 8.39 to find whether or not a polynomial of degree at most three is prime over R. For a polynomial of higher degree it may be exceedingly difficult to determine whether or not it is prime. For example, a polynomial of degree four over R may not have a rational root, and therefore may have no factor of the first degree over R, but may be a product of two prime polynomials of degree two. In this section we shall give some rather special results, which will enable us to show that for *every* positive integer n, there exist polynomials of degree n that are prime over R.

We shall first prove two lemmas, the first of which is the following. As usual, $I[x]$ is the ring of polynomials in the indeterminate x with coefficients in the ring I of integers.

8.42 Lemma. *Let $f(x)$, $g(x)$, and $h(x)$ be elements of the ring $I[x]$ such that $f(x) = g(x)h(x)$. If p is a prime integer which is a divisor of every coefficient of $f(x)$, then p is a divisor of every coefficient of $g(x)$ or a divisor of every coefficient of $h(x)$.*

The proof of this lemma was stated as Exercise 12 at the end of Section 8.2, and one method of proof was suggested in a hint given there.

We here indicate a more elementary proof which, however, does involve a little more calculation. Let us set

$$f(x) = a_0 + a_1 x + \cdots + a_n x^n,$$
$$g(x) = b_0 + b_1 x + \cdots + b_m x^m,$$

and

$$h(x) = c_0 + c_1 x + \cdots + c_k x^k.$$

We are given that each coefficient a_i $(i = 0, 1, \cdots, n)$ is divisible by the prime p. Suppose now that $g(x)$ has at least one coefficient which is not divisible by p, and also that $h(x)$ has at least one coefficient which is not divisible by p, and let us seek a contradiction. To be more precise, let b_s be the *first* coefficient of $g(x)$, when $g(x)$ is written in increasing powers of x, that is not divisible by p; and let c_t be the *first* coefficient of $h(x)$ that is not divisible by p. Since $f(x) = g(x)h(x)$, by considering the coefficients of x^{s+t} on both sides of this equation, we find that

$$a_{s+t} = \cdots + b_{s-1}c_{t+1} + b_s c_t + b_{s+1}c_{t-1} + \cdots.$$

Now, by our choice of s and t, p is seen to be a divisor of every term on the right except the term $b_s c_t$. Since also p is a divisor of a_{s+t}, it follows that p is a divisor of $b_s c_t$. In view of the fact that p is a prime, this implies that p must be a divisor of b_s or a divisor of c_t. We have therefore obtained the desired contradiction. It follows that either $g(x)$ or $h(x)$ must have all coefficients divisible by p, and the proof is completed.

The following lemma, whose proof will be based on the preceding lemma, shows that a polynomial with *integral* coefficients is prime over the field R if and only if it cannot be factored into a product of two polynomials of positive degree with *integral* coefficients. It will then be possible to prove that certain polynomials are prime over R by making use of special properties of the integers.

8.43   Lemma.   *Let $f(x)$ be an element of $I[x]$ such that $f(x) = g(x)h(x)$, where $g(x)$, $h(x) \in R[x]$. Then there exist polynomials $g'(x)$, $h'(x)$ of $I[x]$ having the same degrees as $g(x)$ and $h(x)$, respectively, such that $f(x) = g'(x)h'(x)$.*

Let k be the l.c.m. of the denominators of the coefficients of $g(x)$, so that $kg(x)$ has integral coefficients. Similarly, let l be an integer such that $lh(x)$ has integral coefficients. Since $f(x) = g(x)h(x)$, it follows that

8.44 $$klf(x) = g_1(x)h_1(x),$$

where $g_1(x)$ and $h_1(x)$ have integral coefficients. We may then apply the preceding lemma as follows. If p is a prime divisor of kl, it must be a divisor of all coefficients of $g_1(x)$ or of $h_1(x)$; hence p can be divided from both sides of the equation 8.44, and we still have polynomials with integral coefficients. By a repetition of this process, we can divide out every prime factor of kl and finally get $f(x) = g'(x)h'(x)$, where $g'(x)$ and $h'(x)$ have integral coefficients. It is almost trivial that $g'(x)$ has the same degree as $g(x)$, and also that $h'(x)$ has the same degree as $h(x)$. The proof is therefore completed.

We are now ready to prove the following theorem of Eisenstein.

8.45 Theorem. Let $f(x) = a_0 + a_1x + \cdots + a_nx^n$ be a polynomial of positive degree n over the ring I of integers, and p a prime integer such that $a_i \equiv 0 \pmod{p}$ for $i = 0, 1, \cdots, n - 1$; $a_n \not\equiv 0 \pmod{p}$, and $a_0 \not\equiv 0 \pmod{p^2}$. Then $f(x)$ is a prime polynomial over R.

The preceding lemma shows that we need only prove that $f(x)$ cannot be factored into a product of two factors of positive degree over I. Let us assume that

8.46
$$a_0 + a_1x + \cdots + a_nx^n$$
$$= (b_0 + b_1x + \cdots + b_mx^m)(c_0 + c_1x + \cdots + c_kx^k),$$

where all these coefficients are integers, and clearly $m + k = n$. Since $a_0 = b_0c_0$, the fact that $a_0 \equiv 0 \pmod{p}$ but $a_0 \not\equiv 0 \pmod{p^2}$ shows that exactly one of the integers b_0 and c_0 is divisible by p. Suppose, for convenience of notation, that $c_0 \equiv 0 \pmod{p}$ and that $b_0 \not\equiv 0 \pmod{p}$. Now $a_n = b_mc_k$ and $a_n \not\equiv 0 \pmod{p}$; so $c_k \not\equiv 0 \pmod{p}$. Let s be chosen as the smallest positive integer such that $c_s \not\equiv 0 \pmod{p}$. From what we have just shown we know that there exists such an integer s and that $0 < s \le k$. Now by a consideration of the coefficients of x^s on both sides of 8.46, we see that

$$a_s = b_0c_s + b_1c_{s-1} + \cdots,$$

and, in view of our choice of s, every term on the right with the single exception of b_0c_s is divisible by p. Moreover, $b_0 \not\equiv 0 \pmod{p}$ and $c_s \not\equiv 0 \pmod{p}$, so $a_s \not\equiv 0 \pmod{p}$. However, by our assumptions, the only coefficient of $f(x)$ that is not divisible by p is the leading coefficient a_n. Hence $s = n$, and therefore we must have $k = n$. This shows that in any factorization of $f(x)$ into a product of polynomials with integral coefficients, one of the factors must have degree n. It follows that $f(x)$ is necessarily a prime polynomial over R.

8.47 Corollary. If n is an arbitrary positive integer, there exist polynomials of degree n over R that are prime over R.

This result is easily established by examples. As an illustration, the polynomial $x^n - 2$ over R satisfies all the conditions of the preceding theorem with $p = 2$. Hence, $x^n - 2$ is a prime polynomial over R for each positive integer n. In like manner, each of the following polynomials of degree n over R is prime over R: $x^n + 2$, $x^n + 3$, $3x^n + 2x^{n-1} + 2x^{n-2} + \cdots + 2x + 2$, $x^n + 9x + 3$ $(n > 1)$. The reader will have no difficulty in constructing other examples.

Perhaps we should emphasize that we have not presented a general method for determining whether or not a given polynomial over R is prime over R. This is a difficult problem, and we shall not discuss it further in this book.

8.8 POLYNOMIALS OVER THE REAL OR COMPLEX NUMBERS

In this section we shall discuss some properties of polynomials over the field K of real numbers or the field C of complex numbers. We begin with a few remarks, essentially established in elementary algebra, about quadratic polynomials; that is, polynomials of degree two.

Let

$$g(x) = ax^2 + bx + c, \qquad a \neq 0,$$

be a quadratic polynomial with coefficients in the field C. Then it is well-known that the polynomial $g(x)$ has roots r_1 and r_2, where

8.48 $$r_1 = \frac{-b + \sqrt{b^2 - 4ac}}{2a}, \qquad r_2 = \frac{-b - \sqrt{b^2 - 4ac}}{2a}.$$

We may point out that, by a special case of Theorem 7.15, every nonzero complex number has two square roots. Hence, r_1 and r_2, given by 8.48, are complex numbers and it is easy to verify by direct calculation that

8.49 $$g(x) = a(x - r_1)(x - r_2).$$

Since these first-degree factors have coefficients in C, it is apparent that no quadratic polynomial over C is a prime polynomial over C.

It is customary to call $b^2 - 4ac$ the *discriminant* of the quadratic polynomial $ax^2 + bx + c$. For convenience, let us designate this discriminant by "D".

From 8.48 it follows that $r_1 = r_2$ if and only if $D = 0$. However, the factorization 8.49 holds in any case, so $D = 0$ is a necessary and sufficient condition that the polynomial $g(x)$ have a double root.

Now let us assume that the quadratic polynomial $g(x)$ has *real* coefficients. Then the roots r_1 and r_2 will also be real if and only if $D \geq 0$, for only in this case will D have real square roots. The factorization 8.49 of $g(x)$ into factors of the first degree is therefore a factorization over K if and only if $D \geq 0$. If $D < 0$, $g(x)$ has no real root and $g(x)$ is therefore prime over K.

Let us summarize some of these observations in the following theorem.

.50 Theorem. *No quadratic polynomial over the field C of complex numbers is prime over C. A quadratic polynomial over the field K of real numbers is prime over K if and only if its discriminant is negative.*

We have referred above to Theorem 7.15, where it was proved by use of the trigonometric form of a complex number that every nonzero complex number has n nth roots. It may be worth pointing out that the *square* roots of a complex number may also be computed by an algebraic process. As an illustration, let us seek the roots of the polynomial $x^2 + x - (1 + 3i)$ over C. By 8.48, these roots can immediately be written down in the form

.51
$$\frac{-1 \pm \sqrt{5 + 12i}}{2}.$$

Now in order to express these roots in the usual form of complex numbers, we need to compute the square roots of $5 + 12i$. To do so, suppose that s and t are unknown real numbers such that $s + ti$ is a square root of $5 + 12i$. Thus we have

$$(s + ti)^2 = 5 + 12i,$$

or

$$s^2 - t^2 + 2sti = 5 + 12i.$$

In turn, this implies both of the following equations involving the real numbers s and t:

$$s^2 - t^2 = 5, \qquad 2st = 12.$$

If we solve these two simultaneous equations by elementary methods and remember that s and t are real (so that $s^2 \geq 0$ and $t^2 \geq 0$), we find the solutions to be $s = 3$, $t = 2$ and $s = -3$, $t = -2$. Hence, the square roots of $5 + 12i$ are $\pm (3 + 2i)$. Substituting in 8.51, we find that the roots of the polynomial $x^2 + x - (1 + 3i)$ are $1 + i$ and $-(2 + i)$.

We have shown above that no quadratic polynomial is prime over C. Another special case of some interest is the following. Let us consider a polynomial of the form $ax^n + b$, where a and b are nonzero complex numbers and n is an arbitrary positive integer greater than 1. Since, by Theorem 7.15, the complex number $-b/a$ has n distinct nth roots and these are obviously roots of the polynomial $ax^n + b$, Theorem 8.22 asserts that this polynomial can be factored over C into a product of factors of the first degree. In particular, such a polynomial can never be prime over C.

The general theorem which we shall next state is partially suggested by the special cases already discussed. The theorem was first proved by the famous German mathematician Carl Friedrich Gauss (1777–1855), and is of such importance that it has often been called "The Fundamental Theorem of Algebra." Unfortunately, there is no really elementary proof of this theorem and we shall therefore have to omit the proof.

8.52   Theorem. *If $f(x)$ is an element of $C[x]$ of positive degree, there exists an element of C which is a root of the polynomial $f(x)$.*

If r is a complex number which is a root of the polynomial $f(x)$ of degree n over C, then in $C[x]$ we can use the Factor Theorem and write

$$f(x) = (x - r)f_1(x),$$

where $f_1(x)$ is of degree $n - 1$. It is then apparent from this observation and Theorem 8.36 that the preceding theorem can be expressed in either of the following alternate forms.

8.53   Theorem. *The* only *prime polynomials of $C[x]$ are the polynomials of the first degree.*

8.54   Theorem. *If $f(x)$ is an element of $C[x]$ of positive degree, then $f(x)$ is itself of the first degree or it can be factored in $C[x]$ into a product of polynomials of the first degree.*

We next consider the question of which polynomials over the real field K are prime over K. Of course, the polynomials of the first degree are always prime, and we have shown in Theorem 8.50 that the quadratic polynomials over K that are prime over K are those with negative discriminant. A little later we shall prove that these are the only prime polynomials over K. First, however, we need a preliminary result, which is of some interest in itself.

Let

$$f(x) = a_n x^n + \cdots + a_1 x + a_0$$

be a polynomial of positive degree with real coefficients. Since $K \subset C$, then also $f(x) \in C[x]$ and Theorem 8.52 states that there exists an element r of C such that $f(r) = 0$. We now want to make use of the concept of the conjugate of a complex number, introduced in Section 7.2. We recall that if $u = a + bi$ is a complex number, then the conjugate u^* of u is defined by: $u^* = a - bi$. It was shown that the mapping $u \to u^*$ is a one-one mapping of C onto C, which preserves the operations of addition and multiplication. Now since $f(x)$ is assumed to have real coefficients and a real number is equal to its conjugate, it is not difficult to verify that

$$[f(r)]^* = a_n(r^*)^n + \cdots + a_1 r^* + a_0 = f(r^*).$$

But, since $f(r) = 0$, it follows that $[f(r)]^* = 0$ and therefore $f(r^*) = 0$. That is, r^* is also a root of the polynomial $f(x)$. This result we state as the following theorem.

.55 Theorem. *If r is a complex number which is a root of the polynomial $f(x)$ with real coefficients, then the conjugate r^* of r is also a root of $f(x)$.*

If it happens that r is a real number, then $r^* = r$, and this theorem has no content. However, if r is not real, then r^* and r are distinct roots of $f(x)$. It follows that in $C[x]$ we have

$$f(x) = (x - r)(x - r^*)f_1(x),$$

with the degree of $f_1(x)$ two less than the degree of $f(x)$. If $r = a + bi$, then $r^* = a - bi$, and a simple calculation shows that

$$(x - r)(x - r^*) = x^2 - 2ax + a^2 + b^2.$$

We can therefore write

.56
$$f(x) = (x^2 - 2ax + a^2 + b^2)f_1(x),$$

and the quadratic factor on the right clearly has *real* coefficients. Since also $f(x)$ has real coefficients, it is easy to verify that $f_1(x)$ must have real coefficients (*cf.* Exercise 8, Section 8.4). It follows that 8.56 gives a factorization of $f(x)$ in $K[x]$. If $\deg f(x) > 2$, $f(x)$ can therefore not be a prime polynomial over K. This result, combined with Theorem 8.50, completes the proof of the following theorem.

.57 Theorem. *The only polynomials of $K[x]$ that are prime over K are the polynomials of the first degree and the quadratic polynomials with negative discriminant.*

Now a polynomial of *odd* degree clearly cannot be factored into a product of quadratic polynomials. Therefore, if a polynomial $f(x)$ of $K[x]$ of odd degree is expressed as a product of prime polynomials over K, at least one of these prime polynomials (in fact, an odd number of them) must be of the first degree. This implies that $f(x)$ has at least one real root, and the following is therefore an almost immediate consequence of the preceding theorem.

.58 Corollary. *A polynomial with real coefficients and of odd degree necessarily has a real root.*

Except for quadratic polynomials, and polynomials of the special form $ax^n + b$, we have not given any indication as to how one might actually *find* the real or complex roots of a given polynomial. This is a difficult problem but some information can be found in texts on the "theory of equations." In particular, there do exist algebraic formulas for the roots of polynomials of degrees 3 or 4 with real or complex coefficients. Although these formulas are of great theoretical interest, they are not convenient to use in a numerical case. It is, however, not too difficult to develop methods of approximating the roots to any desired accuracy, and this is what is usually done in practical applications.

_____ **E X E R C I S E S**

1. Find the roots of each of the following polynomials and express each root in the standard form $a + bi$ of a complex number:

· (a) $x^2 - (3i - 2)x - 5 - i$,   (b) $x^2 + ix + 1$,
   (c) $x^2 - (2 + i)x - 1 + 7i$,   (d) $x^2 + x + 4$,
   (e) $x^2 - x + 2 + \sqrt{2}i$,   (f) $x^2 + 2x + i$.

2. Factor each of the following polynomials of $K[x]$ into a product of prime polynomials over K:

   (a) $x^3 - 2x - 4$,   (b) $x^3 - x^2 - 3x + 6$,
   (c) $x^4 + 1$,   (d) $x^4 + 2x^2 - 8$,
   (e) $x^4 + x^3 + 2x^2 + x + 1$,   (f) $x^5 + 1$.

8.9 THE RING OF POLYNOMIALS MODULO $S(X)$

In this section we shall establish a number of results that closely parallel results obtained in the development of the ring of integers modulo n in Section 4.7. We shall omit some of the proofs, but in every case in which a proof is omitted the proof of the corresponding fact for the integers modulo n could be applied with no essential change.

Throughout this section we shall assume that the polynomials being considered have coefficients in a *field* F. However, it may be observed that the proof of the first theorem below is equally valid if F is an arbitrary commutative ring with unity.

Let $s(x)$ be a fixed element of $F[x]$ of positive degree. If $f(x)$, $g(x) \in F[x]$, we shall write

$$f(x) \equiv g(x) \pmod{s(x)}$$

to mean that there exists an element $k(x)$ of $F[x]$ such that $f(x) - g(x) = k(x)s(x)$, and we read this as "$f(x)$ is congruent to $g(x)$ modulo $s(x)$." It is easy to verify that congruence modulo $s(x)$ is an equivalence relation on $F[x]$. Now, since we have an equivalence relation on $F[x]$, we may consider the corresponding equivalence sets. In accordance with previous usage, we shall let $[f(x)]$ denote the equivalence set which contains $f(x)$. We may refer to an equivalence set relative to the equivalence relation of congruence modulo $s(x)$ as "an equivalence set modulo $s(x)$." The elements of the equivalence set $[f(x)]$ are those polynomials of the form $f(x) + h(x)s(x)$, where $h(x) \in F[x]$. Moreover, $[f(x)] = [g(x)]$ if and only if $f(x) \equiv g(x) \pmod{s(x)}$.

We now define addition and multiplication of equivalence sets modulo $s(x)$ as follows:

59
$$[f(x)] + [g(x)] = [f(x) + g(x)],$$

60
$$[f(x)] \cdot [g(x)] = [f(x)g(x)].$$

Just as in the case of congruence modulo n, it can be shown (using an analogue of Theorem 4.40) that addition and multiplication of equivalence sets are well-defined by 8.59 and 8.60. We are now ready to state the following theorem.

61 Theorem. *With respect to the definitions 8.59 and 8.60 of addition and multiplication, the set of all equivalence sets of $F[x]$ modulo $s(x)$ is a commutative ring with unity.*

The ring whose existence is asserted by this theorem will be denoted by $F[x]/(s(x))$. We omit the proof of the theorem inasmuch as it is almost identical with the proof of Theorem 4.43.

The first part of the following theorem parallels the results of Theorems 4.45 and 5.5.

62 Theorem. *The ring $F[x]/(s(x))$ is a field if and only if $s(x)$ is a prime polynomial over F. In any case, $F[x]/(s(x))$ contains a subfield which is isomorphic to the field F.*

First, we observe that $[0]$ is the zero, and if 1 is the unity of F, $[1]$ is the unity of the ring $F[x]/(s(x))$. Suppose that $s(x)$ is not prime over F. Then $s(x) = s_1(x)s_2(x)$, where $s_1(x)$ and $s_2(x)$ are elements of $F[x]$ of positive degree. Since $\deg s_1(x) < \deg s(x)$, $s_1(x)$ cannot be divisible by $s(x)$, and therefore $[s_1(x)] \neq [0]$. Similarly, $[s_2(x)] \neq [0]$. However,

$$[s_1(x)] \cdot [s_2(x)] = [s_1(x)s_2(x)] = [s(x)] = [0].$$

This shows that $F[x]/(s(x))$ is not even an integral domain, and therefore certainly not a field.

Now suppose that $s(x)$ is prime over F, and let $[f(x)]$ be a nonzero element of $F[x]/(s(x))$. Then $f(x)$ is not divisible by $s(x)$. Since $s(x)$ is prime over F, it follows that $f(x)$ and $s(x)$ are relatively prime. By Theorem 8.30, there must then exist elements $h(x)$ and $k(x)$ of $F[x]$ such that

$$1 = f(x)h(x) + s(x)k(x).$$

This equation implies that $f(x)h(x) \equiv 1 \pmod{s(x)}$, and therefore that $[f(x)] \cdot [h(x)] = [1]$. Thus each nonzero element of $F[x]/(s(x))$ has a multiplicative inverse, and hence the ring $F[x]/(s(x))$ is a field. This completes the proof of the first part of the theorem.

For the moment, let F' be the set of all elements of the ring $F[x]/(s(x))$ of the form $[a]$, $a \in F$. Now $[a] = [b]$ if and only if $a \equiv b$ $\pmod{s(x)}$, and since $s(x)$ has positive degree this is true if and only if $a = b$. It follows that the mapping

$$a \to [a], \qquad\qquad a \in F,$$

is a one-one mapping of F onto F'. Moreover, by the definitions of addition and multiplication of equivalence sets, it is clear that addition and multiplication are preserved under this mapping. In other words, the given mapping is an isomorphism of F onto F', and the theorem is established.

In the future we shall find it convenient to identify F' with F; that is, we shall modify the notation and often write "a" in place of "$[a]$", where $a \in F$. With this agreement, it follows that F is actually contained in the ring $F[x]/(s(x))$.

We proceed to point out a convenient, and somewhat more explicit, way to specify the elements of the ring $F[x]/(s(x))$. As soon as we have done this, we shall give a number of examples that may help to clarify the material so far presented in this section.

We have assumed that the fixed polynomial $s(x)$ of $F[x]$ has positive degree, say k. Since $s(x)$ and $cs(x)$, where c is a nonzero element of F, are divisors of exactly the same polynomials, there is no loss of generality in assuming that $s(x)$ is a monic polynomial. This would only involve choosing c to be the multiplicative inverse of the leading coefficient of $s(x)$. We henceforth assume that $s(x)$ is monic, and for later convenience we choose the notation in such a way that

8.63 $$s(x) = x^k - s_{k-1}x^{k-1} - \cdots - s_1 x - s_0,$$

the coefficients being elements of F. Now the elements of the ring $F[x]/(s(x))$ are the different equivalence sets $[f(x)]$, $f(x) \in F[x]$. However, by the Division Algorithm, we have $f(x) = q(x)s(x) + r(x)$, where $r(x) = 0$ or $\deg r(x) < k$, and it follows that $f(x) \equiv r(x) \pmod{s(x)}$.

Furthermore, since the remainder $r(x)$ is *unique*, each polynomial $f(x)$ of $F[x]$ is congruent modulo $s(x)$ to exactly one polynomial which is either zero or has degree less than k. Another way of expressing this fact is to say that the different equivalence sets are those of the form

.64 $[a_0 + a_1x + \cdots + a_{k-1}x^{k-1}],$ $a_i \in F \ (i = 0, 1, \cdots, k-1).$

By use of the definitions of addition and multiplication of equivalence sets, we find that

$$[a_0 + a_1x + \cdots + a_{k-1}x^{k-1}] = [a_0] + [a_1][x] + \cdots + [a_{k-1}][x^{k-1}].$$

Moreover, $[x] \cdot [x] = [x^2]$ and, in general, $[x]^m = [x^m]$ for each positive integer m. By using this fact and also by making use of our previous agreement to identify $[a]$ with a, $a \in F$; we can express an equivalence set 8.64 as follows:

$$[a_0 + a_1x + \cdots + a_{k-1}x^{k-1}] = a_0 + a_1[x] + a_2[x]^2 + \cdots + a_{k-1}[x]^{k-1}.$$

Let us make one final simplification of notation by writing "j" in place of "$[x]$". The different equivalence sets are then expressible uniquely in the simple form

.65 $$a_0 + a_1j + a_2j^2 + \cdots + a_{k-1}j^{k-1},$$

the a's being elements of F. These are then the elements of the ring $F[x]/(s(x))$. The sum of two elements of the form 8.65 is immediately an element of the same form. The product of two elements can be expressed in the form 8.65 by multiplying out in the usual way, and then replacing each power of j higher than the kth by the element of the form 8.65 to which it is equal. For example, since $[s(x)] = 0$, it is easy to see from calculations similar to those used above that $s(j) = 0$; that is, in view of 8.63, that

.66 $$j^k = s_0 + s_1j + \cdots + s_{k-1}j^{k-1},$$

and the right side is of the form 8.65. To compute j^{k+1}, we multiply the preceding equation by j and obtain

$$j^{k+1} = s_0j + s_1j^2 + \cdots + s_{k-2}j^{k-1} + s_{k-1}j^k.$$

Now the right side is not of the form 8.65, but we can get it into this form by substituting for j^k from 8.66 and collecting coefficients of the different powers of j. In this way we obtain

.67 $j^{k+1} = s_{k-1}s_0 + (s_0 + s_{k-1}s_1)j + \cdots + (s_{k-2} + s^2_{-1})j^{k-1}.$

We could proceed in this way to compute higher powers of j. However, the general formulas are not very useful since it is much easier to apply the method directly in any specific case. The following examples will illustrate how this is done.

Example 1. Let F be the field K of real numbers, and let $s(x)$ be the polynomial $x^2 + 1$. Since $x^2 + 1$ is prime over K, we know by Theorem 8.62 that $K[x]/(x^2 + 1)$ is a field. We proceed to describe this field in some detail.

As a special case of the general discussion above, we may observe that since $x^2 + 1$ is of the second degree, every element of $K[x]$ is congruent modulo $x^2 + 1$ to exactly one polynomial of the form $a + bx$, $a, b \in K$. That is, the elements of the field are the equivalence sets $[a + bx]$. However, $[a + bx] = [a] + [b][x]$. Hence, if we set $j = [x]$ and write a for $[a]$ and b for $[b]$, we see that the elements of this field are uniquely expressible in the form

8.68
$$a + bj, \qquad\qquad a, b \in K.$$

This is a special case of 8.65. Let us now characterize the field $K[x]/(x^2 + 1)$ by specifying the operations of addition and multiplication of the elements 8.68. Addition is trivial since

8.69
$$(a + bj) + (c + dj) = (a + c) + (b + d)j,$$

which is immediately of the form 8.68. As for multiplication, we have

8.70
$$(a + bj)(c + dj) = ac + (ad + bc)j + bdj^2,$$

but this is not yet in the form 8.68. However, since $[x^2 + 1] = 0$, we have that $j^2 + 1 = 0$, and it follows that $j^2 = -1$, which is the form that Equation 8.66 takes in this particular example. Replacing j^2 by -1 in Equation 8.70, we find that

8.71
$$(a + bj)(c + dj) = (ac - bd) + (ad + bc)j.$$

We have thus shown how to express the product of two elements of the form 8.68 in the same form. The field $K[x]/(x^2 + 1)$ can now be simply characterized as the field with elements 8.68 and with addition and multiplication given by 8.69 and 8.71, respectively.

Except for an almost trivial difference in notation, the field we have just constructed coincides with the field C of complex numbers as introduced in Chapter 7. More precisely, the field $K[x]/(x^2 + 1)$ is isomorphic to the field C under the mapping

$$a + bj \to a + bi, \qquad\qquad a, b \in K.$$

Hence, we have now given another method of constructing the field of complex numbers from the field of real numbers.

Example 2. Let F be the field $I/(2)$ of integers modulo 2, whose two elements we shall now write as 0 and 1; and let $s(x) = x^2 + x + 1$.

Since neither of the elements of $I/(2)$ is a root of this quadratic polynomial, it follows that this polynomial is prime over $I/(2)$. Hence $(I/(2))/(x^2 + x + 1)$ is a field which, for simplicity, we shall designate by F^*. Since also in this example $s(x)$ is a quadratic polynomial, it follows as in the preceding example that the elements of F^* are uniquely expressible in the form

.72
$$a + bj, \qquad\qquad a, b \in I/(2).$$

As usual, addition of two of these elements is carried out in an almost trivial way as follows:

.73
$$(a + bj) + (c + dj) = (a + c) + (b + d)j.$$

As for multiplication, we have as in the previous example

$$(a + bj)(c + dj) = ac + (ad + bc)j + bdj^2.$$

However, since $s(j) = 0$, in this example we have $j^2 + j + 1 = 0$, or $j^2 = -j - 1$. Since our coefficients are from the field $I/(2)$, we can just as well write $j^2 = j + 1$. Replacing j^2 by $j + 1$ in the above expression for $(a + bj)(c + dj)$, we obtain

.74
$$(a + bj)(c + dj) = (ac + bd) + (ad + bc + bd)j,$$

as the general formula for the product of two elements of F^*. Since there are only two elements of $I/(2)$, and therefore only two choices for a and b in 8.72, we see that F^* has only the four elements $0, 1, j, 1 + j$. Using 8.73 and 8.74 or, better still, simply carrying out the calculations in each case, we can construct the following addition and multiplication tables for F^*.

$(+)$	0	1	j	$1+j$
0	0	1	j	$1+j$
1	1	0	$1+j$	j
j	j	$1+j$	0	1
$1+j$	$1+j$	j	1	0

$(\cdot)$	0	1	j	$1+j$
0	0	0	0	0
1	0	1	j	$1+j$
j	0	j	$1+j$	1
$1+j$	0	$1+j$	1	j

The reader may verify that this field F^* of four elements is isomorphic to the ring of Example 7 of Section 2.3.

Example 3. Let F be the field $I/(2)$, as in the preceding example, but let $s(x) = x^2$. In this case, $s(x)$ is certainly not prime over $I/(2)$. For convenience, let us denote the ring $F[x]/(x^2)$ by T. We know then, by Theorem 8.62, that T is not a field. The elements of T are again of the form

$$a + bj, \qquad\qquad a, b \in I/(2),$$

only this time $j^2 = 0$. Using this fact, we can obtain the following addition and multiplication tables for T.

(+)	0	1	j	$1+j$
0	0	1	j	$1+j$
1	1	0	$1+j$	j
j	j	$1+j$	0	1
$1+j$	$1+j$	j	1	0

(·)	0	1	j	$1+j$
0	0	0	0	0
1	0	1	j	$1+j$
j	0	j	0	j
$1+j$	0	$1+j$	j	1

The addition table coincides with the addition table of Example 2, but the multiplication table is different, as it would have to be since T is not a field.

Example 4. Let $s(x)$ be the polynomial $x^3 + x^2 + 1$ over the field R of rational numbers, and let us next consider the ring $R[x]/(x^3 + x^2 + 1)$, which we shall denote by U. It is easy to verify that $x^3 + x^2 + 1$ has no rational root and, since it is of degree 3, it must therefore be prime over R. Hence, U is a field. Since the degree of $s(x)$ is 3 in this case, it follows by the general argument preceding 8.65 that the elements of U are uniquely expressible in the form

8.75 $$a + bj + cj^2, \qquad a, b, c, \in R,$$

where, as usual, j is the equivalence set $[x]$. Let us consider the product of two of these elements as an illustration of the procedure by which we obtained 8.66 and 8.67. Since $s(j) = 0$, we have that $j^3 + j^2 + 1 = 0$, or

8.76 $$j^3 = -1 - j^2.$$

If we multiply this by j and substitute $-1 - j^2$ for j^3, we get

$$j^4 = -j - j^3 = -j - (-1 - j^2):$$

that is,

8.77 $$j^4 = 1 - j + j^2.$$

The product of two elements 8.75 can now be computed by using the distributive laws and then substituting for j^3 and j^4 from 8.76 and 8.77. If we do so, we finally obtain

8.78 $$(a + bj + cj^2)(d + ej + fj^2) = ad - bf - ce + cf$$
$$+ (ae + bd - cf)j + (af + be + cd - bf - ce + cf)j^2.$$

The field U can therefore be characterized as the field with elements 8.75, with multiplication given by 8.78, and addition carried out in the obvious way. It should perhaps be remarked that the formula 8.78 is obviously too complicated to be of any practical use. For example, it would be extremely difficult to find the multiplicative inverse of a given element of U by using this formula for the product of two elements. Instead, one would use the method of proof of Theorem 8.62 in order to carry out such a calculation

There is one further theorem which is implicit in what we have done, and which is of sufficient importance to warrant an explicit statement as follows.

79 Theorem. *If F is a field and $f(x)$ is an arbitrary element of $F[x]$ of positive degree, there exists a field F' containing F such that $f(x)$ has a root in F'.*

If $f(x)$ has a root in F, then the result is trivial with $F' = F$. Otherwise, there exists a factor $s(x)$ of $f(x)$, which is of degree at least two and is prime over F. Then let us set $F' = F[x]/(s(x))$. We know that F' is a field which contains the field F, and we may therefore also consider $f(x)$ to be a polynomial over F'. Moreover, using the notation in which the equivalence set $[x]$ is denoted by "j", we have $s(j) = 0$. That is, the element j of F' is a root of the polynomial $s(x)$ and is therefore also a root of $f(x)$. The proof is therefore completed.

In the notation of this theorem, since $f(j) = 0$, it follows by the Factor Theorem that in $F'[x]$ the polynomial $f(x)$ has $x - j$ as a factor. If $f(x)$ does not factor entirely into factors of the first degree over F'; that is, if $f(x)$ contains a prime factor over F' which is of degree at least two, the process can be repeated by constructing a field F'' which contains F' and in which $f(x)$ has another root. It is clear that by a continuation of this process, there exists a field F^* containing F such that $f(x)$ factors in $F^*[x]$ into factors of the first degree. This fact plays an important role in the theory of fields, but we shall not discuss it further here.

―――――――――――――――――――― *E X E R C I S E S*

1. Verify that congruence modulo $s(x)$ is an equivalence relation on the set $F[x]$.

2. Show that if $s(x)$ is of the first degree over F, then the field $F[x]/(s(x))$ is isomorphic to F itself.

3. For the given field F and the given polynomial $s(x)$ over F, construct a multiplication table for the ring $F[x]/(s(x))$. Which of these rings are fields?

   (a) $F = I/(2)$, $s(x) = x^2 + 1$;
   (b) $F = I/(3)$, $s(x) = x^2 + 1$;
   (c) $F = I/(3)$, $s(x) = x^2 + x + 2$;
   (d) $F = I/(2)$, $s(x) = x^3 + x + 1$;
   (e) $F = I/(2)$, $s(x) = x^3 + x^2 + 1$.

4. Discuss the field $R[x]/(x^2 - 2)$, and verify that it is isomorphic to the field of all real numbers of the form $a + b\sqrt{2}$, where $a, b \in R$.

5. Discuss the field $R[x]/(x^3 - 2)$, and describe a field of real numbers to which it is isomorphic.

6. It was stated earlier that for each positive integer n and each positive prime p, there exists a polynomial of degree n with coefficients in the field $I/(p)$ which is prime over this field. Use this fact to show that there exists a field with p^n elements.

7. In each case describe a field in which the given polynomial over the specified field has a root. In particular, give a general formula for the product of two elements of the field you describe.

   (a) $x^3 + x + 1$ over R,
   (b) $x^3 + x^2 + x + 2$ over R,
   (c) $x^2 - x + 1$ over K,
   (d) $x^3 + x + 1$ over $I/(2)$.

8. (a) Compute the multiplicative inverse of $1 + j + j^2$ in the field U of Example 4 above, and check by use of Formula 8.78.
   (b) Verify that in $U[x]$,

   $$x^3 + x^2 + 1 = (x - j)(x^2 + (1 + j)x + j + j^2).$$

8.10 PARTIAL FRACTIONS (OPTIONAL)

In calculus, partial fractions are used to carry out the integration of rational functions. In this section we shall briefly outline a proof of the existence of the required partial fraction decompositions.

It was pointed out in Section 5.6 that, starting with an integral domain D, it is possible to construct a quotient field of D whose elements are the formal quotients a/b, where a, $b \in D$ and $b \neq 0$. Now if F is a given field, we know that the polynomial ring $F[x]$ is an integral domain, and we are now interested in the quotient field of this integral domain. An element of this quotient field is therefore expressible as $f(x)/g(x)$, where $f(x)$, $g(x) \in F[x]$, $g(x) \neq 0$. Such an element is called a *rational form* over F, and the field whose elements are these rational forms is often called the field of rational forms (in the indeterminate x) over F. This field is usually denoted by $F(x)$. It should be observed that, by the same conventions we made in constructing the rational numbers from the integers, a polynomial is a special case of a rational form, and therefore $F[x] \subset F(x)$. However, we are not now primarily interested in properties of the field $F(x)$, but only in individual elements of this field.

If $g(x)$ is a polynomial over F of positive degree, we know by Theorem 8.36 that $g(x)$ can be expressed uniquely as a product of its leading coefficient times a product of powers of distinct monic polynomials that are prime over F. This fact is implicitly used in the proof of the following theorem.

80 Theorem. *A rational form $f(x)/g(x)$ over F is expressible as a polynomial over F plus a sum of rational forms over F of the special type $r(x)/[p(x)]^k$, where $p(x)$ is a prime polynomial over F, $[p(x)]^k$ is a divisor of $g(x)$, and deg $r(x) <$ deg $p(x)$.*

The expressing of $f(x)/g(x)$ as described in this theorem is said to be "expressing $f(x)/g(x)$ as a sum of partial fractions."

As an illustration of the theorem, it may be verified that over the field of real numbers

81
$$\frac{x^2 + x - 1}{x^3(x^2 + 1)} = \frac{2}{x} + \frac{1}{x^2} - \frac{1}{x^3} - \frac{2x + 1}{x^2 + 1}.$$

In this case, the polynomial mentioned in the theorem is the zero polynomial. Moreover, there are just two prime factors of the denominator, namely, x and $x^2 + 1$, and therefore only these two choices for $p(x)$.

We prove the theorem in two steps as follows. First, suppose that $g(x) = h(x)k(x)$, where $h(x)$ and $k(x)$ are relatively prime polynomials over F. Then we know that there exist polynomials $s(x)$, $t(x)$ over F such that

$$1 = h(x)s(x) + k(x)t(x),$$

from which it follows that

$$\frac{1}{g(x)} = \frac{s(x)}{k(x)} + \frac{t(x)}{h(x)}.$$

Then, since

$$\frac{f(x)}{g(x)} = \frac{f(x)s(x)}{k(x)} + \frac{f(x)t(x)}{h(x)},$$

we see that $f(x)/g(x)$ is expressible as a sum of rational forms with respective denominators $k(x)$ and $h(x)$. If, say, $h(x)$ is now expressible as a product of two relatively prime polynomials, the same procedure can be applied to the rational form $f(x)t(x)/h(x)$. By a repetition of this process we can finally write $f(x)/g(x)$ as a sum of rational forms having denominators which cannot be expressed as a product of two relatively prime polynomials. Each denominator is then a power of a single prime polynomial and therefore each of these rational forms is of the type $u(x)/[p(x)]^n$, where $p(x)$ is a prime polynomial over F, and $[p(x)]^n$ is a divisor of $g(x)$.

We next consider any one such form of the type $u(x)/[p(x)]^n$. If deg $u(x) <$ deg $p(x)$, $u(x)/[p(x)]^n$ is already one of the rational forms described in the statement of the theorem. If deg $u(x) \geq$ deg $p(x)$, we use the Division Algorithm and write

8.82
$$u(x) = q_0(x)p(x) + r_0(x),$$

where, as usual, $r_0(x) = 0$ or $\deg r_0(x) < \deg p(x)$. If $\deg q_0(x) \geq \deg p(x)$, we divide $q_0(x)$ by $p(x)$ and obtain

$$q_0(x) = q_1(x)p(x) + r_1(x),$$

and by substitution in 8.82 we obtain

$$u(x) = q_1(x)[p(x)]^2 + r_1(x)p(x) + r_0(x).$$

If $\deg q_1(x) \geq \deg p(x)$, we divide $q_1(x)$ by $p(x)$, and continue this process. This procedure is an exact analogue of the proof of Theorem 4.6, and we can show in this way that, for some nonnegative integer m,

8.83 $\quad u(x) = r_m(x)[p(x)]^m + r_{m-1}(x)[p(x)]^{m-1} + \cdots + r_1(x)p(x) + r_0(x),$

where $r_m(x) \neq 0$ and $r_i(x) = 0$ or $\deg r_i(x) < \deg p(x)$ for $i = 0, 1, \cdots, m$. It follows at once from 8.83 that the rational form $u(x)/[p(x)]^n$ is expressible as a polynomial (possibly zero) plus a sum of forms $r(x)/[p(x)]^k$, with $k \leq n$ and therefore $[p(x)]^k$ a divisor of $g(x)$. Since we have already showed that $f(x)/g(x)$ can be expressed as a sum of terms of the form $u(x)/[p(x)]^n$, the proof is therefore completed.

In a numerical case, the steps of the above proof can be actually carried out in order to express a rational form as a sum of partial fractions. Let us give an illustration by carrying out the calculations involved in establishing the example 8.81 given above. Since x^3 and $x^2 + 1$ are relatively prime, by the usual method involving the Euclidean Algorithm, we find that

$$1 = x^3 \cdot x + (x^2 + 1)(1 - x^2),$$

and therefore

$$\frac{1}{x^3(x^2 + 1)} = \frac{x}{x^2 + 1} + \frac{1 - x^2}{x^3}.$$

If we multiply by the given numerator, $x^2 + x - 1$, we obtain

8.84 $\quad \dfrac{x^2 + x - 1}{x^3(x^2 + 1)} = \dfrac{x^3 + x^2 - x}{x^2 + 1} + \dfrac{-x^4 - x^3 + 2x^2 + x - 1}{x^3}.$

We now consider the first term on the right. By the Division Algorithm we see that

$$x^3 + x^2 - x = (x + 1)(x^2 + 1) - 2x - 1,$$

and therefore

$$\frac{x^3 + x^2 - x}{x^2 + 1} = x + 1 - \frac{2x + 1}{x^2 + 1}.$$

Using this equation, we can write Equation 8.84 in the form

$$\frac{x^2 + x - 1}{x^3(x^2 + 1)} = x + 1 - \frac{2x + 1}{x^2 + 1} - x - 1 + \frac{2}{x} + \frac{1}{x^2} - \frac{1}{x^3},$$

and we conclude that

$$\frac{x^2+x-1}{x^3(x^2+1)} = \frac{2}{x} + \frac{1}{x^2} - \frac{1}{x^3} - \frac{2x+1}{x^2+1}.$$

It will be observed that in simplifying each of the terms on the right of 8.84 a nonzero polynomial occurred, but no polynomial occurred in the final result. It can be shown that whenever deg $f(x) <$ deg $g(x)$, as is true in this example, in expressing $f(x)/g(x)$ as a sum of partial fractions no polynomial occurs. Also, it is proved in more advanced texts that the expression of a rational form as a sum of partial fractions is *unique*. However, we shall not prove these facts here.

Over the real field, which is the case of most importance, the only prime polynomials are of the first or second degree. Hence, in this case, the prime polynomials $p(x)$ in the statement of Theorem 8.80 are of the first or second degree. This fact is important in the proof that every rational function can be integrated in terms of elementary functions.

―――――――――――――――――― **E X E R C I S E S**

Use the method of proof of Theorem 8.80 to express each of the following rational forms over the field of real numbers as a sum of partial fractions.

1. $\dfrac{x^2 - x + 1}{x(x^2 + x + 1)}.$

2. $\dfrac{x^2 + x - 2}{x(x^2 - 1)}.$

3. $\dfrac{x+1}{x(x^2 + 1)^2}.$

4. $\dfrac{1}{(x-1)^2(x^2+2)}.$

5. $\dfrac{2x^2 + x - 1}{x(x-1)^3}.$

6. $\dfrac{x^4 + 2x^3 + 4}{(x^2+1)^2}.$

9

Groups

In all the algebraic systems studied so far we have always had two operations, namely, addition and multiplication. We next proceed to study an important class of systems in which there is only one operation. As soon as the definition of a *group* is given in the next section it will be apparent that we already have many examples of groups from previous chapters, although we have not used this terminology. The theory of groups is an important part of modern algebra, and many books have been written on the subject. In this chapter we shall present only a few of the most fundamental properties of groups and give a number of examples that may serve to suggest the wide range of applications of the theory.

9.1 DEFINITION OF A GROUP

We shall now give the definition of a group, and illustrate the definition by some simple examples.

Let "∘" be a binary operation defined on a nonempty set G. We recall that this statement only means that if (a, b) is any ordered pair of elements of G, then $a \circ b$ is a uniquely determined element of G. As a matter of fact, it is customary to call this operation either "addition" or "multiplication," and to use the familiar notation that is associated with these words. However, we shall first state the definition in terms of the unfamiliar symbol "∘".

1 Definition. A nonempty set G on which there is defined a binary operation "∘" is called a *group* (with respect to this operation) provided the following properties are satisfied:

(i) If $a, b, c \in G$, then $(a \circ b) \circ c = a \circ (b \circ c)$
(associative law),

(ii) There exists an element e of G such that $e \circ a = a \circ e = a$ for every element a of G (existence of an identity),

(iii) If $a \in G$, there exists an element x of G such that $a \circ x = x \circ a = e$ (existence of inverses).

As suggested by the indicated names of the second and third properties, e is called an *identity* of the group, and the element x in (iii) is called an *inverse* of the element a. In fact, it is quite easy to prove that the identity is unique, and also that each element has a unique inverse.

In order to give an example of a group it is necessary to specify the elements of the set and to define an operation on this set so that the three properties stated above are satisfied. We now give a few examples of groups.

Example 1. The set I of all integers, with the operation "∘" taken as the usual operation $(+)$ of addition. The first property then merely states that

$$(a + b) + c = a + (b + c),$$

and this is just the associative law of addition for the integers. In this case, the identity of the group is the zero integer since $0 + a = a + 0 = a$ for $a \in I$. The inverse of the element a is the element $-a$ since $a + (-a) = -a + a = 0$, and in the present notation this is just what is required in the statement of the third property. We have therefore verified all three properties, and hence we have a group. This group may be called the *additive group of the integers*.

This example can easily be generalized as follows. Let S be the set of all elements of any *ring*, and let the operation "∘" be taken as the operation of addition already defined in the ring. Then the three properties of a group are precisely the properties P_2, P_3, and P_4 of Section 2.2 required of addition in the ring. Hence, S must be a group relative to the operation of addition. We shall refer to this group as the *additive group of the ring S*.

Example 2. The set T of all nonzero rational numbers, with the operation "∘" taken as the familiar operation of multiplication of rational numbers. Since the product of two nonzero rational numbers is also a nonzero rational number, the set T is closed under multiplication, that is, multiplication is an operation defined on T. If $a, b, c \in T$, then $(ab)c = a(bc)$ by the associative law of multiplication for rational numbers, and this is just 9.1(i) in this case. Moreover, the identity is the rational number 1, and the inverse of an element a of T is the rational number a^{-1}. Hence, T is a group with respect to the operation of multiplication. We may point out that in a group *every* element must have an inverse, and this explains why the set of *all* rational numbers would not be a group with respect to multiplication.

This example can also be generalized as follows. If F is an arbitrary *field*, the set of all nonzero elements of F is a group with respect to the operation of multiplication in the field. This group we shall call the *multiplicative group of the field F*. We emphasize again that there is exactly one element of F, the zero, which is not an element of the multiplicative group of F.

Example 3. The set $\{1, -1, i, -i\}$ consisting of these four complex numbers, with the operation of multiplication of complex numbers. It is easy to verify that the set is closed under multiplication and, of course, the number 1 is the identity. Moreover, 1 and -1 are their own inverses, and i and $-i$ are inverses of each other. The associative law clearly holds since it holds for multiplication of complex numbers in general.

Example 4. The set L of all complex numbers z with $|z| = 1$, again with respect to the operation of multiplication. Since, by Theorem 7.10, we have $|uv| = |u| \cdot |v|$, it follows that if $u \in L$ and $v \in L$, then $uv \in L$, and L is therefore closed under multiplication. Moreover, if $|u| = 1$, it is easy to verify that $|u^{-1}| = 1$. Hence, if $u \in L$, then also $u^{-1} \in L$ and each element of L has an inverse in L. The other properties are obviously satisfied, and therefore L is a group.

Example 5. Let H be the set $\{p, q, r\}$ with an operation, which we shall consider as multiplication, defined by the following table.

$(\cdot)$	p	q	r
p	p	q	r
q	q	r	p
r	r	p	q

Clearly, p is the identity of H. Moreover, p is its own inverse, and q and r are inverses of each other. The associative law is also satisfied, although it is tedious to verify it from the table.

All these examples have an additional property not required by the definition of a group. That is, they are abelian groups according to the following definition.

.2 Definition. If in a group G with operation "$\circ$", $a \circ b = b \circ a$ for all $a, b \in G$, G is said to be an *abelian group* (or a commutative group).

The term "abelian group" is most commonly used for this concept. The name is derived from Niels Henrik Abel (1802–1829), a famous Norwegian mathematician whose fundamental work furnished an inspiration for many later mathematicians.

All the above examples are examples of abelian groups. In Section 9.3 we shall introduce some very important nonabelian groups.

As in the examples, we shall always call the operation in a group either addition or multiplication, and shall use the usual notation associated with these names. We shall never use addition as the operation in a nonabelian group. That is, whenever addition is used as the operation, we shall always assume, whether or not it is explicitly mentioned, that the group is abelian. It follows that in such a group *all* the properties of addition in a ring are satisfied. The identity will be denoted by "0" and called "zero"; the inverse of an element a will be denoted by $-a$; we shall write $b - a$ for $b + (-a)$, and so on.

When the operation in a group is called multiplication, the group may be either abelian or nonabelian. Accordingly, when we come to prove a property of arbitrary groups, we shall think of the operation as multiplication, and use the implied notation. In particular, the inverse of an element a will then be denoted by a^{-1}. We shall usually let e be the identity of the group, and reserve the symbol "1" for the smallest positive integer.

9.2 SOME SIMPLE PROPERTIES OF GROUPS

Let G be an arbitrary group with operation multiplication. The following properties can be easily proved using only trivial modifications of proofs that we have already met in our study of rings and fields. We may emphasize that here multiplication need not be commutative. The first two of these properties have already been stated in the preceding section.

.3 Theorem. *The following hold in every group G:*

   (i)   *The identity of G is unique.*

   (ii) *If $a \in G$, a has a unique inverse a^{-1}.*

  (iii) *If $a, b, c \in G$ such that $ab = ac$, then $b = c$.*

  (iv) *If $a, b, c \in G$ such that $ba = ca$, then $b = c$.*

   (v) *If $a, b \in G$, there exists a unique element x of G such that $ax = b$, and a unique element y of G such that $ya = b$. In fact, $x = a^{-1}b$ and $y = ba^{-1}$.*

(vi)   *The inverse of a product is the product of the inverses in the reverse order, that is, if a, b $\in$ G, then* $(ab)^{-1} = b^{-1}a^{-1}$.

Properties (iii) and (iv) are naturally called the *cancellation laws*. The proofs of the various parts of 9.3 will be assigned as an exercise below.

Just as in the case of multiplication in a ring, the generalized associative law holds, and we can write products without use of parentheses to indicate association.

If $a \in G$, we define $a^0 = e$, where e is the identity of the group. Then, just as though a were a nonzero element of a field, we can define a^n for *every* integer n. Moreover, for all choices of integers m and n, the following laws of exponents hold:

$$a^m \cdot a^n = a^{m+n},$$
$$(a^m)^n = a^{mn}.$$

For an *abelian* group, we also have $(ab)^n = a^n \cdot b^n$, but this is not true in general.

In those cases in which we use addition as the operation, we make use of multiples in place of powers; that is, na takes the place of a^n. Such a group is always assumed to be abelian and we have the following analogues of the above laws of exponents:

$$ma + na = (m + n)a,$$
$$n(ma) = (nm)a,$$
$$n(a + b) = na + nb.$$

These are properties that are already familiar as properties of addition in any ring.

A set H of elements of a group G is naturally called a *subgroup* of G if H is itself a group with respect to the operation already defined on G. The following theorem, whose proof we shall leave as an exercise, is often useful in determining the subgroups of a given group.

9.4   Theorem.   *A nonempty subset K of a group G is a subgroup of G if and only if the following conditions are satisfied:*

(i)   *If a, b $\in$ K, then ab $\in$ K.*
(ii)   *If a $\in$ K, then $a^{-1} \in$ K.*

The concept of isomorphism can be applied to groups in an almost obvious way. Since, however, the operations may be written differently in the two groups, let us state the definition as follows.

9.5   Definition.   Let G be a group with operation "$\circ$" and G' a group with operation "$\square$". A one-one mapping $x \to x'$ of G onto G' is said to be an *isomorphism* of G onto G' provided that for $a, b \in G$, we have

$$a \circ b \rightarrow a' \square b'.$$

If there exists an isomorphism of G onto G', we say that G is *isomorphic* to G' (or that G and G' are isomorphic).

Since the image of $a \circ b$ is $(a \circ b)'$, 9.6 may also be written in the equivalent form: $(a \circ b)' = a' \square b'$.

As an example of isomorphism of groups, let H be the additive group of the ring $I/(4)$, and L the multiplicative group of the field $I/(5)$. In order to distinguish between the elements of these two groups, let us designate the elements of H by 0, 1, 2, 3; and the elements of L by 1*, 2*, 3*, 4*. Then we assert that the one-one mapping of H onto L defined as follows is an isomorphism of H onto L:

$$1 \rightarrow 2^*, \qquad 2 \rightarrow 4^*, \qquad 3 \rightarrow 3^*, \qquad 0 \rightarrow 1^*.$$

For example, we have $2 \rightarrow 4^*$, $3 \rightarrow 3^*$, and it is easily verified that $2 + 3 \rightarrow 4^* \cdot 3^*$ since $2 + 3 = 1$ in H and $4^* \cdot 3^* = 2^*$ in L. The reader may verify that in every case a sum of elements of H has as image the product of the corresponding images in L.

We now mention an important, and familiar, example of an isomorphism as follows. If P is the set of all *positive* real numbers, it is easy to verify that P is a group with respect to the operation of multiplication of real numbers. Let Q be the additive group of all real numbers, and let us consider the mapping

$$x \rightarrow \log_{10} x, \qquad\qquad x \in P,$$

of P into Q. It is known that this is a one-one mapping of P onto Q and, moreover, one of the familiar laws of logarithms assures us that under this mapping

$$ab \rightarrow \log_{10}(ab) = \log_{10} a + \log_{10} b.$$

This is just the property 9.6 required of an isomorphism, and therefore the group P is isomorphic to the group Q. Of course, in place of 10 we could use as a base any fixed positive real number other than 1.

──────────────────────────── *EXERCISES*

1. Prove 9.3(i) − (vi).

2. Which of the following are groups with respect to the indicated operation?

(a) The set $\{1, 3, 7, 9\}$ of elements of $I/(10)$, with operation multiplication.

(b)   The set $\{0, 2, 4, 6, 8\}$ of elements of $I/(10)$, with operation addition.

(c)   The set $\{1, 3, 9\}$ of elements of $I/(10)$, with operation multiplication.

(d)   The set of all rational numbers x such that $0 < x \leq 1$, with operation multiplication.

(e)   The set of all positive rational numbers with operation multiplication.

(f)   The set of all positive irrational real numbers with operation multiplication.

(g)   The set of all integers with operation "$\circ$" defined as follows: $a \circ b = a + b + 1$.

(h)   The set of all integers with operation "$\circ$" defined as follows: $a \circ b = a - b$.

(i)   The set of all rational numbers, other than 1, with operation "$\circ$" defined as follows: $a \circ b = a + b - ab$.

(j)   The set of complex numbers that are nth roots of unity, where n is a fixed positive integer, with operation multiplication.

3. Prove Theorem 9.4.

4. Find all subgroups of each of the following groups:

(a)   The additive group of the ring $I/(12)$.

(b)   The additive group of the ring $I/(5)$.

(c)   The multiplicative group of the field $I/(7)$.

(d)   The multiplicative group of the field $I/(11)$.

5. Show that the set of all elements of the ring $I/(n)$ of the form $[k]$, where k and n are relatively prime, is a group with respect to the operation of multiplication.

6. Prove that $(ab)^2 = a^2b^2$ for all choices of a and b as elements of a group G if and only if G is abelian.

7. Verify that there exists an isomorphism of the additive group of the ring $I/(6)$ onto the multiplicative group of the field $I/(7)$ such that $1 \rightarrow 3^*$.

8. Show that the set of all elements a of a group G such that $ax = xa$ for every element x of G is a subgroup of G.

9. Let $x \rightarrow x'$ be an isomorphism of a group G with operation "$\circ$" onto a group G' with operation "$\square$". If e is the identity of G and $e \rightarrow e'$, show that e' is necessarily the identity of G'. Show also that under this isomorphic mapping the image of the inverse of an element a of G is the inverse of the image of a.

10. What familiar properties of logarithms can you obtain by applying the results of the preceding exercise to the isomorphism $a \to \log_{10} a$ of P onto Q, as given in the example preceding this set of exercises?

9.3 MAPPINGS AND PERMUTATION GROUPS

In this section we shall obtain a new and important class of groups. As a first step, we need to introduce a convenient notation for mappings and to prove a few properties of mappings in general.

Let A and B be two sets. In Chapter 1 we defined a mapping of the set A into the set B, and indicated such a mapping by writing

$$9.7 \qquad\qquad a \to a',$$

where it is understood that a' is the image of a. This notation is reasonably satisfactory when only one mapping is being discussed. However, we shall presently wish to consider at the same time more than one mapping of a set A into a set B, and so we need a more explicit notation. In general, we shall denote a mapping by a Greek letter. For example, let us denote the fixed mapping 9.7 of A into B by α. Then we shall indicate the image of a under the mapping α by $a\alpha$ instead of the previous a', and write 9.7 in the form $a \to a\alpha$.

To illustrate this notation, let $U = \{1, 2, 3, 4\}$ and $V = \{x, y, z\}$. Moreover, let α be the mapping

$$9.8 \qquad\qquad 1 \to y, \qquad 2 \to x, \qquad 3 \to x, \qquad 4 \to z$$

of U into (actually onto) V. Then, since the image of 1 is y, we have that $1\alpha = y$. Similarly, $2\alpha = x$, $3\alpha = x$, and $4\alpha = z$. The mapping α is thus fully defined as soon as we have specified $a\alpha$ for each element a of U.

If both α_1 and α_2 are mappings of a set A into a set B, by $\alpha_1 = \alpha_2$ we naturally mean that $a\alpha_1 = a\alpha_2$ for every element a of A.

Now let A, B, and C be sets, and suppose that we have given a mapping α of A into B, and a mapping β of B into C. We can use these in an almost obvious way to define a mapping of A into C. Under the mapping α an element a of A has image $a\alpha$ in B. We may also express this fact by saying that under the mapping α, a *maps into* $a\alpha$. Now $a\alpha \in B$ and so under the mapping β of B into C, $a\alpha$ maps into a unique element $(a\alpha)\beta$ of C. Thus $a \to (a\alpha)\beta$ clearly defines a mapping of A into C. This mapping of A into C we call the *product* of the mapping α by the mapping β, and designate it by "$\alpha\beta$". Otherwise expressed, the mapping $\alpha\beta$ of A into C is *defined* by

9.9 $a(\alpha\beta) = (a\alpha)\beta,$ $a \in A.$

To illustrate this concept, let α be the mapping 9.8 of U into V. Suppose that $W = \{r, s\}$, and that β is the mapping of V into W given by

$$x \to s, \qquad y \to r, \qquad z \to s$$

or, in our present notation, $x\beta = s$, $y\beta = r$, $z\beta = s$. Then, applying 9.9, we have

$$1(\alpha\beta) = (1\alpha)\beta = y\beta = r,$$
$$2(\alpha\beta) = (2\alpha)\beta = x\beta = s,$$
$$3(\alpha\beta) = (3\alpha)\beta = x\beta = s,$$
$$4(\alpha\beta) = (4\alpha)\beta = z\beta = s.$$

Hence, the mapping $\alpha\beta$ is the mapping

$$1 \to r, \qquad 2 \to s, \qquad 3 \to s, \qquad 4 \to s$$

of U into W.

We should perhaps emphasize that in defining the product of two mappings a certain condition on the sets involved is necessary. Thus, if α is a mapping of A into B, $\alpha\beta$ is defined only if β is a mapping of the set B into some set.

We now take one more step as follows. Let A, B, C, and D be sets, and suppose that α is a mapping of A into B, β is a mapping of B into C, and γ is a mapping of C into D. Then $\alpha\beta$ is a mapping of A into C, and $(\alpha\beta)\gamma$ is a mapping of A into D. In like manner, $\alpha(\beta\gamma)$ is seen to be a mapping of A into D. It is an important fact that these two mappings are equal; that is, that

9.10 $(\alpha\beta)\gamma = \alpha(\beta\gamma).$

By the definition of equality of mappings, we shall prove 9.10 by verifying that

9.11 $a((\alpha\beta)\gamma) = a(\alpha(\beta\gamma))$

for every element a of A.

First, we observe that by the definition of the product of the mappings $\alpha\beta$ and γ, we have

$$a((\alpha\beta)\gamma) = (a(\alpha\beta))\gamma.$$

Then, by the definition of the product $\alpha\beta$, it follows that

$$(a(\alpha\beta))\gamma = ((a\alpha)\beta)\gamma,$$

and so the left side of 9.11 is equal to $((a\alpha)\beta)\gamma$. In like manner, by applying the definition of the product of α by $\beta\gamma$, and then the definition of the product $\beta\gamma$, we obtain

$$a(\alpha(\beta\gamma)) = (a\alpha)(\beta\gamma) = ((a\alpha)\beta)\gamma.$$

Since both sides of 9.11 are equal to $((a\alpha)\beta)\gamma$, we have proved 9.11 and also 9.10. Of course, Equation 9.10 merely states that multiplication of mappings is always associative.

In case α is a *one-one* mapping of a set A onto a set B, it is almost obvious that we can use the mapping α to define a one-one mapping of B onto A. Let us see how this latter mapping can be expressed in the notation which has been introduced. Since α is a one-one mapping of A onto B, if a_1, $a_2 \in A$ such that $a_1 \neq a_2$, then $a_1\alpha \neq a_2\alpha$. Hence, under the mapping $a \to a\alpha$, every element of B is the image of exactly one element of A, and therefore $a\alpha \to a$ then defines a one-one mapping of B onto A. This mapping we denote by α^{-1}. Thus the one-one mapping α^{-1} of B onto A is *defined* by

.12
$$(a\alpha)\alpha^{-1} = a, \qquad\qquad a \in A.$$

Of course, this actually defines a mapping of B onto A only because every element of B is uniquely expressible in the form $a\alpha$ for some $a \in A$.

In connection with our study of groups we are interested in the special case of mappings of a set A onto the *same set A*. Moreover, it is the one-one mappings of A onto A that we wish to study. The following terminology is convenient.

.13 Definition. A one-one mapping of a set A onto itself is called a *permutation* of the set A.

The next theorem will show why we have paused to study mappings in a discussion of groups.

.14 Theorem. *The set S of all permutations of a set A is a group with respect to the operation of multiplication of mappings defined in 9.9.*

First, let us give a formal proof of the almost obvious fact that if α and β are permutations of A, then $\alpha\beta$ is also a permutation of A. Since α and β are mappings of A onto A, the definition

$$a(\alpha\beta) = (a\alpha)\beta, \qquad\qquad a \in A,$$

of $\alpha\beta$ shows that $\alpha\beta$ is certainly a mapping of A *onto* A. We can now show that $\alpha\beta$ is, in fact, a one-one mapping and is therefore a permutation of A. We only need to verify that if $a, b \in A$ such that $a \neq b$, then $a(\alpha\beta) \neq b(\alpha\beta)$. Since α is a one-one mapping and $a \neq b$, it follows that $a\alpha \neq b\alpha$. Then since β is a one-one mapping, we have $(a\alpha)\beta \neq (b\alpha)\beta$, and therefore $a(\alpha\beta) \neq b(\alpha\beta)$. Hence, $\alpha\beta$ is a permutation of the set A, and the set S is closed under the operation of multiplication.

We have already proved (9.10) that multiplication of mappings is necessarily associative, and hence the first requirement of a group is satisfied.

The permutation ϵ of A defined by

$$a\epsilon = a, \qquad\qquad a \in A,$$

and which therefore maps each element into itself, is the identity of the group. For if $\alpha \in S$, we have for each element a of A that

$$a(\alpha\epsilon) = (a\alpha)\epsilon = a\alpha,$$

and therefore $\alpha\epsilon = \alpha$. Similarly,

$$a(\epsilon\alpha) = (a\epsilon)\alpha = a\alpha,$$

and also $\epsilon\alpha = \alpha$.

Finally, we need to show that if $\alpha \in S$, then α has an inverse in S. We shall show, as the notation indicates, that α^{-1}, defined by 9.12, is the inverse of α. Since α is a permutation of A, and therefore the sets A and B being considered in the definition 9.12 are identical, we already know that α^{-1} is a permutation of A. To show that it is the inverse of α, we need to show that $\alpha\alpha^{-1} = \alpha^{-1}\alpha = \epsilon$. If $a \in A$, it follows at once from the definition of a product of mappings and the definition of α^{-1} that

$$a(\alpha\alpha^{-1}) = (a\alpha)\alpha^{-1} = a = a\epsilon,$$

and hence $\alpha\alpha^{-1} = \epsilon$. Using this result, we now see that if $a \in A$, then

$$(a\alpha)(\alpha^{-1}\alpha) = a(\alpha(\alpha^{-1}\alpha)) = a((\alpha\alpha^{-1})\alpha) = a\alpha.$$

But since every element b of A is of the form $a\alpha$ for suitable choice of a in A, we observe that

$$b(\alpha^{-1}\alpha) = b\epsilon$$

for every b in A. Hence, also $\alpha^{-1}\alpha = \epsilon$, and α^{-1} is indeed the inverse of α.

We have now established all the properties required in the definition of a group, and the theorem is therefore established. This group S is naturally called the *group of all permutations of the set* A.

So far, the set A has been a completely arbitrary set. However, we are now primarily interested in the case in which A is restricted to have a finite number of elements. It is, or soon will be, apparent that the group of all permutations of a finite set A depends only on the number of elements of A and not on the notation used for these elements. Accordingly, we make the following definition.

9.15 Definition. Let n be a positive integer. The group of all permutations of a set with n elements is called the *symmetric group* on n symbols, and may be designated by "S_n".

Let us now consider an example in which $A = \{1, 2, 3\}$, a set with three elements. Then the symmetric group S_3, consisting of all permutations of A, contains the six elements $\alpha_1, \alpha_2, \alpha_3, \alpha_4, \alpha_5, \alpha_6$, as follows:

9.16
$$
\begin{aligned}
1\alpha_1 &= 1, & 2\alpha_1 &= 2, & 3\alpha_1 &= 3, \\
1\alpha_2 &= 2, & 2\alpha_2 &= 1, & 3\alpha_2 &= 3, \\
1\alpha_3 &= 3, & 2\alpha_3 &= 2, & 3\alpha_3 &= 1, \\
1\alpha_4 &= 1, & 2\alpha_4 &= 3, & 3\alpha_4 &= 2, \\
1\alpha_5 &= 2, & 2\alpha_5 &= 3, & 3\alpha_5 &= 1, \\
1\alpha_6 &= 3, & 2\alpha_6 &= 1, & 3\alpha_6 &= 2.
\end{aligned}
$$

The product of two of these permutations may, of course, be computed by using the definition of product of mappings. For example, let us compute $\alpha_2\alpha_5$. We have

$$
\begin{aligned}
1(\alpha_2\alpha_5) &= (1\alpha_2)\alpha_5 = 2\alpha_5 = 3, \\
2(\alpha_2\alpha_5) &= (2\alpha_2)\alpha_5 = 1\alpha_5 = 2, \\
3(\alpha_2\alpha_5) &= (3\alpha_2)\alpha_5 = 3\alpha_5 = 1.
\end{aligned}
$$

Hence, $\alpha_2\alpha_5 = \alpha_3$ since under the mapping $\alpha_2\alpha_5$ each element of A has the same image as under the mapping α_3. In like manner we can compute all products and obtain the following multiplication table for the group S_3.

9.17

	α_1	α_2	α_3	α_4	α_5	α_6
α_1	α_1	α_2	α_3	α_4	α_5	α_6
α_2	α_2	α_1	α_5	α_6	α_3	α_4
α_3	α_3	α_6	α_1	α_5	α_4	α_2
α_4	α_4	α_5	α_6	α_1	α_2	α_3
α_5	α_5	α_4	α_2	α_3	α_6	α_1
α_6	α_6	α_3	α_4	α_2	α_1	α_5

It is clear that α_1 is the identity of this group, and from the table one can easily find the inverse of each element. The group S_3 is not an abelian group since, for example, $\alpha_2\alpha_5 = \alpha_3$, whereas $\alpha_5\alpha_2 = \alpha_4$.

Before leaving this example, let us mention still another way of exhibiting the individual permutations of this group. For example, let us consider the element α_2 of S_3, as defined in 9.16. It is sometimes convenient to write

9.18
$$
\alpha_2 = \begin{pmatrix} 1 & 2 & 3 \\ 2 & 1 & 3 \end{pmatrix}
$$

to express the fact that under the mapping α_2 the image of 1 is 2, the image of 2 is 1, and the image of 3 is 3. According to this notation, we merely write the elements of the set A (in any order) in the top row, and under each element of A we write its image under the mapping α_2. In like manner, we see that

$$\alpha_5 = \begin{pmatrix} 1 & 2 & 3 \\ 2 & 3 & 1 \end{pmatrix}.$$

Then to compute the product $\alpha_2\alpha_5$ we observe that under this product 1 maps into 2 and then 2 maps into 3; hence 1 maps into 3. In like manner, 2 maps into 2 and 3 into 1. Hence, we may write

$$\begin{pmatrix} 1 & 2 & 3 \\ 2 & 1 & 3 \end{pmatrix}\begin{pmatrix} 1 & 2 & 3 \\ 2 & 3 & 1 \end{pmatrix} = \begin{pmatrix} 1 & 2 & 3 \\ 3 & 2 & 1 \end{pmatrix} = \alpha_3,$$

and we have again verified that $\alpha_2\alpha_5 = \alpha_3$.

We can use a notation similar to 9.18 to denote a permutation of any finite set. In general, if $i_1, i_2, \cdots, i_n$ is an arrangement of the integers $1, 2, \cdots, n$; by

$$\begin{pmatrix} 1 & 2 & 3 \cdots n \\ i_1 & i_2 & i_3 \cdots i_n \end{pmatrix}$$

we mean the permutation α of the set $A = \{1, 2, \cdots, n\}$ such that $1\alpha = i_1$, $2\alpha = i_2$, $\cdots$, $n\alpha = i_n$. We shall use this notation whenever it seems convenient to do so.

We found above that S_3 has six elements. Let us now determine the number of elements in the symmetric group S_n, that is, the number of permutations of a set $A = \{1, 2, \cdots, n\}$ with n elements. Clearly, the image of 1 may be any element of A, and hence there are n choices for the image of 1. After an image of 1 is selected, there are then $n - 1$ choices for the image of 2, and so on. It follows that there are $n(n-1)(n-2)$ $\cdots 2 \cdot 1$ different permutations of A. This number is usually denoted by $n!$ and called "n factorial." We have therefore shown that S_n has $n!$ elements.

Any group whose elements are permutations is naturally called a *permutation group* or a *group of permutations*. Any subgroup of a symmetric group S_n is certainly a permutation group. For example, from the table 9.17 and Theorem 9.4 it follows that $\{\alpha_1, \alpha_5, \alpha_6\}$ is a subgroup of S_3, and this is therefore an example of a permutation group which is not a symmetric group since it is not the group of all permutations of any set.

It is an important fact, although we shall not give the proof in this book, that *every group is isomorphic to a permutation group.* In view of this theorem, it should not be surprising that there are many different permutation groups.

We conclude this section with a brief indication of how one can construct some interesting permutation groups by use of properties of symmetry of certain geometric figures. As an example, let us consider a square and study all rigid motions of the square into itself. That is, if the square is thought of as being made of some rigid material, such as cardboard, we consider motions such that the figure will look the same after the motion as before. In this, as well as in all other examples we shall consider, the rigid motions will consist of rotations either in the plane or in space. Each rigid motion of the square can be used in an almost obvious way to define a permutation of the vertices of the square. Let us designate the vertices of the square by 1, 2, 3, and 4. Moreover, let E, F, G, and H be the midpoints of the sides, as indicated in Figure 9; and let O be the center of the square. A rotation, in the plane

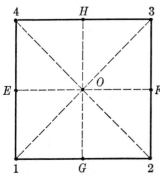

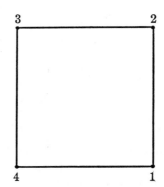

Figure 9   Figure 10

of the square, through an angle of 90° about point O would place the vertices in the position shown in Figure 10. We may interpret the result of this rotation as mapping 1 into 2, 2 into 3, 3 into 4, and 4 into 1; that is, as effecting the permutation

$$\alpha = \begin{pmatrix} 1 & 2 & 3 & 4 \\ 2 & 3 & 4 & 1 \end{pmatrix}$$

of the set $\{1, 2, 3, 4\}$ whose elements denote the vertices. A similar rotation through an angle of 180° or 270° leads to the respective permutations

$$\alpha^2 = \begin{pmatrix} 1 & 2 & 3 & 4 \\ 3 & 4 & 1 & 2 \end{pmatrix} \quad \text{or} \quad \alpha^3 = \begin{pmatrix} 1 & 2 & 3 & 4 \\ 4 & 1 & 2 & 3 \end{pmatrix}.$$

Clearly, $\alpha^4 = \epsilon$, the identity permutation. We also have other rigid motions consisting of rotations in space about a line of symmetry of the square. Let β be the permutation which arises from a rotation through an angle of 180° about the line EF, and γ the permutation which arises from a similar rotation about GH. Then we see that

$$\beta = \begin{pmatrix} 1 & 2 & 3 & 4 \\ 4 & 3 & 2 & 1 \end{pmatrix} \quad \text{and} \quad \gamma = \begin{pmatrix} 1 & 2 & 3 & 4 \\ 2 & 1 & 4 & 3 \end{pmatrix}.$$

There remain two other permutations arising from rotations through 180° about the diagonals of the square. These are

$$\delta = \begin{pmatrix} 1 & 2 & 3 & 4 \\ 1 & 4 & 3 & 2 \end{pmatrix} \quad \text{and} \quad \sigma = \begin{pmatrix} 1 & 2 & 3 & 4 \\ 3 & 2 & 1 & 4 \end{pmatrix}.$$

The set $\{\epsilon, \alpha, \alpha^2, \alpha^3, \beta, \gamma, \delta, \sigma\}$ of permutations obtained in this way is closed under multiplication, as is easily verified by the multiplication table given below.

9.19

	ϵ	α	α^2	α^3	β	γ	δ	σ
ϵ	ϵ	α	α^2	α^3	β	γ	δ	σ
α	α	α^2	α^3	ϵ	σ	δ	β	γ
α^2	α^2	α^3	ϵ	α	γ	β	σ	δ
α^3	α^3	ϵ	α	α^2	δ	σ	γ	β
β	β	δ	γ	σ	ϵ	α^2	α	α^3
γ	γ	σ	β	δ	α^2	ϵ	α^3	α
δ	δ	γ	σ	β	α^3	α	ϵ	α^2
σ	σ	β	δ	γ	α	α^3	α^2	ϵ

Moreover, it is evident that each permutation of this set has an inverse in this set, and we therefore have a group of permutations. This particular group with eight elements is called the *octic group*. Since we obtained this group by a consideration of the rigid motions of a square, we may also say that it is the group of rigid motions of a square.

In a similar way we may construct the group of rigid motions of other geometric figures. We observe that by this process we must actually obtain a *group* of permutations. In the first place, a rigid motion followed by another rigid motion is itself a rigid motion, and hence the set we obtain must be closed under multiplication. Since, also, each rigid motion can be reversed by another rigid motion, the inverse of each permutation in the set will also be in the set. The fact that we obtain a group of permutations then follows from Theorem 9.4.

_____ **E X E R C I S E S**

1. In the following, α and β are the given permutations of the set $A = \{1, 2, 3, 4, 5\}$. Compute, in each case, $\alpha\beta$, $\beta\alpha$, α^2, and β^2.

    (a) $1\alpha = 2$, $2\alpha = 1$, $3\alpha = 3$, $4\alpha = 5$, $5\alpha = 4$;
          $1\beta = 1$, $2\beta = 4$, $3\beta = 2$, $4\beta = 3$, $5\beta = 5$.

    (b) $1\alpha = 4$, $2\alpha = 3$, $3\alpha = 5$, $4\alpha = 1$, $5\alpha = 2$;
          $1\beta = 2$, $2\beta = 3$, $3\beta = 1$, $4\beta = 4$, $5\beta = 5$.

(c) $1\alpha = 2,$ $2\alpha = 1,$ $3\alpha = 4,$ $4\alpha = 5,$ $5\alpha = 3;$
$1\beta = 2,$ $2\beta = 3,$ $3\beta = 4,$ $4\beta = 5,$ $5\beta = 1.$

(d) $\alpha = \begin{pmatrix} 1 & 2 & 3 & 4 & 5 \\ 5 & 4 & 3 & 1 & 2 \end{pmatrix},$ $\beta = \begin{pmatrix} 1 & 2 & 3 & 4 & 5 \\ 3 & 2 & 1 & 5 & 4 \end{pmatrix}.$

(e) $\alpha = \begin{pmatrix} 1 & 2 & 3 & 4 & 5 \\ 1 & 3 & 2 & 5 & 4 \end{pmatrix},$ $\beta = \begin{pmatrix} 1 & 2 & 3 & 4 & 5 \\ 2 & 3 & 1 & 4 & 5 \end{pmatrix}.$

(f) $\alpha = \begin{pmatrix} 1 & 2 & 3 & 4 & 5 \\ 5 & 4 & 3 & 2 & 1 \end{pmatrix},$ $\beta = \begin{pmatrix} 1 & 2 & 3 & 4 & 5 \\ 5 & 4 & 2 & 1 & 3 \end{pmatrix}.$

2. Verify the entry in the table 9.19 giving each of the following products: $\alpha^2\sigma,$ $\beta\gamma,$ $\gamma\beta,$ $\alpha^3\gamma,$ $\delta\sigma.$

3. Find all subgroups of the symmetric group S_3.

4. Find all subgroups of the octic group (9.19).

5. Show that the group of rigid motions of an equilateral triangle is the symmetric group S_3.

6. Find the group of rigid motions of a rectangle that is not a square. Make a multiplication table for this group and show that it is a subgroup of the octic group.

7. How many elements are there in the group of rigid motions of a regular pentagon? A regular hexagon?

9.4 CYCLIC GROUPS

In a later section we shall continue the study of permutation groups, but we now return to the general theory of groups. Inasmuch as we shall not assume that the groups are necessarily abelian, unless otherwise stated we shall consider the operation to be multiplication.

We begin with the following definition.

.20 Definition. If a group H contains an element a such that every element of H is of the form a^l for some integer l, we say that H is a *cyclic group* and that H is *generated by* a or that a is a *generator of H.*

If H is a cyclic group generated by a, then, since H is closed under multiplication, $a^k \in H$ for every positive integer k. Moreover, since the inverse of a^k is a^{-k}, we see that $a^{-k} \in H$ for every positive integer k. Finally, a^0 is the identity e of H by definition, and it therefore follows that $H = \{a^k; \, k \in I\}$. That is, the cyclic group generated by a consists of *all* elements of the form a^k, where k is an arbitrary integer. Of course, not all of these elements need be different.

Suppose, now, that a is an element of an arbitrary group G. It is easy to verify that the set $H = \{a^k; \ k \in I\}$ is a subgroup of G. We see, therefore, that each element of a group G generates a cyclic subgroup of G.

Since $a^i a^j = a^j a^i$ for arbitrary integers i and j, it is clear that a cyclic group is necessarily abelian.

Let us now give some examples of cyclic groups.

Example 1. The multiplicative group of the field $I/(5)$. Let us write the elements as 1, 2, 3, and 4; and remember that multiplication is to be carried out modulo 5. It is easily verified that $2^1 = 2$, $2^2 = 4$, $2^3 = 3$, $2^4 = 1$; hence each element of the group is of the form 2^l for some integer l. It follows that the group must be cyclic with generator 2. The reader may show that 3 is also a generator of this group.

Example 2. The additive group of the ring I of integers. In a ring with addition as the operation, la is the analogue of a^l used above. The integer 1 is a generator of this group since every element is of the form $l \cdot 1$ for some integer l.

Example 3. The additive group of the ring $I/(n)$ of integers modulo n. This group is generated by the element 1 of $I/(n)$. Of course, it may have other generators as well.

Example 4. The group of all complex numbers that are nth roots of unity, where n is a fixed positive integer, with multiplication as the operation. The fact that this group is cyclic is the content of Corollary 7.20, where it was shown that $w = \cos (360°/n) + i \sin (360°/n)$ is a generator.

Example 5. The subgroup $\{\alpha_1, \alpha_5, \alpha_6\}$ of the symmetric group S_3, whose multiplication table is given in 9.17. It is easily verified that $\alpha_5^2 = \alpha_6$ and $\alpha_5^3 = \alpha_1$; hence α_5 is a generator of this subgroup. As a matter of fact, α_6 is also a generator of this same subgroup.

We are now ready to give another definition as follows.

9.21 Definition. (i) If a group G has n elements, where n is a positive integer, G is said to have *finite order* or, more precisely, to have *order n*. If there exists no such positive integer, G is said to have *infinite order*.

(ii) The *order of an element* a of a group G is the order of the cyclic subgroup of G generated by a.

In the language here introduced, we may say that the additive group of the integers has infinite order, the symmetric group S_n has order $n!$, the additive group of the ring $I/(n)$ has order n, and the multiplicative group of the field $I/(p)$ has order $p - 1$. All of these, except the first, are groups of finite order.

The next theorem gives an important characterization of the order of an element of a group.

9.22   Theorem.   *An element a of a group G has order n if and only if n is the smallest positive integer such that $a^n = e$, where e is the identity of G. If no such integer exists, a has infinite order.*

As a first step in the proof, we shall prove the following lemma.

9.23   Lemma.   *Let a be an element of the group G, and suppose that $a^n = e$, with n the smallest such positive integer. If $k \in I$, then $a^k = e$ if and only if $k \equiv 0 \pmod{n}$. More generally, if $i, j \in I$, then $a^i = a^j$ if and only if $i \equiv j \pmod{n}$.*

By the Division Algorithm, we may write any integer k in the form $k = qn + r$, where q and r are integers and $0 \le r < n$. Then, since $a^n = e$, we have

$$a^k = a^{qn+r} = (a^n)^q \cdot a^r = e^q \cdot a^r = a^r.$$

If $a^k = e$, we see that $a^r = e$, and it follows that $r = 0$ since, otherwise, r would be a positive integer less than n and we have assumed that n is the smallest positive integer such that $a^n = e$. Hence, if $a^k = e$, we have $k = qn$ and $k \equiv 0 \pmod{n}$. Conversely, if $k = qn$, it is apparent that $a^k = (a^n)^q = e^q = e$. This establishes the first part of the lemma. The second part now follows easily. For if $a^i = a^j$, it follows that $a^{i-j} = e$, and by what we have just proved, this is true if and only if $i - j \equiv 0 \pmod{n}$ or $i \equiv j \pmod{n}$.

Let us return to the proof of the theorem, and suppose first that $a^n = e$, with n as the smallest such positive integer. We now assert that the elements

9.24 $e, \quad a, \quad a^2, \quad \cdots, \quad a^{n-1}$

are distinct and are all of the elements of the cyclic subgroup of G generated by a. Since no two of the integers $0, 1, 2, \cdots, n - 1$ are congruent modulo n, the preceding lemma shows that the elements 9.24 are distinct. Moreover, since every integer is congruent modulo n to some one of the integers $0, 1, 2, \cdots, n - 1$, it also follows that a^k is equal to one of the elements 9.24, for every integer k. Hence the cyclic subgroup of G generated by a has exactly the n distinct elements 9.24; that is, it has order n and therefore a has order n.

To prove the converse, let us now assume that a has order n. Then not all positive powers of a can be distinct; that is, we must have $a^i = a^j$ for different positive integers i and j. Suppose that $i > j$, and it then follows that $a^{i-j} = e$, with $i - j > 0$. Hence, there exists some positive power of a which is equal to e. Suppose that m is the smallest positive integer such that $a^m = e$. Now, by what we have proved above, a has order m. Since it was given that a has order n, we must have $m = n$. This completes the proof of the first sentence of the theorem.

If there exists no positive integer n such that $a^n = e$, it is easy to show that $a, a^2, a^3, \cdots$ must all be distinct (why?). Hence a must have infinite order, and the theorem is established.

Theorem 9.22 makes it easy to determine the order of an element of a given group. For example, let us find the order of the element 3 of the multiplicative group of $I/(11)$. By computing the successive powers of 3, we find that $3^2 = 9$, $3^3 = 5$, $3^4 = 4$, $3^5 = 1$. Hence, the element 3 has order five. As another example, let us find the order of the element 10 of the additive group of $I/(18)$. By Theorem 9.22, with the proper change of notation, this order will be the least positive integer n such that $n \cdot 10 \equiv 0 \pmod{18}$. It follows easily that $n = 9$, and the element 10 therefore has order 9.

It is not difficult to prove that two cyclic groups are isomorphic if and only if they have the same order. This fact will follow immediately from the following theorem.

9.25 Theorem. (i) *Every cyclic group of infinite order is isomorphic to the additive group of the ring I of integers.*

(ii) *Every cyclic group of order n is isomorphic to the additive group of the ring $I/(n)$ of integers modulo n.*

First, let G be an infinite cyclic group with generator a. Then the mapping

9·26 $$ k \to a^k, \qquad\qquad k \in I, $$

is a mapping of I onto G. Moreover, the mapping is one-one, as we can see as follows. If $a^i = a^j$ with $i > j$, then $a^{i-j} = e$ and Theorem 9.22 would show that a has finite order, whereas we are given that it has infinite order. Hence, if $i, j \in I$ with $i \neq j$, we must have $a^i \neq a^j$, and this proves that 9.26 is a one-one mapping. It is then almost immediate that the mapping is an isomorphism, for we have

$$ i + j \to a^{i+j} = a^i \cdot a^j. $$

Since $i \to a^i$ and $j \to a^j$, we see that sums of elements of I map into the product of the corresponding images in G. Hence, the mapping 9.26 is an isomorphism of the additive group of I onto G.

Next, let G be a cyclic group of order n with generator a. In order to keep the notation straight, we shall now denote the elements of $I/(n)$ by $[k]$, $k \in I$, and we shall show that the mapping

9.27 $$ [k] \to a^k, \qquad\qquad k \in I, $$

is an isomorphism of the additive group of $I/(n)$ onto G. First, we must show that the mapping is well-defined. In other words, we must show that if $i, j \in I$, then $[i] = [j]$ if and only if $a^i = a^j$. However, this follows easily since $[i] = [j]$ if and only if $i \equiv j \pmod{n}$ and, by Theorem 9.22 and Lemma 9.23, we know that $a^i = a^j$ if and only if $i \equiv j \pmod{n}$. Hence, 9.27 actually defines a mapping of the additive group of $I/(n)$ onto G. Moreover, we observe that the mapping is a one-one mapping since we have just pointed out that $[i] \neq [j]$ implies that $a^i \neq a^j$. Now, using the definition of a sum of elements of $I/(n)$ and applying the mapping 9.27, we see that

$$[i] + [j] = [i + j] \to a^{i+j} = a^i \cdot a^j.$$

Since $[i] \to a^i$ and $[j] \to a^j$, we see that sums map into the corresponding products, that is, we have an isomorphism of the additive group of $I/(n)$ onto G. The proof of the theorem is therefore complete.

In Example 1 above, we verified that the multiplicative group of $I/(5)$ is cyclic with generator 2 (or 3), and clearly its order is 4. According to the theorem just proved, it must therefore be isomorphic to the additive group of $I/(4)$. In order to distinguish between them, let us designate the elements of $I/(4)$ by $[0], [1], [2], [3]$; and the nonzero elements of $I/(5)$ by $1, 2, 3, 4$. Using the generator 2 of the latter group, the isomorphism 9.27 is defined by $[k] \to 2^k$, $k \in I$. Written out in detail, this mapping is as follows:

$$[1] \to 2, \quad [2] \to 4, \quad [3] \to 3, \quad [0] \to 1.$$

We can obtain a different isomorphism by using the generator 3 of the multiplicative group of $I/(5)$. This mapping $[k] \to 3^k$ yields the following explicit isomorphism:

$$[1] \to 3, \quad [2] \to 4, \quad [3] \to 2, \quad [0] \to 1.$$

We have thus exhibited two different isomorphisms of these two groups.
Our final theorem about cyclic groups is the following.

9.28 Theorem. *Every subgroup H of a cyclic group G is itself a cyclic group.*

Suppose that G is generated by a, and let H be a subgroup of G. Let m be the smallest positive integer such that $a^m \in H$. We shall show that H is a cyclic group generated by a^m. Since $H \subseteq G$, any element of H is of the form a^k for some integer k. By the Division Algorithm, we may write $k = qm + r$, where $0 \le r < m$. Hence,

$$a^k = a^{qm+r} = (a^m)^q \cdot a^r,$$

and from this it follows that

$$a^r = (a^m)^{-q} \cdot a^k.$$

Since $a^m \in H$ and $a^k \in H$, this equation implies also that $a^r \in H$. In view of the choice of m as the smallest positive integer such that $a^m \in H$, and since $r < m$, we must have $r = 0$. We conclude that $k = qm$, and hence that every element a^k of H is of the form $(a^m)^q$ for some integer q. This shows that H is a cyclic group generated by a^m.

As an almost immediate consequence of the proof of the preceding theorem, we obtain the following result.

9.29 Corollary. *If a cyclic group G has finite order n and is generated by a, every subgroup H of G is generated by an element of the form a^m, where m is a divisor of n.*

Since Theorem 9.22 shows that $a^n = e$, and $e \in H$, we apply the above argument with $k = n$ and obtain $n = qm$. Hence, m is a divisor of n.

Of course, by a simple change in notation, these results apply equally well to the case in which the operation is addition. As an illustration of the preceding corollary, let us find all subgroups of the additive group of the ring $I/(14)$. This is a cyclic group of order 14 generated by the element 1; hence the only subgroups are the cyclic subgroups generated by 1, 2, 7, and 14. The subgroup generated by 14 consists only of the identity 0. The subgroup generated by 2 has order 7 and the subgroup generated by 7 has order 2.

———————————————————— **E X E R C I S E S**

1. Find the order of each element of the octic group (9.19).

2. Find an element of the symmetric group S_4 of order 4. Similarly, find an element of S_5 of order 5; of S_n of order n.

3. It can be proved that for every prime p, the multiplicative group of the field $I/(p)$ is cyclic. Verify this fact for $p = 7, 11$, and 13.

4. Find all subgroups of the additive group of $I/(8)$ and of $I/(12)$.

5. Show that if an abelian group of order 6 contains an element of order 3, G must be a cyclic group.

6. If G is a cyclic group of order n with generator a, show that a^k is also a generator of G if and only if k and n are relatively prime.

7. Show that in any isomorphism of a cyclic group G onto a cyclic group H each generator of G must map into a generator of H.

8. Let G and H be cyclic groups of the same order, and let g be an arbitrary generator of G and h an arbitrary generator of H. Show that there exists an isomorphism of G onto H in which g maps into h.

9. Describe all isomorphisms of the multiplicative group of the field $I/(11)$ onto the additive group of the ring $I/(10)$.

10. Prove that if in an abelian group the element a has order k and the element b has order l, and if k and l are relatively prime, then the element ab has order kl. [Hint: If $(ab)^t = e$, then $a^t = b^{-t}$. Raise both sides to the power k and conclude that t must be divisible by k. Similarly, show that t must be divisible by l.]

9.5 COSETS AND LAGRANGE'S THEOREM

Let G be an arbitrary group, and H a subgroup of G. If $a \in G$, we shall designate by aH the *set* of all elements of G of the form ah, where $h \in H$. That is, $aH = \{ah; \ h \in H\}$.

.30 Definition. If H is a subgroup of the group G and $a \in G$, we call aH a *coset* of H (in G).*

Since $eH = H$, we see that H is itself a coset. Moreover, since $e \in H$, it is clear that $a \in aH$.

An important property of cosets is the following. *If the cosets aH and bH have an element in common; that is, if $aH \cap bH$ is not the empty set, then $aH = bH$.* The proof is as follows. Suppose that $ah_1 = bh_2$, with h_1, $h_2 \in H$. Then $a = bh_2h_1^{-1}$ and any element ah of aH can be expressed in the form $bh_2h_1^{-1}h$. Since $h_2h_1^{-1}h \in H$, it follows that $ah \in bH$. We have therefore shown that $aH \subseteq bH$. In a similar way we can show that $bH \subseteq aH$, and therefore we conclude that $aH = bH$. One way of stating the property we have just proved is to say that two cosets either coincide or have no element in common.

As an example of cosets, consider the symmetric group S_3 with multiplication table 9.17. We know that α_1 is the identity of this group, and it is easy to verify that $K = \{\alpha_1, \alpha_2\}$ is a subgroup. By use of the table, we find the following cosets of K in S_3:

$$\alpha_1 K = \{\alpha_1, \alpha_2\}, \qquad \alpha_4 K = \{\alpha_4, \alpha_5\},$$
$$\alpha_2 K = \{\alpha_2, \alpha_1\}, \qquad \alpha_5 K = \{\alpha_5, \alpha_4\},$$
$$\alpha_3 K = \{\alpha_3, \alpha_6\}, \qquad \alpha_6 K = \{\alpha_6, \alpha_3\}.$$

We see, therefore, that there are three different cosets of K in S_3, that every coset contains two elements, and that every element of S_3 is in exactly one of these three cosets. These observations suggest the method of proof of the following theorem.

*Strictly speaking, this should be called a *left* coset, and one could similarly define a right coset Ha.

9.31 Theorem (Lagrange). *If the group G has order n, the order of every subgroup H of G is a divisor of n.*

Since G has finite order, there are only a finite number, say k, of different cosets of H in G. We know that no two different cosets have an element in common. Moreover, since $a \in aH$, we know that every element of G is in some one, and therefore in exactly one, of these different cosets. Suppose, now, that H has order m. Then we assert that every coset aH has exactly m elements. For if h_1, $h_2 \in H$, $ah_1 = ah_2$ if and only if $h_1 = h_2$; hence aH has the same number of elements as H. Accordingly, the elements of G are distributed into k cosets with m elements in each coset. Since no two cosets have an element in common, G must have exactly km elements. This shows that $n = km$, and the theorem is established.

There are some interesting consequences of this theorem, which we proceed to state. Since the order of an element of a group is the order of the cyclic subgroup generated by that element, we have at once the following corollary.

9.32 Corollary. *The order of an element of a group of finite order is a divisor of the order of the group.*

If the order of a group is a prime p, then every element of the group, other than the identity, must have order p. This yields the next result as follows.

9.33 Corollary. *A group of order p, where p is a prime, is a cyclic group. Moreover, every element except the identity is a generator of the group.*

If the group G has order n, and the element a of G has order m, then, by Corollary 9.32, we have $n = mk$ for some integer k. By Theorem 9.22, we know that $a^m = e$, and hence $a^n = (a^m)^k = e^k = e$. We have established the following corollary.

9.34 Corollary. *If a is an element of a group of order n, then $a^n = e$.*

If we apply this result to the special case of the multiplicative group of $I/(p)$, where p is a prime, we obtain the following theorem of Fermat.

9.35 Corollary. *If s is an integer not divisible by the prime p, then $s^{p-1} \equiv 1 \pmod{p}$.*

————————————————————————— **E X E R C I S E S**

1. Exhibit all cosets of the subgroup $\{\epsilon, \alpha, \alpha^2, \alpha^3\}$ of the octic group (9.19).

2. Exhibit all cosets of the subgroup $\{0, 3, 6, 9\}$ of the additive group of $I/(12)$.

3. Let H be a subgroup of a group G. If $a, b \in G$, let $a \sim b$ mean that $b^{-1}a \in H$. Show that "$\sim$" is an equivalence relation defined on G. If $[a]$ is the equivalence set which contains a, show that $[a] = aH$ and therefore the cosets of H in G are the equivalence sets relative to this equivalence relation.

4. If H is a subgroup of G, define $Ha = \{ha; \ h \in H\}$. If $aH = Ha$ for every element a of G, H is said to be an *invariant* subgroup of G. Now let H be an invariant subgroup of G. Using the notation of the preceding exercise, define multiplication of equivalence sets as follows:

$$[a] \cdot [b] = [ab].$$

Show that multiplication of equivalence sets is well-defined and that with respect to this definition of multiplication the set of all equivalence sets is a group.

9.6 THE SYMMETRIC GROUP S_n

We now return to a further study of permutations of a finite set $A = \{1, 2, \cdots, n\}$. We have already defined the symmetric group S_n to be the group of all permutations of A. Throughout this section the word *permutation* will mean an element of S_n for some positive integer n, and we shall sometimes find it convenient to refer to the elements of A as "symbols."

We shall first study permutations of the particular type described in the following definition.

36 Definition. An element α of S_n is said to be a *cycle of length* k if there exist distinct elements $a_1, a_2, \cdots, a_k$ ($k \geq 1$) of A such that

$$a_1\alpha = a_2, \quad a_2\alpha = a_3, \quad \cdots, \quad a_{k-1}\alpha = a_k, \quad a_k\alpha = a_1,$$

and $i\alpha = i$ for each element i of A other than $a_1, a_2, \cdots, a_k$. This cycle α may be designated by $(a_1 a_2 \cdots a_k)$.

It will be observed that a cycle of length one is necessarily the identity permutation. It sometimes simplifies statements to consider the identity permutation as a cycle, but we shall usually be interested in cycles of length greater than one.

As an example of a cycle, suppose that β is the element of S_6 defined by

$$1\beta = 3, \quad 3\beta = 2, \quad 2\beta = 5, \quad 5\beta = 6, \quad 6\beta = 1, \quad 4\beta = 4.$$

Then β is a cycle of length 5, and we may write $\beta = (13256)$. In a cycle, such as (13256) the symbols appearing are permuted cyclically; that is, each symbol written down maps into the next one, except that the last maps into the first. A symbol, such as 4 in this example, which is not written down is assumed to map into itself. There are other ways of writing the cycle β defined above. For example, $\beta = (32561) = (25613)$, and so on. Also, in another notation introduced in Section 9.3, we have

$$\beta = \begin{pmatrix} 1 & 2 & 3 & 4 & 5 & 6 \\ 3 & 5 & 2 & 4 & 6 & 1 \end{pmatrix}.$$

As further illustrations of all the various notations used, let us consider elements of S_6 and verify that

$$(1345)(146) = \begin{pmatrix} 1 & 2 & 3 & 4 & 5 & 6 \\ 3 & 2 & 6 & 5 & 4 & 1 \end{pmatrix}.$$

In the first factor 1 maps into 3, and in the second factor 3 is unchanged; hence in the product, 1 maps into 3. The symbol 2 does not appear in either factor, hence 2 maps into 2. In the left factor 3 maps into 4, and then in the second factor 4 maps into 6; hence in the product 3 maps into 6. Similarly, the other verifications are easily made.

Now let α be the cycle $(a_1 a_2 \cdots a_k)$ of S_n of length k, and let us consider the powers of α. Under the mapping α^2, we see that a_1 maps into a_3 (if $k \geq 3$), for

$$a_1 \alpha^2 = (a_1 \alpha)\alpha = a_2 \alpha = a_3.$$

Similarly, under the mapping α^3, a_1 maps into a_4 (if $k \geq 4$), and so on. Continuing, we find that $a_1 \alpha^k = a_1$. Since we could just as well write $\alpha = (a_2 a_3 \cdots a_k a_1)$, a similar argument shows that $a_2 \alpha^k = a_2$ and, in general, that $a_i \alpha^k = a_i$ for $i = 1, 2, \cdots, k$. It follows that $\alpha^k = \epsilon$, the identity permutation, and, moreover, k is the smallest power of α which is equal to ϵ. The following result then follows immediately from Theorem 9.22.

9.37 Theorem. *A cycle of length k has order k.*

Two cycles $(a_1 a_2 \cdots a_k)$ and $(b_1 b_2 \cdots b_l)$ of S_n are said to be *disjoint* if the sets $\{a_1, a_2, \cdots, a_k\}$ and $\{b_1, b_2, \cdots, b_l\}$ have no elements in common. More than two cycles are said to be disjoint if each pair of them is disjoint. The next result shows why cycles play an important role in the study of permutations.

9.38 Theorem. *Every element γ of S_n that is not itself a cycle is expressible as a product of disjoint cycles.*

Before considering the proof, let us look at an example. Suppose that

$$\gamma = \begin{pmatrix} 1 & 2 & 3 & 4 & 5 & 6 \\ 3 & 1 & 4 & 2 & 6 & 5 \end{pmatrix},$$

and let us start with any symbol which does not map into itself, for example, the symbol 1. We see that $1\gamma = 3, 3\gamma = 4, 4\gamma = 2,$ and $2\gamma = 1.$ Now take any symbol which has not yet been used and which does not map into itself, for example 5. Then $5\gamma = 6,$ and $6\gamma = 5.$ It is then almost obvious that $\gamma = (1342)(56).$

The proof in the general case follows the same pattern as in this example. Start with any symbol a_1 such that $a_1\gamma \neq a_1,$ and suppose that $a_1\gamma = a_2, a_2\gamma = a_3, a_3\gamma = a_4,$ and so on until we come to the point where, say, $a_k\gamma$ equals some one of the symbols $a_1, a_2, \cdots, a_{k-1}$ already used. Then we must have $a_k\gamma = a_1$ since every other one of these symbols is already known to be the image of some symbol under the mapping $\gamma.$ Thus γ has the same effect on the symbols $a_1, a_2, \cdots, a_k$ as the cycle $(a_1 a_2 \cdots a_k),$ and also effects a permutation of the remaining symbols (if any). If b_1 is a symbol other than $a_1, a_2, \cdots, a_k$ and $b_1\gamma \neq b_1,$ we proceed as above and obtain a cycle $(b_1 b_2 \cdots b_l).$ Now if all symbols that do not map into themselves have been used, we have

$$\gamma = (a_1 a_2 \cdots a_k)(b_1 b_2 \cdots b_l).$$

If there is another symbol c_1 such that $c_1\gamma \neq c_1,$ we can similarly obtain another cycle. Evidently, the process can be continued to obtain the desired result. A complete proof can easily be given by induction.

_____ **E X E R C I S E S**

1. In each of the following, γ is an element of $S_7.$ Express it as a product of disjoint cycles.

   (a) $1\gamma = 3, 2\gamma = 4, 3\gamma = 1, 4\gamma = 7, 5\gamma = 5, 6\gamma = 6, 7\gamma = 2.$
   (b) $1\gamma = 5, 2\gamma = 3, 3\gamma = 4, 4\gamma = 7, 5\gamma = 6, 6\gamma = 1, 7\gamma = 2.$
   (c) $\gamma = \begin{pmatrix} 1 & 2 & 3 & 4 & 5 & 6 & 7 \\ 3 & 4 & 1 & 2 & 6 & 7 & 5 \end{pmatrix}.$
   (d) $\gamma = \begin{pmatrix} 1 & 2 & 3 & 4 & 5 & 6 & 7 \\ 2 & 3 & 1 & 5 & 4 & 7 & 6 \end{pmatrix}.$

2. Express each of the following elements of S_7 as a product of disjoint cycles:

   (a) $(123)(16543),$
   (b) $(213456)(172),$
   (c) $(4215)(3426)(5671),$
   (d) $(1234)(124)(3127)(56).$

The cycles of length 2 are of special interest, and we make the following definition.

9.39 Definition. A cycle of length 2 is called a *transposition*.

A transposition (ij) merely interchanges the symbols i and j, and leaves the other symbols unchanged. Since $(ij)(ij) = \epsilon$, it follows that a transposition is its own inverse.

It is quite easy to show that every cycle of length more than 2 can be expressed as a product of transpositions. In fact, this result follows from the observation that

$$(a_1 a_2 \cdots a_k) = (a_1 a_k)(a_2 a_k) \cdots (a_{k-1} a_k),$$

which can be verified by direct calculation. In view of Theorem 9.38, it follows immediately that *every* permutation can be expressed as a product of transpositions. However, it is easy to verify that there is more than one way to express a permutation as such a product. As examples, we see that

$$(1234) = (14)(24)(34) = (32)(12)(14) = (13)(24)(34)(12)(24),$$
$$(123)(14) = (12)(13)(14) = (14)(24)(34) = (14)(24)(34)(23)(23),$$

and so on. Since $(ij)(ij) = \epsilon$, we can insert as many such pairs of identical transpositions as we wish. Clearly, then, a permutation can be expressed as a product of transpositions in many different ways.

The following theorem, of which the first statement has already been proved, is one of the principal theorems about permutations.

9.40 Theorem. *Every permutation α can be expressed as a product of transpositions. Moreover, if α can be expressed as a product of r transpositions and also as a product of s transpositions, then either r and s are both even or they are both odd.*

Suppose that α is a permutation of the set $A = \{1, 2, \cdots, n\}$. Suppose, further, that

9.41 $$\alpha = \beta_1 \beta_2 \cdots \beta_r = \gamma_1 \gamma_2 \cdots \gamma_s,$$

where each β and each γ is a transposition. In order to show that r and s are both even, or that they are both odd, we proceed as follows. Let $x_1, x_2, \cdots, x_n$ be indeterminates and let P denote the polynomial with integral coefficients defined as follows:

9.42 $$P = \prod_{i < j} (x_i - x_j),$$

it being understood that this stands for the product of all polynomials of the form $x_i - x_j$, where i and j take values from 1 to n, with $i < j$. We now define

43
$$P\alpha = \prod_{i<j} (x_{i\alpha} - x_{j\alpha}),$$

that is, $P\alpha$ is the polynomial obtained by performing the permutation α on the subscripts of the indeterminates.

As an illustration of this notation, if $n = 4$, we have

$$P = (x_1 - x_2)(x_1 - x_3)(x_1 - x_4)(x_2 - x_3)(x_2 - x_4)(x_3 - x_4).$$

Moreover, if

$$\alpha = \begin{pmatrix} 1 & 2 & 3 & 4 \\ 4 & 1 & 2 & 3 \end{pmatrix},$$

we find that

$$P\alpha = (x_4 - x_1)(x_4 - x_2)(x_4 - x_3)(x_1 - x_2)(x_1 - x_3)(x_2 - x_3),$$

and it is easily verified that $P\alpha = -P$. In general, it is fairly clear that always $P\alpha = \pm P$, with the sign depending in some way on the permutation α. We next prove the following lemma.

44 Lemma, *If $\delta = (kl)$ is a transposition, then $P\delta = -P$.*

Now $k \neq l$, and there is no loss of generality in assuming that $k < l$. Hence, one of the factors in P is $x_k - x_l$ and in $P\delta$ the corresponding factor is $x_l - x_k$; that is, this factor is just changed in sign under the mapping δ on the subscripts. Any factor of P of the form $x_i - x_j$, where neither i nor j is equal to k or l, is clearly unchanged under the mapping δ. All other factors of P can be paired to form products of the form $\pm (x_i - x_k)(x_i - x_l)$, with the sign determined by the relative magnitudes of i, k, and l. But since the effect of δ is just to interchange x_k and x_l, any such product is unchanged. Hence, the only effect of δ is to change the sign of P, and the lemma is established.

The proof of the theorem now follows easily. Since, by 9.41, $P\alpha$ can be computed by performing in turn the r transpositions $\beta_1, \beta_2, \cdots \beta_r$, and by the lemma each of these merely changes the sign of P, it follows that $P\alpha = (-1)^r P$. In like manner, using the fact that $\alpha = \gamma_1 \gamma_2 \cdots \gamma_s$, we see that also $P\alpha = (-1)^s P$. Hence, we must have $(-1)^r P = (-1)^s P$ from which it follows that $(-1)^r = (-1)^s$. This implies that r and s are both even or they are both odd, and the proof is completed.

45 Definition. A permutation is called an *even* permutation or an *odd* permutation according as it can be expressed as a product of an even or an odd number of transpositions.

If the permutation α can be expressed as a product of k transpositions, and the permutation β can be expressed as a product of l transpositions, it is obvious that $\alpha\beta$ can be expressed as a product of $k + l$ transpositions. It follows that the product of two even, or of two odd, permutations is an even permutation, whereas the product of an odd permutation and an even permutation is an odd permutation.

Another observation of some importance is the following. Suppose that α is a product of k transpositions, say $\alpha = \alpha_1\alpha_2 \cdots \alpha_k$. Then, since a transposition is its own inverse, it is easy to see that $\alpha^{-1} = \alpha_k\alpha_{k-1} \cdots \alpha_1$. It follows that α^{-1} is an even permutation if and only if α is an even permutation. We shall conclude our study of permutation groups by proving the following theorem.

9.46 Theorem. *The set A_n of all even permutations of the symmetric group S_n is a subgroup of S_n of order $n!/2$.*

The fact that A_n is a subgroup of S_n follows at once from the preceding remarks and Theorem 9.4. This subgroup A_n of S_n is usually called the *alternating group* on n symbols.

Let us now consider the order of A_n. If β is a fixed odd permutation, all the elements of the coset βA_n are odd permutations since the product of an odd permutation by an even permutation is necessarily an odd permutation. We proceed to show that *all* odd permutations of S_n are in the coset βA_n. If γ is an arbitrary odd permutation, we may write $\gamma = \beta(\beta^{-1}\gamma)$, and $\beta^{-1}\gamma$ is an even permutation since β^{-1} and γ are both odd. It follows that $\beta^{-1}\gamma \in A_n$ and hence that $\gamma \in \beta A_n$. We have shown that the coset βA_n consists of all the odd permutations, and hence that there are just the two cosets A_n and βA_n of A_n in S_n. Since these cosets have the same number of elements and S_n has order $n!$, it follows that the alternating group A_n has order $n!/2$.

_____ *E X E R C I S E S*

1. Verify that a cycle of length k is an even or an odd permutation according as k is odd or even, respectively.

2. Prove that every even permutation is a cycle of length three or can be expressed as a product of cycles of length three. [Hint: $(12)(13) = (123)$, and $(12)(34) = (134)(321)$.]

3. Let G be a subgroup of the symmetric group S_n, which contains at least one odd permutation. Prove that the set of all even permutations in G is a subgroup of G, and then prove that G contains the same number of odd permutations as of even permutations.

10

Vector Spaces

In this chapter we shall introduce and study a new class of algebraic systems called *vector spaces*. The concept of a vector, used here to indicate an element of a vector space, is a generalization and abstraction of the concept of vector as the term is used in physics. We begin with a short discussion of vectors in the latter sense, as a partial motivation of the material to follow. We then proceed to give the abstract definition of a vector space and to establish some of the most important properties of such systems.

10.1 VECTORS IN A PLANE

Physical entities such as displacements, forces, and velocities have both magnitude and direction, and are usually called *vectors*. Geometrically, a vector may be represented by a directed line segment, the length of the segment indicating the magnitude of the vector and the direction of the segment specifying the direction of the vector. We shall here consider vectors in a given coordinate plane and, moreover, shall represent the vectors by directed segments emanating from the origin of coordinates. A vector X, as shown in Figure 11, is then completely determined by the coordinates (r, s) of its terminal point. Accordingly, we may just as well call (r, s) the vector; that is, we may identify the

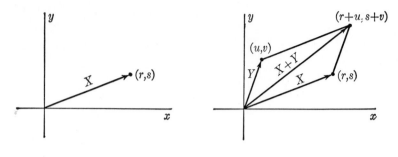

Figure 11   Figure 12

vector X with the ordered pair of real numbers that specifies its terminal point, and write $X = (r, s)$.

If X and Y are vectors in the same plane, the so-called parallelogram law states that the *sum* (or resultant) $X + Y$ of these vectors is the vector determined by the diagonal of the parallelogram two of whose adjacent sides are the line segments representing the vectors X and Y, respectively (Figure 12). If $X = (r, s)$ and $Y = (u, v)$, it is not difficult to show that

10.1
$$X + Y = (r + u, s + v).$$

From our point of view, we propose to take 10.1 as the *definition* of the sum of two vectors. Let us now denote by "V_2" the set of all vectors (x, y), where x and y are real numbers. Then, using 10.1 as the definition of addition, we have an operation of addition defined on V_2, and it is easy to verify that V_2 is an abelian group with respect to this operation. The identity $(0, 0)$ of this group we may call the *zero vector*.

When using vectors in physical problems it is customary to consider, for example, that $2X$ is a vector having twice the magnitude of X and the same direction as X. The vector $(-2)X$ is considered to be the vector having twice the magnitude of X and the opposite direction to X. In general, if a is a real number, aX has magnitude $|a|$ times the magnitude of X and has the same or opposite direction to X according as $a > 0$ or $a < 0$. If $X = (r, s)$, simple geometric considerations show that if a is any real number,

10.2
$$aX = a(r, s) = (ar, as).$$

Now real numbers are often called *scalars* to distinguish them from vectors, so 10.2 gives us a multiplication of vectors by scalars. Again, although this scalar multiplication was suggested by a procedure used in physics, we propose to take 10.2 as the *definition* of scalar multiplication.

The set V_2 with addition defined by 10.1 and scalar multiplication defined by 10.2 is an example of a vector space according to the definition to be given presently. Actually, since the scalars are real numbers, it is customary to call V_2 a vector space *over the field K* of real numbers and to recognize this fact by the more explicit notation $V_2(K)$, instead of V_2 as used so far.

It is apparent that the above procedure could be generalized in various ways. For example, a consideration of vectors in space instead of in a plane would lead to vectors designated by ordered triples of real numbers, and the set of all such vectors with analogous definitions of addition and scalar multiplication would be a vector space which we might denote by "$V_3(K)$". From a purely algebraic point of view, there is no reason why we might not go on and consider vectors to be ordered n-tuples of real numbers, and likewise the field K might be replaced by any other field. Actually, we shall not be so much concerned with the nature of the vectors themselves as with certain formal properties involving addition and scalar multiplication of vectors. Of course, the particular properties which are of primary interest are those which will be exhibited in the definition of a vector space we now proceed to give.

10.2 DEFINITION AND SIMPLE PROPERTIES OF A VECTOR SPACE

The following definition will assign a precise meaning to some of the terms which have been used in the preceding section.

.3 Definition. Let F be a field, and V a nonempty set on which there is defined an operation of addition. The elements of F and of V may be called *scalars* and *vectors*, respectively. We assume that there is also defined on V a scalar multiplication by elements of F; that is, if $a \in F$ and $X \in V$, then aX is a uniquely determined element of V. The set V is then called a *vector space over the field F* if the following conditions are satisfied:

(i) V is an abelian group with respect to addition,

(ii) $a(X + Y) = aX + aY$, $\qquad\qquad a \in F;\ X, Y \in V,$

(iii) $(a + b)X = aX + bX$, $\qquad\qquad a, b \in F;\ X \in V,$

(iv) $a(bX) = (ab)X$, $\qquad\qquad\qquad a, b \in F;\ X \in V,$

(v) $1X = X$, $\qquad\qquad\qquad\qquad\quad$ 1 the unity of F.

When it is desirable to exhibit explicitly the particular field F over which V is a vector space, we shall find it convenient to designate the vector space by "$V(F)$". However, we shall omit the "F" when the context makes it clear what field is being considered.

Let us now clarify the preceding definition by several examples.

Example 1. Let F be an arbitrary field, n a positive integer, and let $V_n(F)$ be the set of all ordered n-tuples of elements of F. That is, the elements of $V_n(F)$ are of the form $(a_1, a_2, \cdots, a_n)$, where $a_i \in F$ $(i = 1, 2, \cdots, n)$. In $V_n(F)$ we define addition as follows:

10.4 $(a_1, a_2, \cdots, a_n) + (b_1, b_2, \cdots, b_n) = (a_1 + b_1, a_2 + b_2, \cdots, a_n + b_n)$.

Moreover, if $c \in F$, we define scalar multiplication in the following way:

10.5 $$c(a_1, a_2, \cdots, a_n) = (ca_1, ca_2, \cdots, ca_n).$$

It is then easy to verify that all properties of a vector space are satisfied, and hence that $V_n(F)$ is a vector space over the field F. Vector spaces of this type are of great importance and will be referred to often in the future. We shall consistently use the notation "$V_n(F)$" to designate this vector space.

It is obvious that 10.4 and 10.5 are generalizations of 10.1 and 10.2, so that the use of "$V_2(K)$" to designate the vector space discussed in the preceding section is consistent with the more general notation introduced in this example.

Example 2. We now modify the preceding example by using *infinite* sequences of elements of F. Let $W(F)$ be the set of all infinite sequences of elements of F; that is, all expressions of the form

$$(a_1, a_2, a_3, \cdots), \qquad\qquad a_i \in F \ (i = 1, 2, 3, \cdots).$$

In $W(F)$ we define addition and scalar multiplication as follows:

$$(a_1, a_2, a_3, \cdots) + (b_1, b_2, b_3, \cdots) = (a_1 + b_1, a_2 + b_2, a_3 + b_3, \cdots),$$

and

$$c(a_1, a_2, a_3, \cdots) = (ca_1, ca_2, ca_3, \cdots).$$

Then $W(F)$ is a vector space over F.

If, instead of using *all* infinite sequences of elements of F, we use just those infinite sequences in which at most a finite number of elements of F are different from zero, we again obtain a vector space. (*Cf.* Exercise 8 at the end of this section.)

Example 3. Let H be a given field and F a subfield of H. We can consider H to be a vector space over the field F if we use as addition the addition already defined in the field H, and define scalar multiplication in the following obvious way. If $a \in F$ and $c \in H$, let ac be the product of these elements as already defined in the field H. The vector space that we obtain in this way might be designated by "$H(F)$." In this special case, Property (i) of Definition 10.3 is satisfied since we are using the additive group of the field H. Properties (ii) and (iii) follow from the distributive laws in H, and Property (iv) is just the associative law in H.

Example 4. Let $P(F)$ be the set of polynomials in an indeterminate x over a field F. We use the usual addition of polynomials, and scalar multiplication is defined in the following way. If $a \in F$ and $f(x) \in P(F)$, then $af(x)$ is the polynomial obtained from $f(x)$ by multiplying all its coefficients by a. Of course, this coincides with the product of two polynomials, as defined previously, where one of the polynomials is just a. It is easily verified that $P(F)$ is then a vector space over the field F.

Examples 3 and 4 have a common generalization as follows. Let R be a ring which contains a field F as a subring, with R and F having the same unity. Then R is a vector space over F, using addition as already defined in R and scalar multiplication as ring multiplication of elements of R by elements of F. The vector space of Example 3 is obtained by specializing the ring R to be a field, and the vector space of Example 4 by taking R to be the ring $F[x]$ of polynomials in x over F.

Example 5. Let Q be the set of all polynomials in an indeterminate x over a field F that have degree at most three, together with the zero polynomial. Then Q is a vector space over F if we define addition and scalar multiplication as in the preceding example. We may point out, however, that Q is not a ring since it is not closed under multiplication of polynomials.

Now that we have given the definition of a vector space and exhibited some examples, let us prove a few simple properties of vector spaces in general. If X is an element of a vector space V, we shall use the familiar notations of abelian groups with respect to the operation of addition. In particular, we shall denote the additive inverse of X by $-X$. The identity of the abelian group V we shall call the *zero vector* and, for the moment, we shall designate it by "O" to distinguish it from the zero "0" of the field F. The most fundamental properties of vector spaces are stated in the following theorem.

0.6 Theorem. *Let V be a vector space over the field F, and let O be the zero vector of V. The following are then true:*

(i) *If $a \in F$, then $aO = O$,*
(ii) *If $X \in V$, then $0X = O$,*
(iii) *If $a \in F$ and $X \in V$, then $a(-X) = (-a)X = -(aX)$,*
(iv) *If $aX = O$, then $a = 0$ or $X = O$.*

We shall prove (i) and (iii), and leave the proofs of the others as as exercises.

To prove (i), let $a \in F$ and $X \in V$. Then

$$aX = a(X + O) = aX + aO,$$

by Definition 10.3 (ii). This shows that aO is the zero vector; that is, that $aO = O$.

One part of (iii) is a consequence of the following calculation:

$$O = aO = a(X - X) = aX + a(- X).$$

It follows that $a(- X)$ is the additive inverse of aX, and hence that $a(- X) = - (aX)$. In this calculation we have tacitly used 10.3 (ii) and 10.6 (i). To get the other part of (iii) we use the following calculation in which we assume the truth of 10.6 (ii) although the proof has not been written out, and also make use of 10.3 (iii):

$$O = 0X = (a - a)X = aX + (- a)X.$$

Hence, $(- a)X = - (aX)$, as we wished to show.

Up to this point we have used different symbols to designate the zero vector and the zero element of the field F. However, in the future we shall not find it necessary to distinguish between these zeros since the context will always make it clear which one is intended. Accordingly, we shall henceforth use the familiar symbol "0" to designate either the zero vector or the zero scalar.

If V is a vector space over a field F, a nonempty subset U of V is naturally called a *subspace* of V if U is itself a vector space over F with respect to the addition and scalar multiplication already defined in V. The following theorem is helpful in identifying subspaces of a given vector space.

10.7 Theorem. *A nonempty subset U of a vector space V over a field F is a subspace of V if and only if U is closed under addition and scalar multiplication.*

If U is a subspace of V, it is trivial that U must be closed under addition and scalar multiplication. To show the converse, suppose that U is a nonempty subset of the vector space V, which is closed under addition and scalar multiplication, and let us show that U is indeed a vector space. If $X \in U$ and 1 is the unity of F, we have $(- 1)X \in U$. But, by 10.6 (iii) and 10.3 (v), we see that

$$(- 1)X = - (1X) = - X,$$

so that the additive inverse $- X$ of X is in U. Since U is closed under addition, Theorem 9.4 now shows that U is a subgroup of V; that is, that part (i) of Definition 10.3 is satisfied. Properties (ii)–(v) hold in U since they hold in the larger set V. Hence, U is a vector space over F and therefore is a subspace of V.

As an illustration of the use of this theorem, let us show that the set W of all elements of the vector space $V_3(F)$ of the form $(x + 2y, y, -x + 3y)$, where x and y are elements of F, is a subspace of $V_3(F)$. If $(a + 2b, b, -a + 3b)$ and $(c + 2d, d, -c + 3d)$ are elements of W, we see that their sum can be written in the form

$$(a + c + 2(b + d), b + d, -(a + c) + 3(b + d)),$$

and this is seen to be the element of W in which $x = a + c$ and $y = b + d$. This shows that W is closed under addition. Also, if $(a + 2b, b, -a + 3b)$ is an element of W and $r \in F$, it follows that

$$r(a + 2b, b, -a + 3b) = (ra + 2rb, rb, -ra + 3rb),$$

and we have the desired form with $x = ra$ and $y = rb$. Hence, W is also closed under scalar multiplication and, by the preceding theorem, W is therefore a subspace of $V_3(F)$.

_____ **E X E R C I S E S**

1. In each case, using natural definitions of addition and scalar multiplication, which of the following are vector spaces over the indicated field?

   (*a*)   The set of all real numbers of the form $a + b\sqrt{2} + c\sqrt[3]{3}$, where a, b, and c are elements of the field R of rational numbers; field R.

   (*b*)   The set of all polynomials of degree greater than five over a field F; field F.

   (*c*)   The set of all real functions f such that $f(x + 1) = f(x)$; field K of real numbers.

   (*d*)   The set $\{0, x + 2, 2x + 4, 3x + 1, 4x + 3\}$ of polynomials in the indeterminate x over the field $I/(5)$; field $I/(5)$.

   (*e*)   The set of all polynomials with zero constant terms over a field F; field F.

2. Prove Theorem 10.6 (ii) and (iv).

3. Let V be a vector space over a field F. Prove each of the following "cancellation laws":

   (*i*)   If a, $b \in F$ and X is a nonzero element of V such that $aX = bX$, then $a = b$.

   (*ii*)   If X, $Y \in V$ and a is a nonzero element of F such that $aX = aY$, then $X = Y$.

4. If F is a field and a_1, a_2, and a_3 are fixed elements of F, show that the set of all ordered triples (x_1, x_2, x_3) of elements of F such that $a_1x_1 + a_2x_2 + a_3x_3 = 0$ is a subspace of $V_3(F)$.

5. Find all subspaces of $V_2(I/(2))$; of $V_3(I/(2))$.

6. (a) How many elements are there in the vector space $V_n(I/(p))$?
   (b) Show that the number of elements in any subspace of $V_n(I/(p))$ is of the form p^k for some nonnegative integer k.

7. Which of the following are subspaces of $V_3(K)$?

   (a) The set of all elements of the form $(x, 2y, 3z)$, where x, y, $z \in K$.

   (b) The set of all elements of the form (x, y, z), where x, y, and z are rational numbers.

   (c) The set of all elements of the form $(x, 2x, x + 1)$, where $x \in K$.

   (d) The set of all elements of the form $(x, 0, z)$, where x, $z \in K$.

   (e) The set of all elements of the form $(x, y, 2)$, where x, $y \in K$.

   (f) The set of all elements of the form $(x + 2y, \ x - 3z, \ 2x + y + z)$, where x, y, $z \in K$.

8. Verify that the set of all elements of the vector space $W(F)$ of Example 2 in which at most a finite number of elements of F are different from zero is a subspace of $W(F)$.

10.3 LINEAR DEPENDENCE

Throughout this section V will denote a vector space over a field F. Unless otherwise explicitly stated, when we refer to a set $\{X_1, X_2, \cdots, X_m\}$ of vectors, it will be understood that m is a positive integer and the set is therefore a nonempty finite set. The concept which we now define plays a central role in the study of vector spaces.

10.8 Definition. A set $\{X_1, X_2, \cdots, X_m\}$ of vectors of a vector space V is said to be a *linearly dependent* set if there exist elements $a_1, a_2, \cdots, a_m$ of F, *not all of which are zero*, such that

10.9 $$a_1X_1 + a_2X_2 + \cdots + a_mX_m = 0.$$

If the set $\{X_1, X_2, \cdots, X_m\}$ is not linearly dependent, it is said to be *linearly independent*.

As a matter of language, we shall also sometimes say that the vectors $X_1, X_2, \cdots, X_m$ are linearly dependent or independent according as the set $\{X_1, X_2, \cdots, X_m\}$ is linearly dependent or independent.

Let us emphasize the meaning of the definition by the following remarks. Certainly, a relation of the form 10.9 will always hold if the a's are all equal to zero. If such a relation holds *only* in this case, the set $\{X_1, X_2, \cdots, X_m\}$ is linearly independent. However, if a relation 10.9 holds with at least one of the a's unequal to zero, the set $\{X_1, X_2, \cdots, X_m\}$ is linearly dependent.

Example 1. Let us consider the set $\{X_1, X_2, X_3\}$, where these are the following vectors of $V_3(K)$: $X_1 = (1, 3, 2)$, $X_2 = (1, -7, -8)$, $X_3 = (2, 1, -1)$. It is easily verified that $3X_1 + X_2 - 2X_3 = 0$, and hence that this set is linearly dependent.

Example 2. Find whether the vectors $X_1 = (2, 1, 1, 1)$, $X_2 = (1, 3, 1, -2)$, and $X_3 = (1, 2, -1, 3)$ of $V_4(K)$ are linearly dependent or independent.

In order to solve this problem we need to determine whether there exist real numbers y_1, y_2, y_3, not all of which are zero, such that

0.10 $$y_1X_1 + y_2X_2 + y_3X_3 = 0.$$

Using the definitions of addition and scalar multiplication in $V_4(K)$, Equation 10.10 is equivalent to the following system of simultaneous equations in the unknowns y_1, y_2, and y_3:

$$2y_1 + y_2 + y_3 = 0,$$
$$y_1 + 3y_2 + 2y_3 = 0,$$
$$y_1 + y_2 - y_3 = 0,$$
$$y_1 - 2y_2 + 3y_3 = 0.$$

Systems of equations of this form will be studied in detail in the next chapter, but a systematic use of the methods of elementary algebra is sufficient for our present purpose. First, we proceed as follows to eliminate y_1 from every equation but one. Let us multiply the second equation by 2 and subtract it from the first; then also subtract the second equation from the third and from the fourth. There then results the following system of equations:

$$-5y_2 - 3y_3 = 0,$$
$$y_1 + 3y_2 + 2y_3 = 0,$$
$$-2y_2 - 3y_3 = 0,$$
$$-5y_2 + y_3 = 0.$$

We could, by a similar method, proceed to eliminate y_2 from all the equations of this new system except, say, the first. However, it is not necessary to do so, for if we subtract the first equation from the last, we find that $4y_3 = 0$, and hence we must have $y_3 = 0$. Now, setting $y_3 = 0$ in the first equation, we see that $y_2 = 0$. Finally, if we set $y_2 = y_3 = 0$

in the second equation, it follows that $y_1 = 0$. We have shown that if y_1, y_2, y_3 are real numbers such that 10.10 holds, then $y_1 = y_2 = y_3 = 0$, and the vectors X_1, X_2, X_3 are therefore linearly independent.

We now state in the following theorem a number of simple, but fundamental, properties of linear dependence or independence.

10.11 Theorem. *In the following, the indicated vectors are elements of a vector space V over a field F.*

(i)   *The set $\{X_1, X_2, \cdots, X_m\}$ is a linearly dependent set if at least one of the vectors of the set is the zero vector.*

(ii)   *The set $\{X\}$, consisting of the one vector X, is linearly independent if and only if $X \neq 0$.*

(iii)   *If the set $\{X_1, X_2, \cdots, X_m\}$ is linearly independent, then any nonempty subset of this set is linearly independent.*

(iv)   *If the set $\{X_1, X_2, \cdots, X_m\}$ is linearly dependent, then the set $\{X_1, X_2, \cdots, X_m, X\}$ is linearly dependent for each $X \in V$.*

(v)   *If $\{X_1, X_2, \cdots, X_m\}$ is a linearly independent set and if b_i, $c_i \in F$ $(i = 1, 2, \cdots, m)$ such that*
$$b_1 X_1 + b_2 X_2 + \cdots + b_m X_m = c_1 X_1 + c_2 X_2 + \cdots + c_m X_m,$$
then $b_i = c_i$ $(i = 1, 2, \cdots, m)$.

(vi)   *If $X_i \in V$ $(i = 1, 2, \cdots, m)$ and $r_i \in F$ $(i = 2, 3, \cdots, m)$, are such that the set $\{X_2 + r_2 X_1, X_3 + r_3 X_1, \cdots, X_m + r_m X_1\}$ is a linearly dependent set, then the set $\{X_1, X_2, \cdots, X_m\}$ is a linearly dependent set.*

The reader should try to prove the various parts of this theorem before looking at the proofs below. There should be no difficulty in carrying out the proofs provided the definitions of a vector space and of linear dependence and independence are clearly in mind.

Proof of (i). Suppose, for convenience of notation, that $X_1 = 0$. Then, since $1X_1 = 0$ by 10.3 (v), and $0X_i = 0$ by 10.6 (ii), it follows that
$$1X_1 + 0X_2 + \cdots + 0X_m = 0.$$

This relation is of the form 10.9 with $a_1 \neq 0$; hence the set $\{X_1, X_2, \cdots, X_m\}$ is linearly dependent.

Proof of (ii). Suppose that $X \neq 0$. If $aX = 0$, it follows from 10.6 (iv) that $a = 0$. Hence, the set $\{X\}$ is linearly independent. Of course, in this case a relation of the form 10.9 has just one term on its left side. If $X = 0$, the special case of (i) in which $m = 1$ shows at once that the set $\{X\}$ is linearly dependent.

Proof of (iii). For convenience of notation, let us consider a subset of the form $\{X_1, \cdots, X_i\}$, where $1 \leq i < m$, and suppose that $a_1 X_1 + \cdots + a_i X_i = 0$. Then, obviously,
$$a_1 X_1 + \cdots + a_i X_i + 0X_{i+1} + \cdots + 0X_m = 0.$$

Since the set $\{X_1, \cdots, X_m\}$ is linearly independent, it follows that we must have $a_1 = a_2 = \cdots = a_i = 0$. We have therefore shown that $a_1 X_1 + \cdots + a_i X_i = 0$ only if all a's are equal to zero, and hence that the set $\{X_1, \cdots, X_i\}$ is linearly independent.

Proof of (iv). Suppose that $a_1 X_1 + \cdots + a_m X_m = 0$ with $a_j \neq 0$, where j is some integer such that $1 \leq j \leq m$. Then

$$a_1 X_1 + \cdots + a_m X_m + 0X = 0,$$

and since $a_j \neq 0$, we conclude that the set $\{X_1, \cdots, X_m, X\}$ is a linearly dependent set.

Proof of (v). From what is given it follows that

$$b_1 X_1 + b_2 X_2 + \cdots + b_m X_m - (c_1 X_1 + c_2 X_2 + \cdots + c_m X_m) = 0.$$

Then, using 10.6 (iii), 10.3 (iii), and the fact that V is an abelian group with respect to addition, it is not difficult to show that

$$(b_1 - c_1)X_1 + (b_2 - c_2)X_2 + \cdots + (b_m - c_m)X_m = 0.$$

Since the set $\{X_1, \cdots, X_m\}$ is linearly independent, this equation implies that $b_i - c_i = 0$ and therefore that $b_i = c_i$ $(i = 1, 2, \cdots, m)$.

Proof of (vi). By what is given we know that there must exist elements a_i $(i = 2, 3, \cdots, m)$ of F, not all of which are zero, such that

$$a_2(X_2 + r_2 X_1) + a_3(X_3 + r_3 X_1) + \cdots + a_m(X_m + r_m X_1) = 0.$$

However, it follows from this equation that

$$(a_2 r_2 + \cdots + a_m r_m)X_1 + a_2 X_2 + \cdots + a_m X_m = 0$$

and, since the a's are not all zero, we see that the set $\{X_1, X_2, \cdots, X_m\}$ is a linearly dependent set. This completes the proof of the theorem.

_____ EXERCISES

1. Determine whether each of the following sets of vectors of $V_3(K)$ is linearly dependent or independent:

    (a) $\{(-1, 2, 1), (3, 1, -2)\}$,
    (b) $\{(1, 3, 2), (2, 1, 0), (0, 5, 4)\}$,
    (c) $\{(2, -1, 1), (1, 2, 3), (0, 1, 2)\}$,
    (d) $\{(1, 0, 0), (0, 1, 0), (0, 0, 1)\}$,
    (e) $\{(1, -2, 1), (0, 1, 2), (1, 1, 1)\}$,
    (f) $\{(1, 0, -1), (2, 1, 3), (-1, 0, 0), (1, 0, 1)\}$.

2. Determine whether each of the following sets of vectors of $V_4(K)$ is linearly dependent or independent:

(a) $\{(1, -1, 2, 1), (2, 1, 1, 2)\}$,
(b) $\{(1, 2, 1, 2), (0, 1, 1, 0), (1, 4, 3, 2)\}$,
(c) $\{(0, 1, 0, 1), (1, 2, 3, -1), (1, 0, 1, 0), (0, 3, 2, 0)\}$,
(d) $\{(1, 2, -1, 1), (0, 1, -1, 2), (2, 1, 0, 3), (1, 1, 0, 0)\}$.

3. Determine whether each of the following sets of vectors of $V_3(I/(5))$ is linearly dependent or independent:

(a) $\{(1, 3, 2), (2, 1, 3)\}$,
(b) $\{(1, 1, 2), (2, 1, 0), (0, 4, 1)\}$,
(c) $\{(2, 1, 0), (1, 1, 2), (3, 0, 2)\}$.

4. Prove, giving the reason for each step, that a set consisting of *two* vectors of a vector space is a linearly dependent set if and only if one of these vectors is equal to a scalar times the other.

5. If X_1 and X_2 are vectors of a vector space over the field F, and $a, b \in F$, show that the set $\{X_1, X_2, aX_1 + bX_2\}$ is a linearly dependent set.

6. Let X_1, X_2, and X_3 be vectors of a vector space over the field F, and let a and b be arbitrary elements of F. Show that the set $\{X_1, X_2, X_3\}$ is a linearly dependent set if and only if $\{X_1 + aX_2 + bX_3, X_2, X_3\}$ is a linearly dependent set.

10.4 LINEAR COMBINATIONS AND SUBSPACES

We shall continue to let V be a vector space over a field F.

10.12 Definition. A vector of the form $a_1X_1 + a_2X_2 + \cdots + a_mX_m$, where $X_i \in V$ and $a_i \in F$ $(i = 1, 2, \cdots, m)$, is called a *linear combination* (over F) of the vectors $X_1, X_2, \cdots, X_m$.

In the linear combination $a_1X_1 + a_2X_2 + \cdots + a_mX_m$, it is sometimes convenient to call a_i the *coefficient* of X_i $(i = 1, 2, \cdots, m)$.

We shall now verify the important fact that *the set U of all linear combinations of given vectors $X_1, X_2, \cdots, X_m$ of V is a subspace of V*. By Theorem 10.7, we only need to show that U is closed under addition and scalar multiplication. Suppose that Y and Z are elements of U. Then,

$$Y = c_1X_1 + c_2X_2 + \cdots + c_mX_m$$

and

$$Z = d_1X_1 + d_2X_2 + \cdots + d_mX_m,$$

where the c's and d's are elements of F. It follows that

$$Y + Z = (c_1 + d_1)X_1 + (c_2 + d_2)X_2 + \cdots + (c_m + d_m)X_m.$$

Hence, $Y + Z$ is a linear combination of $X_1, X_2, \cdots, X_m$; and therefore an element of U. This shows that U is closed under addition. Now if $r \in F$ and Y is as above, we see that

$$rY = r(c_1X_1 + c_2X_2 + \cdots + c_mX_m) = (rc_1)X_1 + (rc_2)X_2 + \cdots (rc_m)X_m.$$

It follows that $rY \in U$; that is, that U is also closed under scalar multiplication. We have therefore proved that U is a subspace of V.

We now make the following definition.

0.13 Definition. If $X_1, X_2, \cdots, X_m$ are elements of a vector space V, the subspace of V which consists of all linear combinations of these vectors will be designated by $[X_1, X_2, \cdots, X_m]$, and called the subspace *generated* by the vectors $X_1, X_2, \cdots, X_m$.

Perhaps we should emphasize the distinction between the sets $\{X_1, X_2, \cdots, X_m\}$ and $[X_1, X_2, \cdots, X_m]$. The former is the set consisting of just the m vectors $X_1, X_2, \cdots, X_m$; whereas the latter consists of all vectors which are expressible as linear combinations of the vectors $X_1, X_2, \cdots, X_m$. Since

$$X_1 = 1X_1 + 0X_2 + \cdots + 0X_m,$$

it is clear that X_1 is a linear combination of the vectors $X_1, X_2, \cdots, X_m$; and hence that $X_1 \in [X_1, X_2, \cdots, X_m]$. In like manner we see that $X_i \in [X_1, X_2, \cdots, X_m]$ for $i = 1, 2, \cdots, m$; and it follows that

$$\{X_1, X_2, \cdots, X_m\} \subseteq [X_1, X_2, \cdots, X_m].$$

Actually, $[X_1, X_2, \cdots, X_m]$ is the smallest subspace of V which contains all the vectors $X_1, X_2, \cdots, X_m$; and this is the reason that we call it the subspace of V *generated by* these vectors.

As a consequence of the fact that $[X_1, X_2, \cdots, X_m]$ is a subspace of V, or by a simple direct calculation, it follows that a linear combination of vectors, each of which is a linear combination of $X_1, X_2, \cdots, X_m$, is itself a linear combination of $X_1, X_2, \cdots, X_m$. Otherwise expressed, if $Y_1, Y_2, \cdots, Y_k$ are elements of the subspace $[X_1, X_2, \cdots, X_m]$, then

$$[Y_1, Y_2, \cdots, Y_k] \subseteq [X_1, X_2, \cdots, X_m].$$

Moreover, we have that

$$[Y_1, Y_2, \cdots, Y_k] = [X_1, X_2, \cdots, X_m]$$

if and only if each of the Y's is a linear combination of the X's, and each of the X's is a linear combination of the Y's. This observation is frequently useful in proving the equality of two subspaces of V.

As an illustration of a subspace generated by given vectors, let us consider the vector space $V_3(K)$ and let $X = (1, 0, -1)$ and

$Y = (2, 1, 3)$. Then the subspace $[X, Y]$ of $V_3(K)$ is the set of all vectors of the form $aX + bY$, where $a, b \in K$. However,

$$aX + bY = a(1, 0, -1) + b(2, 1, 3) = (a + 2b, b, -a + 3b),$$

and hence $[X, Y]$ may be characterized as the set of all vectors of the form $(a + 2b, b, -a + 3b)$, with $a, b \in K$.

Now let n be an arbitrary positive integer, and consider the vector space $V_n(F)$, where F is an arbitrary field. Let $E_1, E_2, \cdots, E_n$ be the following vectors of $V_n(F)$:

$$E_1 = (1, 0, 0, \cdots, 0),$$
$$E_2 = (0, 1, 0, \cdots, 0),$$
$$E_3 = (0, 0, 1, \cdots, 0),$$
$$\cdot \quad \cdot \quad \cdot \quad \cdot \quad \cdot \quad \cdot \quad \cdot \quad \cdot$$
$$E_n = (0, 0, 0, \cdots, 1).$$

These are often called the *unit vectors* of $V_n(F)$, and we shall in the future use the notation we have introduced here for these vectors. We observe now that these unit vectors are linearly independent since

$$a_1 E_1 + a_2 E_2 + \cdots + a_n E_n = (a_1, a_2, \cdots, a_n),$$

and this is the zero vector if and only if all a's are equal to zero. It is also almost obvious that the entire space $V_n(F)$ is generated by these unit vectors, that is, that

$$V_n(F) = [E_1, E_2, \cdots, E_n].$$

For if $(c_1, c_2, \cdots, c_n)$ is an arbitrary element of $V_n(F)$, we have

$$(c_1, c_2, \cdots, c_n) = c_1 E_1 + c_2 E_2 + \cdots + c_n E_n,$$

and hence every element of $V_n(F)$ is a linear combination of the unit vectors.

Before stating the next theorem let us observe that in the notation introduced in this section, Theorem 10.11 (v) may be stated in the following convenient form.

10.14 Corollary. *If $X_1, X_2, \cdots, X_m$ are linearly independent vectors of V, each vector of the subspace $[X_1, X_2, \cdots, X_m]$ of V is uniquely expressible as a linear combination of $X_1, X_2, \cdots, X_m$.*

Several important properties are collected in the following theorem.

10.15 Theorem. *Let m be a positive integer and let $X_1, X_2, \cdots, X_m$ be vectors of the vector space V over the field F. The following are then true:*

(i)   The subspace $[X_1, X_2, \cdots, X_m]$ is unchanged if a vector X_k $(1 \le k \le m)$ is replaced by aX_k, where a is a nonzero scalar; that is,

$$[X_1, \cdots, X_k, \cdots, X_m] = [X_1, \cdots, aX_k, \cdots, X_m].$$

(ii)   The subspace $[X_1, X_2, \cdots, X_m]$ is unchanged if a vector X_k $(1 \le k \le m)$ is replaced by $X_k + bX_l$, where $1 \le l \le m$, $l \ne k$, and b is any scalar. That is, we have

$$[X_1, \cdots, X_k, \cdots, X_l, \cdots, X_m] = [X_1, \cdots, X_k + bX_l, \cdots, X_l, \cdots, X_m].$$

(iii)   If $Y = a_1X_1 + a_2X_2 + \cdots + a_mX_m$, with $a_k \ne 0$, then

$$[X_1, \cdots, X_k, \cdots, X_m] = [X_1, \cdots, Y, \cdots, X_m].$$

(iv)   If $X \in V$, then $[X_1, X_2, \cdots, X_m, X] = [X_1, X_2, \cdots, X_m]$ if and only if X is a linear combination of $X_1, X_2, \cdots, X_m$.

(v)   If $\{X_1, X_2, \cdots, X_m\}$ is a linearly independent set and $X \notin [X_1, X_2, \cdots, X_m]$, then $\{X_1, X_2, \cdots, X_m, X\}$ is a linearly independent set.

We shall prove parts (ii) and (v) of this theorem, and leave the proofs of the other parts as exercises.

First, let us prove part (ii) and, for convenience, let us set

$$A = \{X_1, \cdots, X_k, \cdots, X_l, \cdots, X_m\},$$

and

$$B = \{X_1, \cdots, X_k + bX_l, \cdots, X_l, \cdots, X_m\}.$$

Since $X_k = 1(X_k + bX_l) - bX_l$, it follows that X_k is a linear combination of the vectors in the set B. Moreover, each vector X_j with $j \ne k$ occurs in both sets, and hence every vector in the set A is a linear combination of the vectors in the set B. The converse is obviously true, and we therefore conclude that

$$[X_1, \cdots, X_k, \cdots, X_l, \cdots, X_m] = [X_1, \cdots, X_k + bX_l, \cdots, X_l, \cdots, X_m].$$

To prove part (v), suppose that $c_1, c_2, \cdots, c_m, c$ are scalars such that

10.16
$$c_1X_1 + c_2X_2 + \cdots + c_mX_m + cX = 0.$$

If $c \ne 0$, we may write

$$X = -c^{-1}(c_1X_1 + c_2X_2 + \cdots + c_mX_m),$$

and it follows that $X \in [X_1, X_2, \cdots, X_m]$. However, it is given that X is not an element of this subspace, and hence we must have $c = 0$. If we substitute $c = 0$ in 10.16, it follows also that $c_i = 0$ $(i = 1, 2, \cdots, m)$, since the vectors $X_1, X_2, \cdots, X_m$ are given to be linearly independent.

We have therefore shown that a relation of the form 10.16 can hold only if all the coefficients are zero, and this proves that the vectors $X_1, X_2, \cdots, X_m, X$ are linearly independent.

We conclude this section with the following theorem, which will prove to be extremely useful in the further study of vector spaces.

10.17 Theorem. *If $X_1, X_2, \cdots, X_m$ are vectors in the vector space V, any $m + 1$ vectors in the subspace $[X_1, X_2, \cdots, X_m]$ of V are linearly dependent.*

The proof is by induction on m. For the case in which $m = 1$ we need only show that any two vectors of $[X_1]$ are linearly dependent. Let $Y_1 = aX_1$ and $Y_2 = bX_1$ be two vectors of the subspace $[X_1]$. If $a = 0$, then $Y_1 = 0$ and the equation $1 Y_1 + 0 Y_2 = 0$ shows that Y_1 and Y_2 are linearly dependent. If $a \neq 0$, the equation $- b Y_1 + a Y_2 = 0$ shows that Y_1 and Y_2 are linearly dependent. This disposes of the case in which $m = 1$.

To complete the proof by induction, let k be a positive integer such that the statement of the theorem is true for $m = k$, and let us prove it for $m = k + 1$. We shall do so by showing that if Y_1, $Y_2, \cdots, Y_{k+2}$ are arbitrary vectors in the subspace $[X_1, X_2, \cdots, X_{k+1}]$, then these vectors are linearly dependent. Since each Y_i is a linear combination of $X_1, X_2, \cdots, X_{k+1}$, we can write

$$Y_1 = a_1 X_1 + a_2 X_2 + \cdots + a_{k+1} X_{k+1},$$
$$Y_2 = b_1 X_1 + b_2 X_2 + \cdots + b_{k+1} X_{k+1},$$

10.18
$$Y_3 = c_1 X_1 + c_2 X_2 + \cdots + c_{k+1} X_{k+1},$$
$$\cdots \cdots \cdots \cdots \cdots \cdots \cdots \cdots$$
$$Y_{k+2} = s_1 X_1 + s_2 X_2 + \cdots + s_{k+1} X_{k+1},$$

it being understood that the various coefficients are elements of F. If it happens that in these equations the coefficients of X_1 are all zero, then the Y's are, in fact, linear combinations of the k vectors $X_2, X_3, \cdots, X_{k+1}$. This means that they are elements of the subspace $[X_2, X_3, \cdots, X_{k+1}]$ and, by our assumption that the statement of the theorem is true for $m = k$, we see that any $k + 1$ vectors of the set $\{Y_1, Y_2, \cdots, Y_{k+2}\}$ are linearly dependent. Theorem 10.11 (iv) then shows that the set $\{Y_1, Y_2, \cdots, Y_{k+2}\}$ is linearly dependent and we have the desired result.

There remains to dispose of the case in which not all the coefficients of X_1 in Equations 10.18 are zero. Let us assume, for convenience of notation, that $a_1 \neq 0$. Then from the first of Equations 10.18 we have that

$$a_1^{-1} Y_1 = X_1 + a_1^{-1} a_2 X_2 + \cdots + a_1^{-1} a_{k+1} X_{k+1},$$

and from this and the second of Equations 10.18 it follows that the vector $Y_2 - b_1 a_1^{-1} Y_1$ is a linear combination of $X_2, \cdots, X_{k+1}$; and is therefore an element of $[X_2, \cdots, X_{k+1}]$. Similarly, using the third of Equations 10.18, we see that $Y_3 - c_1 a_1^{-1} Y_1$ is an element of $[X_2, \cdots, X_{k+1}]$. Continuing in this manner, we find that the $k + 1$ vectors

$$Y_2 - b_1 a_1^{-1} Y_1, \; Y_3 - c_1 a_1^{-1} Y_1, \cdots, \; Y_{k+2} - s_1 a_1^{-1} Y_1$$

are elements of $[X_2, \cdots, X_{k+1}]$. But by our assumption that the statement of the theorem is true for $m = k$, these $k + 1$ vectors must be linearly dependent. Theorem 10.11 (vi) then shows that the vectors $Y_1, Y_2, \cdots, Y_{k+2}$ are linearly dependent, and the proof of the theorem is completed.

The following simple corollary of this theorem follows immediately from the observation made above that if $E_1, E_2, \cdots, E_n$ are the unit vectors of $V_n(F)$, then $V_n(F) = [E_1, E_2, \cdots, E_n]$.

10.19 Corollary. *Any $n + 1$ vectors of $V_n(F)$ are linearly dependent.*

_____ E X E R C I S E S

1. Prove that if $\{X_1, X_2, \cdots, X_m\}$ (where $m > 1$) is a linearly dependent set of vectors, then some one of these vectors is a linear combination of the others.

2. Prove Theorem 10.15 (i), (iii), and (iv).

3. Show that if the set $\{X_1, X_2, \cdots, X_m\}$ is linearly independent but the set $\{X_1, X_2, \cdots, X_m, X\}$ is linearly dependent, then X is a linear combination of the vectors $X_1, X_2, \cdots, X_m$.

4. If $m > 1$, $X \in [X_1, X_2, \cdots, X_m]$, and $X \notin [X_1, X_2, \cdots, X_{m-1}]$, prove that $X_m \in [X_1, X_2, \cdots, X_{m-1}, X]$.

5. If $X \in [X_1, X_2, \cdots, X_m]$, show that the set $\{X, X_1, X_2, \cdots, X_m\}$ is a linearly dependent set.

6. Show that if $[X_1, X_2, \cdots, X_m] = [Y_1, Y_2, \cdots, Y_n]$ with $m \neq n$, then at least one of the sets $\{X_1, X_2, \cdots, X_m\}$ and $\{Y_1, Y_2, \cdots, Y_n\}$ is a linearly dependent set.

7. Show that if the nonzero vectors $X_1, X_2, \cdots, X_m$ $(m \geq 2)$ are linearly dependent, there exists an integer k with $2 \leq k \leq m$ such that X_k is a linear combination of $X_1, X_2, \cdots, X_{k-1}$.

10.5 BASIS AND DIMENSION

We now make the following definition.

10.20 Definition. The set $\{X_1, X_2, \cdots, X_n\}$ of elements of a vector space V is said to be a *basis* of V if the following two conditions are satisfied:

(i) The set $\{X_1, X_2, \cdots, X_n\}$ is a linearly independent set.

(ii) V is generated by $X_1, X_2, \cdots, X_n$; that is,

$$V = [X_1, X_2, \cdots, X_n].$$

In view of Corollary 10.14, we see that if the set $\{X_1, X_2, \cdots, X_n\}$ is a basis of V, every vector of V is *uniquely* expressible as a linear combination of the vectors $X_1, X_2, \cdots, X_n$.

As an example of the concept of basis of a vector space, we have already observed that the set $\{E_1, E_2, \cdots, E_n\}$ of unit vectors of $V_n(F)$ has both the defining properties and is therefore a basis of $V_n(F)$. In particular, let us now consider the vector space $V_3(K)$. Then, as a special case of the observation just made, the set $\{(1, 0, 0), (0, 1, 0), (0, 0, 1)\}$ is a basis of $V_3(K)$. However, $V_3(K)$ may have other bases as well. For example, let us consider the set $A = \{(1, 2, 1), (2, 1, 0), (1, -1, 2)\}$ of elements of $V_3(K)$. By the method used in Section 10.3 it can be shown that this is a linearly independent set, and we shall not give the details here. Moreover, that each of the unit vectors is a linear combination of the vectors of this set A follows from the following easily verified equations:

$$(1, 0, 0) = -\tfrac{2}{9}(1, 2, 1) + \tfrac{5}{9}(2, 1, 0) + \tfrac{1}{9}(1, -1, 2),$$
$$(0, 1, 0) = \quad\tfrac{4}{9}(1, 2, 1) - \tfrac{1}{9}(2, 1, 0) - \tfrac{2}{9}(1, -1, 2),$$
$$(0, 0, 1) = \quad\tfrac{1}{3}(1, 2, 1) - \tfrac{1}{3}(2, 1, 0) + \tfrac{1}{3}(1, -1, 2).$$

Since $V_3(K)$ is generated by the unit vectors, we see therefore that every element of $V_3(K)$ is a linear combination of the vectors of the set A. Hence, the vectors of this set form a basis of $V_3(K)$.

We have just indicated that a vector space may have more than one basis. However, it is easy to verify that not every vector space has a basis according to our definition.* As an example of a vector space without a basis, let us consider the vector space $P(F)$ of polynomials in an indeterminate x over a field F (Example 4 of Section 10.2). If n is an arbitrary positive integer and $f_1, f_2, \cdots, f_n$ are any n elements of $P(F)$, then no linear combination of these vectors can have a degree exceeding the maximum of the degrees of $f_1, f_2, \cdots, f_n$. Hence, there exist elements

---

*In more advanced treatises, what we have called a basis is usually called a *finite* basis, and every vector space has either a finite or an infinite basis.

of $P(F)$ that are not in the subspace $[f_1, f_2, \cdots, f_n]$, and condition (ii) of Definition 10.20 cannot be satisfied. This shows that the vector space $P(F)$ cannot have a basis. Another example of a vector space without a basis is the vector space $W(F)$ of Example 2 of Section 10.2. However, we shall be primarily concerned with vector spaces that do have bases, and for them the following theorem is fundamental.

10.21 Theorem. *If the vector space V has a basis consisting of n vectors, then every basis of V has exactly n vectors.*

Suppose that $\{X_1, X_2, \cdots, X_n\}$ and $\{Y_1, Y_2, \cdots, Y_m\}$ are bases of V, and let us show that necessarily $m = n$. We observe that $V = [X_1, X_2, \cdots, X_n] = [Y_1, Y_2, \cdots, Y_m]$ and apply Theorem 10.17 as follows. If $m > n$, any $n + 1$ of the vectors $Y_1, Y_2, \cdots, Y_m$ are linearly dependent, and hence the entire set $\{Y_1, Y_2, \cdots, Y_m\}$ is linearly dependent. However, this contradicts the fact that $\{Y_1, Y_2, \cdots, Y_m\}$ is a basis of V. We conclude therefore that we cannot have $m > n$. By interchanging the roles of the X's and the Y's in this argument, we find also that we cannot have $n > m$. Hence, $m = n$, and the proof is completed.

Since all bases of a vector space have the same number of elements, it is convenient to have a name for the number of such elements.

10.22 Definition. A vector space V is said to have *dimension* n $(n \geq 1)$ if V has a basis consisting of n elements. The vector space consisting of only the zero vector is said to have *dimension zero*. A vector space is said to have *finite* dimension if it has dimension m for some nonnegative integer m.

We shall write dim $V = n$, to indicate that the vector space V has dimension n.

It is now clear that dim $V_n(F) = n$, since $V_n(F)$ has the basis $\{E_1, E_2, \cdots, E_n\}$. In particular, the vector space $V_2(K)$ discussed in Section 10.1, and which we described geometrically as the set of all vectors in a plane, has dimension 2. This fact should at least help to make our definition of dimension seem a reasonable one.

We shall now prove the following theorem.

10.23 Theorem. *If dim $V = n$ with $n > 0$, the following are true:*

(i) *Any $n + 1$ vectors of V are linearly dependent.*
(ii) *Any set of n linearly independent vectors of V is a basis of V.*
(iii) *V cannot be generated by fewer than n vectors.*
(iv) *If $V = [Z_1, Z_2, \cdots, Z_n]$, then $\{Z_1, Z_2, \cdots, Z_n\}$ is necessarily a linearly independent set and therefore a basis of V.*

If $\{X_1, X_2, \cdots, X_n\}$ is a basis of V, then $V = [X_1, X_2, \cdots, X_n]$ and the first statement of the theorem follows at once from Theorem 10.17.

To prove the second statement, let $\{Y_1, Y_2, \cdots, Y_n\}$ be a set of n linearly independent vectors of V. If this set were not a basis, there would exist an element Y of V such that $Y \notin [Y_1, Y_2, \cdots, Y_n]$. By Theorem 10.15 (v), this would imply that the set $\{Y_1, Y_2, \cdots, Y_n, Y\}$ is a linearly independent set. However, this is impossible by the first part of the present theorem, and we conclude that $\{Y_1, Y_2, \cdots, Y_n\}$ must be a basis of V.

If V were generated by m vectors with $m < n$, Theorem 10.17 would show that V could not contain n linearly independent vectors. However, dim $V = n$ implies that there do exist n linearly independent vectors in V, and we have established part (iii) of the theorem.

To prove part (iv), suppose that $V = [Z_1, Z_2, \cdots, Z_n]$, and let us assume that the set $\{Z_1, Z_2, \cdots, Z_n\}$ is linearly dependent and seek a contradiction. The case in which $n = 1$ is trivial, so we may assume that $n > 1$. Then the linear dependence of the set $\{Z_1, Z_2, \cdots, Z_n\}$ implies that some one of these vectors is a linear combination of the others. (See Exercise 1 of the preceding set.) For convenience of notation, let us suppose that Z_1 is a linear combination of $Z_2, \cdots, Z_n$. By Theorem 10.15 (iv), we then see that

$$V = [Z_1, Z_2, \cdots, Z_n] = [Z_2, \cdots, Z_n].$$

However, this violates part (iii) of the present theorem since we now have V generated by fewer than n vectors. This contradiction shows that the set $\{Z_1, Z_2, \cdots, Z_n\}$ is linearly independent, and the proof of the theorem is therefore completed.

The next theorem shows that any set of linearly independent vectors of a vector space of finite dimension is a part of a basis of the space.

10.24 Theorem. *Let V be a vector space of dimension $n > 1$. If $\{X_1, X_2, \cdots, X_r\}$, where $1 \le r < n$, is a set of linearly independent vectors of V, there exist vectors $X_{r+1}, \cdots, X_n$ of V such that $\{X_1, X_2, \cdots, X_n\}$ is a basis of V.*

This result is easily established as follows. Since $r < n$, the set $\{X_1, X_2, \cdots, X_r\}$ is not a basis of V and hence there exists a vector X_{r+1} of V such that $X_{r+1} \notin [X_1, X_2, \cdots, X_r]$. By Theorem 10.15 (v), the set $\{X_1, X_2, \cdots, X_r, X_{r+1}\}$ is a linearly independent set. If $r + 1 < n$, we can repeat the argument. Continuing in this way, we must eventually obtain a set of n linearly independent vectors and, by the preceding theorem, this set is a basis of V.

We next consider a few questions about the dimensions of subspaces of a given vector space.

0.25 Theorem. *If dim $V = n$ and U is a subspace of V, then U has finite dimension and dim $U \leq n$. Moreover, $U = V$ if and only if dim $U = n$.*

The statement is trivial if $n = 0$; hence we assume that $n > 0$. If U consists only of the zero vector, dim $U = 0$ and clearly dim $U \leq n$, so there is nothing to prove. Suppose, then, that X_1 is a nonzero vector in U. If $U \neq [X_1]$, let X_2 be an element of U which is not in $[X_1]$. Then X_1 and X_2 are linearly independent. If $U \neq [X_1, X_2]$, let X_3 be an element of U which is not in $[X_1, X_2]$, and again we know that X_1, X_2, and X_3 are linearly independent. Continuing in this way, we must eventually come to the point at which $U = [X_1, X_2, \cdots, X_r]$, where $r \leq n$ since there can exist at most n linearly independent vectors in V. This shows that dim $U = r \leq n$, and the first statement of the theorem is established. The proof of the last statement is left to the reader.

If U_1 and U_2 are subspaces of the same vector space V, let us define

0.26 $$U_1 + U_2 = \{X + Y; \ X \in U_1, Y \in U_2\}.$$

As will soon be stated in the next theorem, it can be shown that $U_1 + U_2$ is a *subspace* of V. We may remark that since the subspace U_2 contains the zero vector, it follows that if $X \in U_1$, then $X = X + 0$ is also an element of $U_1 + U_2$. That is, $U_1 \subseteq U_1 + U_2$; and, similarly, $U_2 \subseteq U_1 + U_2$. However, in general, $U_1 + U_2$ will contain many vectors other than those in U_1 or U_2. It is quite easy to show that the intersection $U_1 \cap U_2$ of the two subspaces U_1 and U_2 is also a subspace of V. An interesting relationship between the subspaces U_1, U_2, $U_1 + U_2$, and $U_1 \cap U_2$ is given in the second part of the following theorem.

0.27 Theorem. *Let U_1 and U_2 be subspaces of a vector space V. Then*

(i) *$U_1 \cap U_2$ and $U_1 + U_2$ are subspaces of V,*

(ii) *If V has finite dimension,*
$$dim \ (U_1 + U_2) = dim \ U_1 + dim \ U_2 - dim \ (U_1 \cap U_2).$$

We shall leave as exercises the proof of part (i) of this theorem and the proof of part (ii) for the special case in which dim $(U_1 \cap U_2) = 0$. We then proceed to the proof of part (ii) under the assumption that dim $(U_1 \cap U_2) > 0$. We may remark that since $U_1 \cap U_2$ is a subspace of U_1, it follows that

$$dim \ (U_1 \cap U_2) \leq dim \ U_1,$$

and, similarly,

$$dim \ (U_1 \cap U_2) \leq dim \ U_2.$$

First, we dispose of an easy special case as follows. Suppose that

$$\dim (U_1 \cap U_2) = \dim U_1,$$

which implies that $U_1 \cap U_2 = U_1$. It follows that $U_1 \subseteq U_2$, and 10.26 then shows that $U_1 + U_2 = U_2$. Hence, in this case, 10.27 (ii) takes the form

$$\dim U_2 = \dim U_1 + \dim U_2 - \dim U_1,$$

which is obviously true. Similar remarks hold if it happens that

$$\dim (U_1 \cap U_2) = \dim U_2.$$

Let us now set $\dim (U_1 \cap U_2) = r$, $\dim U_1 = r + s$, and $\dim U_2 = r + t$. In view of the preceding remarks, we henceforth assume that $r > 0$, $s > 0$, and $t > 0$. The proof will be completed by showing that

$$\dim (U_1 + U_2) = r + s + t.$$

Let $\{X_1, \cdots, X_r\}$ be a basis of $U_1 \cap U_2$. Then, by Theorem 10.24, there exist vectors $Y_1, \cdots, Y_s$ such that $\{X_1, \cdots, X_r, Y_1, \cdots, Y_s\}$ is a basis of U_1; and vectors $Z_1, \cdots, Z_t$ such that $\{X_1, \cdots, X_r, Z_1, \cdots, Z_t\}$ is a basis of U_2. It now follows from 10.26 that every vector of the subspace $U_1 + U_2$ is a linear combination of vectors of the set

10.28 $$\{X_1, \cdots, X_r, Y_1, \cdots, Y_s, Z_1, \cdots, Z_t\}.$$

We shall now show that this is a linearly independent set and hence a basis of $U_1 + U_2$.

Suppose that

10.29 $$a_1 X_1 + \cdots + a_r X_r + b_1 Y_1 + \cdots + b_s Y_s + c_1 Z_1 + \cdots + c_t Z_t = 0,$$

where all the coefficients are elements of F. Let $Z = c_1 Z_1 + \cdots + c_t Z_t$. It is then clear that $Z \in U_2$, and we see from 10.29 that

$$Z = - (a_1 X_1 + \cdots + a_r X_r + b_1 Y_1 + \cdots + b_s Y_s),$$

and hence also $Z \in U_1$. This shows that $Z \in (U_1 \cap U_2)$, and hence Z is a linear combination of the basis elements $X_1, \cdots, X_r$ of $U_1 \cap U_2$. Thus there exist scalars $e_1, \cdots. e_r$ such that

$$Z = c_1 Z_1 + \cdots + c_t Z_t = e_1 X_1 + \cdots + e_r X_r,$$

and from this it follows that

$$e_1 X_1 + \cdots + e_r X_r - c_1 Z_1 - \cdots - c_t Z_t = 0.$$

But since $\{X_1, \cdots, X_r, Z_1, \cdots, Z_t\}$ is a basis of U_2, this is a linearly independent set and hence all e's and all c's must equal zero. Now, setting all c's equal to zero in 10.29, the linear independence of the set

$\{X_1, \cdots, X_r, Y_1, \cdots, Y_s\}$ shows that we must have all a's and all b's equal to zero. Hence, a relation of the form 10.29 holds only if all coefficients are zero. This shows that the set 10.28 is a linearly independent set and therefore a basis of $U_1 + U_2$. Finally, we see that dim $(U_1 + U_2) = r + s + t$ since this is the number of vectors in the basis 10.28. The proof is therefore completed.

$E\ X\ E\ R\ C\ I\ S\ E\ S$

1. Prove Theorem 10.27 (i).

2. Prove Theorem 10.27 (ii) for the case in which dim $(U_1 \cap U_2) = 0$.

3. Find a basis for $V_3(K)$ which contains the vectors $(1, -1, 0)$ and $(2, 1, 3)$.

4. If $C(K)$ is the vector space of the field of complex numbers over the field K of real numbers (*cf.* Example 3 of Section 10.2),

   (*i*)   Find the dimension of $C(K)$,

   (*ii*) Show that $\{a + bi, c + di\}$ is a basis of $C(K)$ if and only if $ad - bc \neq 0$.

5. Let $A = \{X_1, X_2, \cdots, X_m\}$ be a set of nonzero vectors of a vector space V. A subset $\{Y_1, Y_2, \cdots, Y_k\}$ of A is said to be a *maximal linearly independent subset* of A if (i) the set $\{Y_1, Y_2, \cdots, Y_k\}$ is a linearly independent set, and (ii) the set $\{Y_1, Y_2, \cdots, Y_k, Y\}$ is a linearly dependent set for each Y in A other than $Y_1, Y_2, \cdots, Y_k$. Show that if $\{Y_1, Y_2, \cdots, Y_k\}$ is a maximal linearly independent subset of A, then

$$\dim [X_1, X_2, \cdots, X_m] = k.$$

6. Find the dimension of the subspace

$$[(1, 2, 1, 0), (-1, 1, -4, 3), (2, 3, 3, -1), (0, 1, -1, 1)]$$
   of $V_4(K)$.

7. Let T be the set of all subspaces of $V_2(I/(2))$, and let an operation of addition be defined on the set T by 10.26. Verify that T is not a group with respect to this operation of addition.

8. Let U_1 and U_2 be subspaces of $V_4(K)$ as follows: $U_1 = [(1, 2, -1, 0), (2, 0, 1, 1)]$ and $U_2 = [(0, 0, 0, 1), (1, 0, 1, 0), (0, 4, -3, -1)]$. Find dim U_1, dim U_2, dim $(U_1 \cap U_2)$, dim $(U_1 + U_2)$, and verify the truth of Theorem 10.27 (ii) in this particular case.

10.6 ISOMORPHISM OF VECTOR SPACES

The concept of isomorphism of two vector spaces over the same field is introduced in the following definition.

10.30 Definition. Let V and V' be vector spaces over the same field F. A one-one mapping $X \to X'$ of V onto V' is called an *isomorphism* of V onto V' if the following are true:

$$\text{(i)} \quad X + Y \to X' + Y', \qquad\qquad X, Y \in V,$$
$$\text{(ii)} \quad rX \to rX', \qquad\qquad r \in F, X \in V.$$

If there exists an isomorphism of V onto V', we say also that V is *isomorphic to V'*.

The next theorem will show why the vector spaces $V_n(F)$ play such an important role in the study of vector spaces.

10.31 Theorem. *If a vector space V over the field F has dimension n with $n > 0$, then V is isomorphic to the vector space $V_n(F)$.*

Let $\{X_1, X_2, \cdots, X_n\}$ be a basis of V; hence the elements of V are just the linear combinations of these basis elements. We shall show that the mapping

10.32
$$c_1 X_1 + c_2 X_2 + \cdots + c_n X_n \to (c_1, c_2, \cdots, c_n)$$

is an isomorphism of V onto $V_n(F)$. It is obvious that this is a one-one mapping of V onto $V_n(F)$ since, by Corollary 10.14, the elements of V are *uniquely* expressible as linear combinations of the basis elements. We proceed to verify the two required properties 10.30 (i) and (ii) of an isomorphism. Let

$$X = a_1 X_1 + a_2 X_2 + \cdots + a_n X_n$$
and
$$Y = b_1 X_1 + b_2 X_2 + \cdots + b_n X_n$$

be elements of V, so that under the mapping 10.32, $X \to (a_1, a_2, \cdots, a_n)$ and $Y \to (b_1, b_2, \cdots, b_n)$. We now observe that

$$X + Y = (a_1 + b_1)X_1 + (a_2 + b_2)X_2 + \cdots + (a_n + b_n)X_n,$$

and therefore

$$X + Y \to (a_1 + b_1, a_2 + b_2, \cdots, a_n + b_n)$$
$$= (a_1, a_2, \cdots, a_n) + (b_1, b_2, \cdots, b_n).$$

Hence, addition is preserved under the mapping 10.32, and this establishes property 10.30 (i). Moreover, if X is as above and $r \in F$, we have

$$rX = (ra_1)X_1 + (ra_2)X_2 + \cdots + (ra_n)X_n \to (ra_1, ra_2, \cdots, ra_n)$$
$$= r(a_1, a_2, \cdots, a_n).$$

This verifies 10.30 (ii), and we have therefore shown that the mapping 10.32 is an isomorphism of V onto $V_n(F)$.

The content of this theorem suggests that when studying vector spaces of finite dimension we could limit ourselves to vector spaces of the form $V_n(F)$. However, it is often simpler not to make this restriction. Moreover, the most important properties of vector spaces do not depend on the notation used to designate the vectors, and it is therefore appropriate to establish these properties by using only the defining properties of a vector space. This is the reason that we have waited until now to prove Theorem 10.31.

10.7   INNER PRODUCTS IN $V_n(F)$

The concept to be introduced in this section will be useful in the following chapter.

0.33   Definition.   If $X = (a_1, a_2, \cdots, a_n)$ and $Y = (b_1, b_2, \cdots, b_n)$ are elements of $V_n(F)$, the *inner product* $X \cdot Y$ of X and Y is defined as follows:

$$X \cdot Y = a_1 b_1 + a_2 b_2 + \cdots + a_n b_n.$$

It is clear that the inner product of two vectors is a scalar; that is, it is an element of F. The following theorem gives the most important properties of inner products. Since the proofs are quite simple, we leave them as exercises.

0.34   Theorem.   (i)   *If $X, Y \in V_n(F)$, then $X \cdot Y = Y \cdot X$.*

(ii)   *If $X, Y, Z \in V_n(F)$, then $(X + Y) \cdot Z = X \cdot Z + Y \cdot Z$.*

(iii)   *If $X, Y \in V_n(F)$ and $a \in F$, then*
$$(aX) \cdot Y = X \cdot (aY) = a(X \cdot Y).$$

(iv)   *If $Y, X_1, X_2, \cdots, X_m$ are elements of $V_n(F)$, and $a_1, a_2, \cdots, a_m$ are elements of F, then*

$$(a_1 X_1 + a_2 X_2 + \cdots + a_m X_m) \cdot Y$$
$$= a_1(X_1 \cdot Y) + a_2(X_2 \cdot Y) + \cdots + a_m(X_m \cdot Y).$$

1. Prove that two vector spaces over the same field and having finite dimension are isomorphic if and only if they have the same dimension.

2. Show that the vector space Q of Example 5 of Section 10.2 is isomorphic to $V_4(F)$.

3. Prove Theorem 10.34.

4. If X and Y are nonzero elements of $V_2(K)$, show that $X \cdot Y = 0$ if and only if the directed line segments which represent these vectors, in the sense described in Section 10.1, are perpendicular.

5. If $Y \in V_n(F)$, use Theorem 10.34 to show that the set of all vectors X of $V_n(F)$ such that $X \cdot Y = 0$ is a subspace of $V_n(F)$.

11

Systems of Linear Equations

There are several different ways of approaching the study of systems of linear equations. In this chapter we shall apply the theory of vector spaces as developed in the preceding chapter. After determinants have been introduced in the next chapter we shall then indicate how the theory of determinants may be used as an alternate approach to the subject.

Section 11.2 is devoted to a systematic procedure which can be used to determine whether or not a given system of linear equations has a solution and, if it does have a solution, for finding all solutions. However, we shall be primarily interested in obtaining theoretical results such as various conditions under which a system of linear equations will have a solution. Matrices will be introduced in Section 11.3 and a few simple properties will be established. Finally, these properties will be used to obtain additional results about systems of linear equations.

11.1 NOTATION AND SIMPLE RESULTS

If F is a given field and x_1, x_2, $\cdots$, x_n are indeterminates, it is customary to call a polynomial of the form $a_1x_1 + a_2x_2 + \cdots + a_nx_n$, where the coefficients are elements of F, a *linear form* (over F). Using the "sigma" notation for sums, with which the reader is no doubt already familiar, such a linear form may be written as

$$\sum_{k=1}^{n} a_k x_k.$$

This notation indicates a sum in which k takes on the successive values 1. 2, $\cdots$, n, that is,

$$\sum_{k=1}^{n} a_k x_k = a_1 x_1 + a_2 x_2 + \cdots + a_n x_n.$$

Of course, any other symbol can be used in place of k in this notation Hence,

$$\sum_{k=1}^{n} a_k x_k = \sum_{i=1}^{n} a_i x_i = \sum_{j=1}^{n} a_j x_j,$$

and so on. In the future we shall use this "sigma" notation for sums whenever it seems convenient or appropriate.

The linear form in which all coefficients are zero may be called the *zero linear form* and designated simply by "0".

Now let m and n be positive integers and let us consider a system of linear equations which we may write in the following explicit form:

11.1
$$
\begin{aligned}
a_{11}x_1 + a_{12}x_2 + \cdots + a_{1n}x_n &= b_1, \\
a_{21}x_1 + a_{22}x_2 + \cdots + a_{2n}x_n &= b_2, \\
&\;\;\vdots \\
a_{m1}x_1 + a_{m2}x_2 + \cdots + a_{mn}x_n &= b_m.
\end{aligned}
$$

It is understood that all the coefficients a_{ij}, as well as the *constant terms* b_i, are elements of a given field F. If we wish to emphasize the particular field involved, we shall speak of a system of linear equations *over* F.

As a matter of notation, it should be observed that a_{ij} is the coefficient of x_j in the ith equation. That is, the first subscript of a_{ij} specifies the equation and the second one the indeterminate of which it is the coefficient.

Now the left sides of Equations 11.1 are linear forms over F, and the right sides are elements of F. Since a linear form over F is not an element of F, it is clear that the "=" is being used in a different sense than heretofore. However, it is common practice to write Equations 11.1 with the understanding that what we really mean is that we are seeking elements $t_1, t_2, \cdots, t_n$ of F such that if we replace x_i by t_i ($i = 1, 2, \cdots, n$), each equation will yield a true equality of elements of F. Then, if $t_1, t_2, \cdots, t_n$ are such elements, it is customary to say that

$x_1 = t_1,\ x_2 = t_2,\ \cdots,\ x_n = t_n$ is a *solution* of the Equations 11.1; also that in this solution x_i has the *value* t_i $(i = 1, 2, \cdots, n)$. Of course, it is quite possible for a given system of linear equations not to have any solution. In fact, we shall eventually obtain various tests for the existence of a solution.

The symbols $x_1, x_2, \cdots, x_n$ are often called *unknowns*, and we may therefore call 11.1 a *system of m linear equations in n unknowns*.

There are various alternative ways of writing the Equations 11.1, each of which is convenient for certain purposes. First, we observe that we may write them in the following form:

1.2
$$\sum_{j=1}^{n} a_{ij}x_j = b_i, \qquad (i = 1, 2, \cdots, m).$$

In this form, each value of i gives one equation, and in each equation j takes values from 1 to n. We next introduce a quite different notation which will be most useful.

Let us define elements of the vector space $V_n(F)$ as follows:

1.3
$$A_1 = (a_{11}, a_{12}, \cdots, a_{1n}),$$
$$A_2 = (a_{21}, a_{22}, \cdots, a_{2n}),$$
$$\cdot \quad \cdot \quad \cdot \quad \cdot \quad \cdot \quad \cdot \quad \cdot \quad \cdot$$
$$A_m = (a_{m1}, a_{m2}, \cdots, a_{mn}).$$

It will be noted that A_i is composed of the coefficients in the ith equation of the system 11.1. Let us also formally write $X = (x_1, x_2, \cdots, x_n)$. Then in terms of the inner product of vectors as defined in the last section of the preceding chapter, we may write the system 11.1 in the following form:

1.4
$$A_1 \cdot X = b_1, \quad A_2 \cdot X = b_2, \quad \cdots, \quad A_m \cdot X = b_m.$$

A *solution* of this system of equations is then an element $T = (t_1, t_2, \cdots, t_n)$ of $V_n(F)$ such that

1.5
$$A_1 \cdot T = b_1, \quad A_2 \cdot T = b_2, \quad \cdots, \quad A_m \cdot T = b_m.$$

It is now fairly easy to give one condition which must hold provided this system of linear equations has a solution. First, let us make the following definition.

1.6 Definition. The system 11.4 of linear equations is said to be *compatible* if for every choice of elements s_i of F such that $\sum_{i=1}^{m} s_i A_i = 0$, then necessarily $\sum_{i=1}^{m} s_i b_i = 0$ also.

We shall now show that if the system 11.4 of linear equations has a solution, the system is compatible. For if T is a solution and

$$\sum_{i=1}^{m} s_i A_i = 0,$$

it follows from 11.5 and Theorem 10.34 that

$$\sum_{i=1}^{m} s_i b_i = \sum_{i=1}^{m} s_i (A_i \cdot T) = \sum_{i=1}^{m} (s_i A_i) \cdot T = \left(\sum_{i=1}^{m} s_i A_i\right) \cdot T = 0 \cdot T = 0,$$

and the system is therefore compatible.

It should be clear that when we say that a system is compatible, we are only saying in a precise way that if the system has a solution and if there exist elements of F such that when we multiply both sides of the equations by these elements of F and add corresponding members we obtain the zero linear form on the left, then we must also obtain the zero element of F on the right. Later on we shall prove the converse of what was proved above, that is, we shall prove that if a system of linear equations is compatible, the system necessarily has a solution. This is a fairly deep result and in order to prove it we shall have to wait until the proper machinery is available.

There is still another useful way of writing Equations 11.1 (or 11.2 or 11.4). First, we shall introduce elements of $V_m(F)$ consisting of coefficients in our system of equations that lie in a fixed vertical line. Let us set

11.7 $\quad A^1 = \begin{bmatrix} a_{11} \\ a_{21} \\ \vdots \\ a_{m1} \end{bmatrix}, \quad A^2 = \begin{bmatrix} a_{12} \\ a_{22} \\ \vdots \\ a_{m2} \end{bmatrix}, \quad \cdots, \quad A^n = \begin{bmatrix} a_{1n} \\ a_{2n} \\ \vdots \\ a_{mn} \end{bmatrix}, \quad B^1 = \begin{bmatrix} b_1 \\ b_2 \\ \vdots \\ b_m \end{bmatrix}.$

The elements 11.3 of $V_n(F)$ are written as *row vectors*, and we may call these elements 11.7 of $V_m(F)$ *column vectors* to indicate that we have used a vertical arrangement instead of a horizontal one. Heretofore we have always used row vectors only because they are simpler to write. When we have occasion to use column vectors we shall use superscripts (not to be confused with exponents) to indicate this fact. Now in terms of the column vectors defined in 11.7 the entire system 11.1 of linear equations can be written in the following vector form:

11.8 $\qquad\qquad x_1 A^1 + x_2 A^2 + \cdots + x_n A^n = B^1.$

In the notation used here we may now observe that *the Equation 11.8 (or the system 11.1) has a solution if and only if the vector B^1 is a linear combination of the vectors $A^1, A^2, \cdots, A^n$.* We shall refer to this fact again in a later section.

The usual method of finding solutions of a given system of linear equations involves a procedure for simplifying the form of the system. The following concept is a useful one in this connection.

1.9   Definition.   Two systems of linear equations are said to be *equivalent* if they have exactly the same solutions.

There are simple operations on a system of linear equations that always yield equivalent systems. In order to simplify the wording, we shall speak of multiplying an equation by an element of F to mean the multiplying of both members of the equation by this element. Also, we shall speak of adding two equations to mean the adding of corresponding members of the two equations.

1.10   Definition.   We shall say that we perform an *elementary operation* on a system of linear equations if we do any one of the following:
  Type 1.   Interchange two equations.
  Type 2.   Multiply an equation by a nonzero element of F.
  Type 3.   Add to one equation d times a different equation, where $d \in F$.

As suggested by what was said above, the importance of these elementary operations stems from the following theorem.

1.11   Theorem.   *If a system of linear equations is obtained from a given system by applying in turn a finite number of elementary operations, the two systems are equivalent.*

It is obvious that we need only show that *one* elementary operation always yields an equivalent system. The desired result is quite trivial for an elementary operation of Type 1 or 2, and so we consider an elementary operation of Type 3. Let us write our given system of equations in the form 11.4 and, for convenience of notation, suppose that the operation consists of multiplying the second equation by $d \in F$ and adding it to the first equation. Using the fact that

$$A_1 \cdot X + d(A_2 \cdot X) = (A_1 + dA_2) \cdot X,$$

the resulting system can be written in the following form:

1.12 $(A_1 + dA_2) \cdot X = b_1 + db_2, \quad A_2 \cdot X = b_2, \quad \cdots, \quad A_m \cdot X = b_m.$

Now if T is a solution of 11.4 so that, in fact, $A_i \cdot T = b_i$ for $i = 1,$ $2, \cdots, m$, it is clear that T is also a solution of 11.12. Conversely, let T be a solution of 11.12, so that, in particular, $(A_1 + dA_2) \cdot T = b_1 + db_2$ and $A_2 \cdot T = b_2$. Since

$$(A_1 + dA_2) \cdot T = A_1 \cdot T + d(A_2 \cdot T) = b_1 + db_2,$$

it follows that $A_1 \cdot T = b_1$. Moreover, the two systems 11.4 and 11.12 are identical except for the first equation, and hence T is a solution of every equation of the system 11.4. We have thus shown that every solution of either of these systems is a solution of the other and they are therefore equivalent.

If one of the equations of a system is the *zero equation*; that is, if all the coefficients and the constant term are zero, the deletion of this equation from the system will clearly yield an equivalent system. We shall not call this an elementary operation, but we shall use this operation without hesitation whenever it is helpful to do so.

Theorem 11.11, together with the operation of deletion of one or more zero equations, may be applied in a systematic way to find all solutions (if any) of a given system. What we do is to apply a sequence of operations until a system is obtained in a simple enough form that the solutions are apparent. These solutions must then be the solutions of the original system. Although it is a very simple procedure, we shall find that it leads to interesting theoretical results as well as to a practical method for actually finding the solutions of a given system. This procedure will be discussed in detail in the following section.

11.2 ECHELON SYSTEMS

We shall begin by discussing two examples which will clarify the ideas involved. First, let us consider the following system of four equations in five unknowns over the field R of rational numbers:

11.13
$$x_1 + x_2 + x_3 + 2x_4 + 3x_5 = 13,$$
$$-2x_1 - 2x_2 + x_3 + 3x_4 - 4x_5 = 5,$$
$$3x_1 + 3x_2 + x_4 + 5x_5 = 10,$$
$$x_1 + x_2 + 2x_3 - x_4 + 9x_5 = 18.$$

In order to eliminate x_1 from all equations but the first, we perform, in turn, the following three elementary operations of Type 3 on this system. First, we multiply the first equation by 2 and add it to the second equation, then multiply the first equation by -3 and add it to the third, and finally multiply the first equation by -1 and add it to the last equation. We thus obtain the following system which, by Theorem 11.11, must be equivalent to the system 11.13:

$$x_1 + x_2 + x_3 + 2x_4 + 3x_5 = 13,$$
$$3x_3 + 7x_4 + 2x_5 = 31,$$
$$-3x_3 - 5x_4 - 4x_5 = -29,$$
$$x_3 - 3x_4 + 6x_5 = 5.$$

We now proceed to eliminate x_3 from all these equations but one. Since in the last equation the coefficient of x_3 is unity, we shall work with this equation and, in order to systematize the procedure, we use an elementary operation of Type 1 to interchange the second and fourth equation in order to get this equation in the second position. We then eliminate x_3 from all the equations except this new second one by multiplying it in turn by the proper elements of R and adding to the other equations. In this way we obtain the system

$$x_1 + x_2 \quad\; + 5x_4 - \; 3x_5 = 8,$$
$$x_3 - \; 3x_4 + \; 6x_5 = 5,$$
$$- 14x_4 + 14x_5 = -14,$$
$$16x_4 - 16x_5 = 16.$$

It is now clear that the third equation (as well as the fourth) can be simplified by an elementary operation of Type 2. Accordingly, we divide the third equation by -14 (multiply it by $-1/14$), and then proceed as above to eliminate x_4 from all equations except the third. We thus obtain the following system of equations:

$$x_1 + x_2 \quad\;\; + 2x_5 = 3,$$
$$x_3 \quad\; + 3x_5 = 8,$$
$$x_4 - \; x_5 = 1,$$
$$0 = 0.$$

Finally, we omit the last equation and rewrite the system in the following form:

1.14
$$x_1 = 3 - x_2 - 2x_5,$$
$$x_3 = 8 \quad\quad - 3x_5,$$
$$x_4 = 1 \quad\quad + x_5.$$

This system is equivalent to the given system 11.13, and in the present form its solutions are apparent. If x_2 and x_5 are replaced by arbitrary elements of R, and the other unknowns are calculated from 11.14, we obtain a solution; and all solutions can be obtained in this way. To express this fact algebraically, let s and t be arbitrary elements of R. Then

$$x_1 = 3 - s - 2t, \quad x_2 = s, \quad x_3 = 8 - 3t, \quad x_4 = 1 + t, \quad x_5 = t$$

is a solution of the system 11.14, and any solution is of this form for suitable choices of s and t. We have therefore found all solutions of the given system 11.13 since it is equivalent to the system 11.14.

In the example just discussed, we found many solutions of the given system of equations. In other cases there might be exactly one solution or no solution. As a simple illustration of what happens when there is no solution, let us attempt to solve the following system of equations by the same method used above:

11.15
$$x_1 + x_2 - x_3 = 5,$$
$$x_1 + 2x_2 - 3x_3 = 8,$$
$$x_2 - 2x_3 = 1.$$

First, we multiply the first equation by -1 and add it to the second equation, obtaining the following system:

$$x_1 + x_2 - x_3 = 5,$$
$$x_2 - 2x_3 = 3,$$
$$x_2 - 2x_3 = 1.$$

Of course, it is obvious that this system has no solution, but let us proceed to eliminate x_2 from the first and third equations. After doing this, we have the system

$$x_1 + x_3 = 2,$$
$$x_2 - 2x_3 = 3,$$
$$0 = -2.$$

Finally, in order to standardize the procedure, we divide the third equation by -2 and then multiply the new third equation by -2 and add it to the first; and also multiply the new third equation by -3 and add it to the second. We obtain in this way the following system of equations which is equivalent to the given system 11.15:

11.16
$$x_1 + x_3 = 0,$$
$$x_2 - 2x_3 = 0,$$
$$0 = 1.$$

Now the symbol "0" on the left in the last of these equations stands for the zero linear form $0x_1 + 0x_2 + 0x_3$. It is clear that if the unknowns in this zero linear form are replaced by arbitrary elements of the field R, we obtain the zero element of R. Hence the last equation has no solution, and therefore the system 11.16 has no solution. We shall presently see that any system of linear equations which does not have a solution is reducible to a system in which one of the equations takes the form $0 = 1$.

We have considered these two examples in detail as illustrations of the procedure which can be applied to any system of linear equations. Suppose, now, that we wish to solve an arbitrary system 11.1 of m linear equations in n unknowns. We shall assume that not *all* the coefficients a_{ij} are zero since, otherwise, the problem is completely trivial. Moreover, if all the coefficients of x_1 were zero, we could just as well consider only $x_2, \cdots, x_n$ as the unknowns and ignore x_1. However, to use a general notation, let us suppose that x_{k_1} is the *first* one of the unknowns x_1, x_2, $\cdots$, x_n which has a nonzero coefficient in any of the equations. Normally, of course, we will have $k_1 = 1$. By interchanging equations, if necessary, we can obtain an equivalent system in which the coefficient of x_{k_1} is not zero in the *first* of our equations. Then, by dividing the first equation by the coefficient of x_{k_1} in this equation, we can obtain unity as the coefficient of x_{k_1}. Next, by elementary operations of Type 3, as in the examples, we can obtain a system in which the coefficient of x_{k_1} is zero in every equation other than the first. The system is then of the following type:

$$x_{k_1} + b_{1\,k_1+1}x_{k_1+1} + \cdots + b_{1n}x_n = c_1,$$
$$b_{2\,k_1+1}x_{k_1+1} + \cdots + b_{2n}x_n = c_2,$$
$$\cdot \quad \cdot \quad \cdot \quad \cdot \quad \cdot \quad \cdot \quad \cdot \quad \cdot \quad \cdot \quad \cdot \quad \cdot \quad \cdot$$
$$b_{m\,k_1+1}x_{k_1+1} + \cdots + b_{mn}x_n = c_m.$$

Now suppose that x_{k_2} is the first one of the unknowns $x_{k_1+1}, \cdots, x_n$ which has a nonzero coefficient in any of these equations *except the first*. By interchanging equations, if necessary, we can be sure that the coefficient of x_{k_2} is not zero in the second equation. We can then use elementary operations to make this coefficient unity and the coefficient of x_{k_2} zero in all equations except the second. By continuing this process, we find that for some positive integer r, with $r \leq m$ and $r \leq n$, there exist positive integers $k_1 < k_2 < \cdots < k_r$ such that our system of equations can be reduced by use of elementary operations to a system of the following form:

$$x_{k_1} + \cdots + 0x_{k_2} + \cdots + 0x_{k_r} + \cdots = d_1,$$
$$x_{k_2} + \cdots + 0x_{k_r} + \cdots = d_2.$$
$$\cdot \quad \cdot \quad \cdot \quad \cdot \quad \cdot \quad \cdot \quad \cdot \quad \cdot \quad \cdot \quad \cdot \quad \cdot$$
$$x_{k_r} + \cdots = d_r,$$
$$0 = d_{r+1},$$
$$\cdot \quad \cdot \quad \cdot \quad \cdot$$
$$0 = d_m.$$

11.17

In this system if i is an integer such that $1 \leq i \leq r$, the coefficient of x_{k_i} is different from zero *only* in the ith equation. For example, the coefficients of $x_{k_2}, \cdots, x_{k_r}$ are all zero in the first equation, but if there are any other unknowns, their coefficients need not be zero. In the second equation the coefficient of x_j is zero for all $j < k_2$; also, the coefficients of $x_{k_3}, \cdots, x_{k_r}$ are zero. Corresponding remarks hold for the other equations. If it happens that $r = m$, then there will be no equations with 0 as left member.

Let us now assume that the given system 11.1, and therefore also the equivalent system 11.17, has a solution. It is then apparent that we must have $d_{r+1} = \cdots = d_m = 0$. Accordingly, we conclude that *if the system 11.1 has a solution, it can be reduced by elementary operations, together with the possible deletion of zero equations, to a system of the form*

11.18
$$x_{k_1} + \cdots + 0x_{k_2} + \cdots + 0x_{k_r} + \cdots = d_1,$$
$$x_{k_2} + \cdots + 0x_{k_r} + \cdots = d_2,$$
$$\cdot \quad \cdot \quad \cdot \quad \cdot \quad \cdot \quad \cdot \quad \cdot \quad \cdot \quad \cdot \quad \cdot$$
$$x_{k_r} + \cdots = d_r,$$

with the same understanding about zero coefficients as in 11.17. We now observe that it is easy to find all solutions of the system 11.18. If we assign arbitrary values from the field F to the unknowns (if any) other than $x_{k_1}, x_{k_2}, \cdots, x_{k_r}$, the value of x_{k_1} is uniquely determined from the first equation, the value of x_{k_2} is uniquely determined from the second equation, and so on. Not only does this procedure give a method of finding solutions but, since the values of $x_{k_1}, x_{k_2}, \cdots, x_{k_r}$ are uniquely determined by the values of the other unknowns, it follows that *every* solution of the system 11.18 can be obtained by the process just described.

Let us next assume that the given system 11.1, and therefore also the equivalent system 11.17, does not have a solution. If $d_{r+1} = \cdots = d_m = 0$, the argument given above would show that the system has a solution. Accordingly, at least one of the equations in 11.17 must be of the form $0 = d$ with $d \neq 0$. For theoretical purposes it is helpful to continue our simplification procedure a little further as follows. By interchanging equations, if necessary, we can consider this equation $0 = d$ to be the first one of those with 0 as left member. Then, by elementary operations, we can write this equation in the form $0 = 1$ and also reduce the constant terms in all other equations to 0. Finally, after deleting any zero equations, our system takes the following form:

11.19
$$x_{k_1} + \cdots + 0x_{k_2} + \cdots + 0x_{k_r} + \cdots = 0,$$
$$x_{k_2} + \cdots + 0x_{k_r} + \cdots = 0,$$
$$\cdot \quad \cdot \quad \cdot \quad \cdot \quad \cdot \quad \cdot \quad \cdot \quad \cdot \quad \cdot \quad \cdot$$
$$x_{k_r} + \cdots = 0,$$
$$0 = 1.$$

A system of linear equations either of the form 11.18 or of the form 11.19 is said to be an *echelon* system.

The conclusions we have reached above may be summarized in the following theorem.

11.20 Theorem. *Any system 11.1 of linear equations with coefficients over a field F can be reduced by means of elementary operations, and the possible deletion of zero equations, to an echelon system.*

The given system has a solution if and only if it is reducible to an echelon system of the form 11.18. In this case, the unknowns (if any) other than x_{k_1}, x_{k_2}, $\cdots$, x_{k_r} can be assigned arbitrary values from F, and the corresponding values of x_{k_1}, x_{k_2}, $\cdots$, x_{k_r} are then uniquely determined from the Equations 11.18. Moreover, all solutions can be obtained in this way.

The given system does not have a solution if and only if it is reducible to an echelon system of the form 11.19.

If $r = n$, the Equations 11.18 take the form $x_1 = d_1$, $x_2 = d_2$, $\cdots$, $x_n = d_n$; and the system clearly has exactly one solution. If $r < n$, there is at least one unknown which can be assigned arbitrary values; hence there will be more than one solution. The following result is therefore an immediate consequence of the preceding theorem.

11.21 Corollary. *A system 11.1 of linear equations has a* unique *solution if and only if the number r of equations in the corresponding echelon system 11.18 is equal to the number n of unknowns.*

EXERCISES

Reduce each of the following systems of linear equations to an echelon system, and find all solutions.

In Exercises 1–6, the equations are over the field of rational numbers.

1.
$$x_1 - \ x_2 + 2x_3 = 5,$$
$$2x_1 + \ x_2 - \ x_3 = 2,$$
$$2x_1 - \ x_2 - \ x_3 = 4,$$
$$x_1 + 3x_2 + 2x_3 = 1.$$

2.
$$2x_1 - 2x_2 + 2x_3 - \ 3x_4 = 11,$$
$$x_1 - \ x_2 + \ x_3 - \ 2x_4 = \ 4,$$
$$-x_1 + \ x_2 \qquad + \ 6x_4 = -3,$$
$$9x_1 - 9x_2 + 7x_3 - 23x_4 = 43.$$

3.
$$2x_1 - \ x_2 + \ x_3 = 4,$$
$$3x_1 + \ x_2 - 5x_3 = 1,$$
$$x_1 - 5x_2 + 8x_3 = 5,$$
$$2x_1 - 2x_2 + \ x_3 = 3.$$

4.
$$2x_1 - 4x_2 + 3x_3 - 5x_4 = -3,$$
$$4x_1 + 2x_2 + \ x_3 \qquad = 4,$$
$$6x_1 - 2x_2 + 4x_3 - 5x_4 = 1.$$

5. $2x_1 - x_2 - x_3 + x_4 + 8x_5 = -4,$
$x_1 + x_2 + 4x_3 + x_4 + 4x_5 = 3,$
$-3x_1 + 2x_2 + 3x_3 + x_4 - 5x_5 = 3,$
$2x_1 - 2x_2 - 3x_3 + 2x_4 + 12x_5 = -10.$

6. $3x_1 - x_2 + x_3 - x_4 = 1,$
$2x_1 + 3x_2 - x_3 + 5x_4 = 7,$
$2x_1 + 5x_2 - x_3 + 12x_4 = 8,$
$x_1 - 2x_2 + 2x_3 + x_4 = 5.$

In Exercises 7–9, the equations are over the field $I/(3)$. Find the number of solutions in each case and actually exhibit all of them.

7. $x_1 + 2x_2 + x_3 = 2,$
$2x_1 + x_2 + 2x_3 = 1,$
$x_1 + x_2 + x_3 = 2.$

8. $x_1 + 2x_2 + x_3 \qquad = 0,$
$x_2 + x_3 + x_4 = 0,$
$2x_1 + 2x_2 + x_3 \qquad = 2,$
$2x_2 \qquad + x_4 = 2.$

9. $2x_1 + x_2 + 2x_3 + x_4 = 1,$
$x_1 + 2x_2 + x_3 + 2x_4 = 2.$

11.3 MATRICES

The concept of a matrix arises naturally in mathematics in several different ways. For example, in carrying out the calculations of the preceding section it is obvious that we could avoid writing down the unknowns, as well as the signs of addition and equality, and just work with the array of coefficients and constant terms. This possibility suggests the introduction of some suitable notation and terminology for discussing rectangular arrays of elements of a field. We proceed to give the necessary definitions and to establish those properties which will be particularly useful in the study of systems of linear equations. Matrices will be studied in somewhat more detail in Chapter 13.

Let p and q be positive integers, and let c_{ij} $(i = 1, 2, \cdots, p;$ $j = 1, 2, \cdots, q)$ be elements of a field F. The rectangular array C defined by

11.22
$$C = \begin{bmatrix} c_{11} & c_{12} & \cdots & c_{1q} \\ c_{21} & c_{22} & \cdots & c_{2q} \\ \cdot & \cdot & \cdots & \cdot \\ c_{p1} & c_{p2} & \cdots & c_{pq} \end{bmatrix}$$

is called a *matrix* (over F) with p rows and q columns, or simply a $p \times q$

matrix. As suggested by this language, the elements of the matrix C that occur in a horizontal line constitute a *row* of the matrix, and those in a vertical line a *column* of the matrix. It will be observed that an element c_{ij} occurs at the intersection of the ith row and jth column.

The rows of the matrix C may be considered to be elements of the vector space $V_q(F)$. More precisely, we may define the *row vectors* of C to be the following vectors of $V_q(F)$:

$$C_1 = (c_{11}, c_{12}, \cdots, c_{1q}),$$
$$C_2 = (c_{21}, c_{22}, \cdots, c_{2q}),$$
$$\cdot \quad \cdot \quad \cdot \quad \cdot \quad \cdot \quad \cdot \quad \cdot \quad \cdot \quad \cdot \quad \cdot \quad \cdot$$
$$C_p = (c_{p1}, c_{p2}, \cdots, c_{pq}).$$

Similarly, the *column vectors* of C are defined to be the following vectors of $V_p(F)$:

$$C^1 = \begin{bmatrix} c_{11} \\ c_{21} \\ \vdots \\ c_{p1} \end{bmatrix}, \quad C^2 = \begin{bmatrix} c_{12} \\ c_{22} \\ \vdots \\ c_{p2} \end{bmatrix}, \quad \cdots, \quad C^q = \begin{bmatrix} c_{1q} \\ c_{2q} \\ \vdots \\ c_{pq} \end{bmatrix}.$$

It will be observed that a row vector of the matrix C may be considered to be a matrix with one row and q columns, and likewise a column vector may be considered to be a matrix with p rows and one column.

The concepts introduced in the following definition play an important role in the sequel.

11.23 Definition. The subspace of $V_q(F)$ generated by the row vectors of C, that is, in the notation of 10.13, the subspace $[C_1, C_2, \cdots, C_p]$ of $V_q(F)$, is called the *row space* of the matrix C. The dimension of this row space is called the *row rank* of the matrix C.

Similarly, the subspace of $V_p(F)$ generated by the column vectors of C; that is, the subspace $[C^1, C^2, \cdots, C^q]$ of $V_p(F)$, is called the *column space* of C and its dimension is the *column rank* of C.

In order to compute the row rank, or the column rank, of a given matrix, we may use a method suggested by the way in which we simplified a system of linear equations in the preceding section. Let us first define elementary operations on a matrix as follows (*cf.* 11.10).

11.24 Definition. Let C be a matrix over a field F. We shall say that we perform an *elementary row (column) operation* on C if we do any one of the following:

Type 1. Interchange two rows (columns).

Type 2. Multiply the elements of one row (column) by a non-zero element of F.

Type 3. Add to the elements of one row (column) d times the corresponding elements of a different row (column), where $d \in F$.

We thus have three different types of elementary row operations, and three types of elementary column operations. For simplicity of statement, we now restrict attention to elementary row operations. From our present point of view, the importance of the elementary row operations is that if a matrix D is obtained from a matrix C by means of an elementary row operation, C and D have the same row spaces and therefore also the same row rank. This fact is obvious for an elementary row operation of Type 1, and parts (i) and (ii) of Theorem 10.15 assure us that it is also true for operations of Types 2 and 3. Since the row rank of a matrix is not changed by application of *one* elementary row operation, the same must also be true for a finite sequence of elementary row operations. Of course, similar remarks hold for column operations, and we summarize these remarks in the following theorem.

11.25 Theorem. *If one matrix is obtained from another by a finite sequence of elementary row (column) operations, the two matrices have the same row space (column space), and therefore also the same row rank (column rank).*

In view of this theorem, we may compute the row rank of a given matrix by applying elementary row operations until a matrix is obtained in a form in which its row rank is apparent. This row rank must then also be the row rank of the given matrix. Let us illustrate this procedure by finding the row rank of the following matrix over the field R of rational numbers:

11.26
$$\begin{bmatrix} 0 & -1 & 3 & -1 & 0 & 2 \\ -1 & 1 & -2 & -2 & 1 & -3 \\ 2 & -1 & 4 & 4 & -1 & 8 \\ 1 & -2 & 5 & 1 & -1 & 5 \end{bmatrix}.$$

It will be observed that the procedure is essentially that used in the preceding section to reduce a system of linear equations to an echelon system.

First, we get an element 1 in the upper left-hand position by interchanging the first two rows and then multiplying the new first row by -1. We then have the matrix

$$\begin{bmatrix} 1 & -1 & 2 & 2 & -1 & 3 \\ 0 & -1 & 3 & -1 & 0 & 2 \\ 2 & -1 & 4 & 4 & -1 & 8 \\ 1 & -2 & 5 & 1 & -1 & 5 \end{bmatrix}.$$

Next we use elementary row operations of Type 3 to reduce all elements of the first column, except this first element, to zero. More specifically, we multiply the first row by -2 and add it to the third row; also multiply the first row by -1 and add it to the fourth row. This gives us the matrix

$$\begin{bmatrix} 1 & -1 & 2 & 2 & -1 & 3 \\ 0 & -1 & 3 & -1 & 0 & 2 \\ 0 & 1 & 0 & 0 & 1 & 2 \\ 0 & -1 & 3 & -1 & 0 & 2 \end{bmatrix}.$$

Now if we add the third row to each of the other rows, and then interchange the second and third rows, we obtain

$$\begin{bmatrix} 1 & 0 & 2 & 2 & 0 & 5 \\ 0 & 1 & 0 & 0 & 1 & 2 \\ 0 & 0 & 3 & -1 & 1 & 4 \\ 0 & 0 & 3 & -1 & 1 & 4 \end{bmatrix}.$$

We next multiply the third row by -1 and add it to the last row, obtaining a row consisting entirely of zeros. We then multiply the third row by $1/3$ in order to get 1 as its first nonzero element. Finally, we multiply the third row by -2 and add it to the first row. This gives the matrix

$$\begin{bmatrix} 1 & 0 & 0 & 8/3 & -2/3 & 7/3 \\ 0 & 1 & 0 & 0 & 1 & 2 \\ 0 & 0 & 1 & -1/3 & 1/3 & 4/3 \\ 0 & 0 & 0 & 0 & 0 & 0 \end{bmatrix}.$$

Since the unit vectors $(1, 0, 0)$, $(0, 1, 0)$, and $(0, 0, 1)$ of $V_3(R)$ are linearly independent, it is easy to see that the first three rows of this matrix are linearly independent, and hence that its row rank is 3. Since this matrix has been obtained from the given matrix by use of elementary row operations, it follows that the matrix 11.26 also has row rank 3.

In this example, we have computed the *row* rank of the given matrix. It is obvious that we could similarly apply elementary column operations to determine the column rank of the matrix. However, the next theorem is of considerable theoretical importance and will show us that both of these ranks are known as soon as one of them has been determined.

11.27 Theorem. *The row rank of any matrix is equal to its column rank.*

Let C be the $p \times q$ matrix 11.22 over a field F, and suppose that the row rank of C is r and that its column rank is s. The main part of the proof consists in showing that any $r + 1$ column vectors of C are linearly dependent, and hence that $s \leq r$. If $r = p$, this is clearly true since, by Corollary 10.19, any $p + 1$ vectors of $V_p(F)$ are linearly dependent. Suppose, then, that $r < p$. Since the row rank is r, there must exist r row vectors that constitute a basis of the row space of C. Let us rearrange the rows (if necessary) so that the first r rows are a basis of the row space. It is not difficult to see that this cannot change the linear dependence or independence of column vectors, and hence it does not change the column rank. As a matter of notation, we may therefore assume, without loss of generality, that the *first* r rows of C form a basis of the row space of C. Since we wish to show that the column rank s of C cannot exceed r, we may certainly assume that $q > r$ since, otherwise, there is nothing to prove. Let us now write our matrix C in a somewhat more explicit form as follows:

$$C = \begin{bmatrix} c_{11} & c_{12} & \cdots & c_{1r} & c_{1\,r+1} & \cdots & c_{1q} \\ c_{21} & c_{22} & \cdots & c_{2r} & c_{2\,r+1} & \cdots & c_{2q} \\ \cdot & \cdot & \cdot & \cdot & \cdot & \cdot & \cdot \\ c_{r1} & c_{r2} & \cdots & c_{rr} & c_{r\,r+1} & \cdots & c_{rq} \\ \cdot & \cdot & \cdot & \cdot & \cdot & \cdot & \cdot \\ c_{p1} & c_{p2} & \cdots & c_{pr} & c_{p\,r+1} & \cdots & c_{pq} \end{bmatrix}.$$

As introduced earlier, let $C_1, C_2, \cdots, C_p$ be the row vectors, and $C^1, C^2, \cdots, C^q$ the column vectors of C. Moreover, let

$$S^1 = \begin{bmatrix} c_{11} \\ c_{21} \\ \vdots \\ c_{r1} \end{bmatrix}, \quad S^2 = \begin{bmatrix} c_{12} \\ c_{22} \\ \vdots \\ c_{r2} \end{bmatrix}, \quad \cdots, \quad S^q = \begin{bmatrix} c_{1q} \\ c_{2q} \\ \vdots \\ c_{rq} \end{bmatrix}$$

be elements of $V_r(F)$ consisting of column vectors taken from the first r rows of C. We shall now prove the following lemma.

11.28 Lemma. *If $t_i \in F$ $(i = 1, 2, \cdots, q)$ such that*

$$\sum_{i=1}^{q} t_i S^i = 0, \quad \text{then also} \quad \sum_{i=1}^{q} t_i C^i = 0.$$

If $T = (t_1, t_2, \cdots, t_q)$, then $\sum_{i=1}^{q} t_i S^i = 0$ can be expressed using inner products of vectors as follows:

11.29 $$C_1 \cdot T = 0, \quad C_2 \cdot T = 0, \quad \cdots, \quad C_r \cdot T = 0.$$

Now if C_k is an arbitrary row vector of C, then C_k is a linear combination of the vectors $C_1, C_2, \cdots, C_r$, since they form a basis of the row space of C. That is, there exist elements a_j $(j = 1, 2, \cdots, r)$ of F such that

$$C_k = a_1 C_1 + a_2 C_2 + \cdots + a_r C_r.$$

It follows from Theorem 10.34 (iv) that

$$C_k \cdot T = (a_1C_1 + a_2C_2 + \cdots + a_rC_r) \cdot T$$
$$= a_1(C_1 \cdot T) + a_2(C_2 \cdot T) + \cdots + a_r(C_r \cdot T).$$

Hence, in view of 11.29, we see that $C_k \cdot T = 0$. Again, changing the notation, the fact that $C_k \cdot T = 0$ for $k = 1, 2, \cdots, p$ assures us that

$$\sum_{i=1}^{q} t_i C^i = 0,$$

as we wished to prove. The lemma is therefore established.

It is now easy to complete the proof that any $r + 1$ column vectors of C are linearly dependent. Merely for convenience of notation, let us show that the first $r + 1$ column vectors $C^1, C^2, \cdots, C^{r+1}$ are linearly dependent. We know that the column vectors $S^1, S^2, \cdots, S^{r+1}$ must be linearly dependent since we have $r + 1$ vectors of $V_r(F)$. Hence, there exist elements b_i $(i = 1, 2, \cdots, r + 1)$ of F, not all zero, such that

$$\sum_{i=1}^{r+1} b_i S^i = 0.$$

The lemma then asserts that also

$$\sum_{i=1}^{r+1} b_i C^i = 0,$$

and since the coefficients are not all zero we have shown that the first $r + 1$ column vectors of C are linearly dependent. Similarly, any set of $r + 1$ column vectors of C is a linearly dependent set, and we have therefore shown that $s \leq r$.

We may restate what we have proved up to this point as follows. *The column rank of an arbitrary matrix cannot exceed the row rank of the matrix.* One simple way to complete the proof of the theorem is as follows. If C is the matrix 11.22, let us write a new matrix C', called the *transpose* of C, obtained from C by interchanging rows and columns. That is, C' is defined as follows:

$$C' = \begin{bmatrix} c_{11} & c_{21} & \cdots & c_{p1} \\ c_{12} & c_{22} & \cdots & c_{p2} \\ \cdot & \cdot & \cdot & \cdot \\ c_{1q} & c_{2q} & \cdots & c_{pq} \end{bmatrix}.$$

Now the row space and column space of the matrix C' are, respectively, the column space and the row space of C. Hence, the row rank of the matrix C' is s and its column rank is r. Since we have already proved that the column rank of a matrix can never exceed the row rank, we see that $r \leq s$. Moreover, we already know that $s \leq r$, and we conclude that $s = r$. The proof of the theorem is therefore completed.

In view of this theorem, we need not distinguish between the row rank and the column rank of a matrix. Accordingly, we make the following definition.

11.30 Definition. The common value of the row rank and the column rank of a matrix is called simply the *rank* of the matrix.

We shall sometimes find it convenient to refer to the (row) rank of a matrix by which we shall mean that the truth of the statement we are making is most easily seen by consideration of the *row* rank.

_____ **E X E R C I S E S**

In each of Exercises 1–5, use elementary row operations to determine the (row) rank of the given matrix over the rational field.

1.
$$\begin{bmatrix} -1 & 2 & 1 \\ 1 & -1 & 2 \\ 1 & 1 & 4 \end{bmatrix}.$$

2.
$$\begin{bmatrix} 2 & -1 & 1 \\ 3 & 1 & 2 \\ 1 & 0 & -1 \\ 0 & 1 & 0 \end{bmatrix}.$$

3.
$$\begin{bmatrix} 1 & 3 & -1 & 2 \\ 0 & 1 & 2 & -5 \\ 2 & 3 & -8 & 19 \end{bmatrix}.$$

4.
$$\begin{bmatrix} 0 & 1 & -1 & 2 \\ 2 & -1 & 0 & 1 \\ 1 & 1 & 1 & 1 \end{bmatrix}.$$

5.
$$\begin{bmatrix} 1 & 2 & -1 & 3 \\ 4 & 1 & 2 & 1 \\ 3 & -1 & 1 & 2 \\ 1 & 2 & 0 & 1 \end{bmatrix}.$$

6. Use elementary row operations to determine the rank of the following matrix over the field $I/(5)$:

$$\begin{bmatrix} 2 & 1 & 1 & 3 & 4 \\ 4 & 1 & 2 & 1 & 2 \\ 1 & 2 & 1 & 1 & 2 \\ 1 & 3 & 0 & 2 & 1 \end{bmatrix}.$$

7. Show that, by use of both elementary row and column operations, the matrix

$$\begin{bmatrix} -1 & -2 & 1 & 3 \\ 1 & 0 & 1 & 1 \\ 3 & 2 & 1 & -1 \\ 1 & -4 & 5 & 9 \end{bmatrix}$$

over the rational field can be reduced to the matrix

$$\begin{bmatrix} 1 & 0 & 0 & 0 \\ 0 & 1 & 0 & 0 \\ 0 & 0 & 0 & 0 \\ 0 & 0 & 0 & 0 \end{bmatrix}.$$

8. Determine the dimension of each of the following subspaces of the appropriate vector space $V_n(R)$. [Hint: Form a matrix whose row vectors are the given vectors and find the (row) rank of the matrix.]

(a) $[(1, 2, -1), (3, 1, 2), (1, -3, 4)]$,

(b) $[(3, -1, 4), (2, 1, 3), (1, 0, 2)]$,

(c) $[(0, 1, 1, 2), (-2, 1, 0, 1), (3, 1, 5, 2), (1, 0, 3, -1)]$,

(d) $[(-1, 2, -1, 0), (0, 3, 1, 2), (1, 1, -2, 2), (2, 1, 0, -1)]$.

11.4 APPLICATIONS TO SYSTEMS OF LINEAR EQUATIONS

We shall now apply the results of the preceding section to a further study of systems of linear equations.

Associated with the system 11.1 of m linear equations in n unknowns are two matrices. The $m \times n$ matrix

$$\begin{bmatrix} a_{11} & a_{12} & \cdots & a_{1n} \\ a_{21} & a_{22} & \cdots & a_{2n} \\ \cdot & \cdot & \cdots & \cdot \\ a_{m1} & a_{m2} & \cdots & a_{mn} \end{bmatrix}$$

consisting of the coefficients of the various unknowns, is called the *matrix of the coefficients* of the given system. The $m \times (n + 1)$ matrix

$$\begin{bmatrix} a_{11} & a_{12} & \cdots & a_{1n} & b_1 \\ a_{21} & a_{22} & \cdots & a_{2n} & b_2 \\ \cdot & \cdot & \cdots & \cdot & \cdot \\ a_{m1} & a_{m2} & \cdots & a_{mn} & b_m \end{bmatrix}$$

is called the *augmented matrix* of the system. The augmented matrix differs from the matrix of the coefficients only in that it has an additional column which consists of the constant terms of the equations.

Now an elementary operation on a system of linear equations, as defined in 11.10, has the same effect on the augmented matrix of the system as the corresponding elementary row operation on this matrix, as defined in 11.24. Hence, if the given system is reduced to an echelon system of equations by a sequence of elementary operations and, possibly, the deletion of zero equations, we know that the augmented matrix of the echelon system can be obtained from the augmented matrix of the given system by a sequence of elementary row operations and the possible deletion of zero rows.

In view of these observations, we see that the process of reducing a given system of linear equations to an echelon system can be carried out by working with the augmented matrix of the system. For example, suppose that we wish to solve the following system of linear equations over the rational field:

$$x_1 + 2x_2 + 2x_3 = \quad 5,$$
$$x_1 - 3x_2 + 2x_3 = -5,$$
$$2x_1 - \quad x_2 + \quad x_3 = -3.$$

The augmented matrix of this system is the matrix

$$\begin{bmatrix} 1 & 2 & 2 & 5 \\ 1 & -3 & 2 & -5 \\ 2 & -1 & 1 & -3 \end{bmatrix}.$$

We omit the details, but by use of elementary row operations this matrix can be reduced to the form

$$\begin{bmatrix} 1 & 0 & 0 & -1 \\ 0 & 1 & 0 & 2 \\ 0 & 0 & 1 & 1 \end{bmatrix}.$$

This is clearly the augmented matrix of the following echelon system of equations, which must be equivalent to the given system:

$$x_1 \quad\quad\quad = -1,$$
$$x_2 \quad\quad = \quad 2,$$
$$x_3 = \quad 1.$$

Accordingly, we conclude that the only solution of the given system is $x_1 = -1$, $x_2 = 2$, $x_3 = 1$.

As indicated by this example, there is some economy of effort in working with the augmented matrix instead of with the equations themselves. However, it is of more importance that we can apply these ideas to obtain some general theoretical results.

Since the presence or absence of a zero row cannot affect the row space of a matrix, we conclude from Theorem 11.25 that the row space of the augmented matrix of a given system of linear equations is equal to the row space of the augmented matrix of the echelon system 11.18 or 11.19 to which the given system is equivalent. Moreover, an elementary row operation on the augmented matrix of a system of linear equations induces an elementary row operation on the matrix of coefficients as well.

If a system 11.1 of linear equations has a solution, we know that it is reducible to an echelon system of the form 11.18. The (row) rank of the matrix of the coefficients, and also of the augmented matrix, of this echelon system is easily seen to be r. Hence, in view of the observations made above, and Theorem 11.25, we know that the ranks of the matrix of the coefficients and of the augmented matrix of the given system 11.1 must both be equal to r. If the given system does not have a solution, it is reducible to an echelon system of the form 11.19. For this system, the (row) rank of the matrix of coefficients is r, whereas the (row) rank of the augmented matrix is $r + 1$.

These observations, together with Theorem 11.20, yield the following result.

11.31 Theorem. *A system 11.1 of linear equations over a field F has a solution if and only if the rank of the matrix of the coefficients of the system is equal to the rank of the augmented matrix of the system. If these ranks are both equal to r, and r is less than the number n of unknowns, certain $n - r$ of the unknowns can be assigned arbitrary values from F and the values of the other r unknowns are then uniquely determined. Moreover, all solutions can be obtained in this way. The system has a unique solution if and only if $r = n$.*

We may point out that the first statement of the theorem can be easily established as follows without any consideration of echelon systems. It was observed immediately following Equation 11.8 that the system has a solution if and only if the column vector B^1 of constant terms is a linear combination of the column vectors $A^1, A^2, \cdots, A^n$ of the matrix of coefficients. In turn, Theorem 10.15 (iv) implies that this is true if and only if the column space of the augmented matrix coincides with the column space of the matrix of coefficients. Hence, the given system of equations has a solution if and only if the (column) rank of the augmented matrix is equal to the (column) rank of the matrix of coefficients.

Let us now return to a consideration of the compatibility condition as defined in 11.6. We have already proved that if a system of linear equations has a solution, it is compatible. We shall now complete the proof of the following theorem.

11.32 Theorem. *A system of linear equations over a field F has a solution if and only if it is compatible.*

It will be convenient to write our system in the following form (11.4):

11.33
$$A_1 \cdot X = b_1, \quad A_2 \cdot X = b_2, \quad \cdots, \quad A_m \cdot X = b_m.$$

We now assume that the system 11.33 is compatible, and shall show that it has a solution. Let us suppose that it does not have a solution, and seek a contradiction. Since it does not have a solution, we know that it is reducible to an echelon system of the form 11.19. Moreover, the row space of the augmented matrix of the system 11.33 will coincide with the row space of the augmented matrix of the echelon system 11.19. In particular, the last row of this matrix, all of whose elements are zero except for a 1 in the last place, is a linear combination of the rows of the augmented matrix of the system 11.33. We conclude that there exist elements s_i $(i = 1, 2, \cdots, m)$ of F such that

$$\sum_{i=1}^{m} s_i A_i = 0, \qquad \sum_{i=1}^{m} s_i b_i = 1.$$

However, this violates the assumption that the system is compatible, and we have obtained the desired contradiction. The system therefore has a solution and the proof is completed.

The next theorem will show that we may be able to delete some of the equations of a given system without affecting the solutions of the system. Let us indicate the row vectors of the augmented matrix of the system 11.33 by (A_1, b_1), (A_2, b_2), $\cdots$, (A_m, b_m). We shall proceed to prove the following result.

11.34 Theorem. *If the row vectors (A_{l_1}, b_{l_1}), (A_{l_2}, b_{l_2}), $\cdots$, (A_{l_r}, b_{l_r}) form a basis of the row space of the augmented matrix of the system 11.33, then the system is equivalent to the system consisting of the following r equations:*

11.35
$$A_{l_1} \cdot X = b_{l_1}, \quad A_{l_2} \cdot X = b_{l_2}, \quad \cdots, \quad A_{l_r} \cdot X = b_{l_r}.$$

It is obvious that any solution of the entire system 11.33 is also a solution of the subsystem 11.35. To prove the theorem, we therefore need only show that any solution T of the system 11.35 is also a solution of the system 11.33. If $A_j \cdot X = b_j$ is an arbitrary one of the Equations 11.33, we shall show that $A_j \cdot T = b_j$. Since the row vector (A_j, b_j) is a linear combination of the given basis of the row space of the augmented matrix, there exist elements d_i $(i = 1, 2, \cdots, r)$ of F such that

$$A_j = \sum_{i=1}^{r} d_i A_{l_i}, \qquad b_j = \sum_{i=1}^{r} d_i b_{l_i}.$$

Using these equations, simple properties of the inner product, and the fact that T is a solution of the system 11.35, we find that

$$A_j \cdot T = \left(\sum_{i=1}^{r} d_i A_{l_i} \right) \cdot T = \sum_{i=1}^{r} d_i (A_{l_i} \cdot T) = \sum_{i=1}^{r} d_i b_{l_i} = b_j.$$

Hence, T is, in fact, a solution of each equation of the system 11.33, and the proof is completed.

11.5 SYSTEMS OF LINEAR HOMOGENEOUS EQUATIONS

In this section we briefly discuss a special case of some importance. A linear equation is said to be *homogeneous* if its constant term is zero. A system of m linear homogeneous equations can then be written in the form 11.33 with all b's equal to zero. That is, such system is of the form

.36 $$A_1 \cdot X = 0, \quad A_2 \cdot X = 0, \quad \cdots, \quad A_m \cdot X = 0.$$

Since the augmented matrix of this system differs from the matrix of coefficients only by having an additional zero column, the ranks of these matrices are the same. Theorem 11.31 then asserts that the system must have a solution. However, this fact is also immediately obvious from the observation that the equations are satisfied if we set $x_1 = 0$, $x_2 = 0$, $\cdots$, $x_n = 0$; otherwise expressed, $X = 0$ is a solution of the system. This solution, in which all the unknowns are assigned the value zero, is usually called the *trivial solution* of the system. Any other solution is a nontrivial solution.

The principal theorem about the solutions of a system of linear homogeneous equations is the following.

.37 Theorem. *If r is the rank of the matrix of coefficients of a system 11.36 of linear homogeneous equations in n unknowns over a field F, then the solutions of the system form a subspace of dimension $n - r$ of the vector space $V_n(F)$.*

First, let us verify that the set of all solutions is a subspace of $V_n(F)$. If S and T are solutions of the system 11.36, so that $A_i \cdot S = 0$ and $A_i \cdot T = 0$ for $i = 1, 2, \cdots, m$, then also

$$A_i \cdot (S + T) = A_i \cdot S + A_i \cdot T = 0,$$

so that $S + T$ is a solution. Similarly, if S is a solution and $c \in F$, then $A_i \cdot (cS) = c(A_i \cdot S) = c0 = 0$ for $i = 1, 2, \cdots, m$; and cS is also a solution. We have thus shown that the subset of $V_n(F)$ consisting of all solutions of the system 11.36 is closed under addition and scalar multiplication. This subset is then a subspace of $V_n(F)$ by Theorem 10.7. We now proceed to prove that this subspace has dimension $n - r$.

If $r = n$, we know from Theorem 11.31 that there is a unique solution, and it must therefore be the trivial solution. The subspace of all solutions is then the zero vector space and, by definition, it has dimension zero. Having disposed of this simple case, we shall henceforth assume that $r < n$.

By Theorem 11.20, we know that our system 11.36 can be reduced to an echelon system of the form 11.18 in which all the d's are zero. For convenience of notation, let us suppose that $k_1 = 1$, $k_2 = 2$, $\cdots$, $k_r = r$. Then this echelon system, which is equivalent to our given system, can be written in the form

11.38
$$x_1 = c_{1\ r+1}x_{r+1} + \cdots + c_{1n}x_n,$$
$$x_2 = c_{2\ r+1}x_{r+1} + \cdots + c_{2n}x_n,$$
$$\cdots \cdots \cdots \cdots \cdots \cdots \cdots$$
$$x_r = c_{r\ r+1}x_{r+1} + \cdots + c_{rn}x_n.$$

where the c's are fixed elements of F. We can get a particular solution by setting $x_{r+1} = 1$, $x_{r+2} = \cdots = x_n = 0$, and solving for the corresponding values of $x_1, x_2, \cdots, x_r$. In this way we obtain the solution

$$T_1 = (c_{1\ r+1}, \cdots, c_{r\ r+1}, 1, 0, \cdots, 0).$$

In like manner, each of the following is seen to be a solution:

$$T_2 = (c_{1\ r+2}, \cdots, c_{r\ r+2}, 0, 1, \cdots, 0),$$
$$\cdots \cdots \cdots \cdots \cdots \cdots \cdots \cdots$$
$$T_{n-r} = (c_{1n}, \cdots, c_{rn}, 0, 0, \cdots, 1).$$

By a consideration of the last $n - r$ entries in these vectors, it is clear that $T_1, T_2, \cdots, T_{n-r}$ are linearly independent elements of $V_n(F)$. Moreover, if $T = (t_1, t_2, \cdots, t_n)$ is an arbitrary solution of the system 11.38, and therefore of 11.36, a straightforward calculation will show that $T = t_{r+1}T_1 + \cdots + t_nT_{n-r}$. We have therefore shown that the set $\{T_1, T_2, \cdots, T_{n-r}\}$ is a basis of the subspace of $V_n(F)$ consisting of all solutions of the system 11.36. The dimension of this subspace is thus $n - r$, and the proof of the theorem is completed.

Since a vector space of positive dimension must contain nonzero vectors, we have at once the following corollary.

11.39 Corollary. *A system of linear homogeneous equations has a nontrivial solution if and only if the rank of the matrix of coefficients of the system is less than the number of unknowns.*

The following result is an immediate consequence of the fact that the rank of a matrix cannot exceed the number of rows in the matrix.

11.40 Corollary. *A system of linear homogeneous equations with fewer equations than unknowns always has a nontrivial solution.*

In each of Exercises 1–3, solve the given system of linear equations over the rational field by working only with the augmented matrix of the system.

1.
$$x_1 - 2x_2 + x_3 = -6,$$
$$3x_1 + 4x_2 + 2x_3 = 5,$$
$$-x_1 + 3x_2 - x_3 = 8.$$

2.
$$2x_1 - x_2 + 3x_3 = 3,$$
$$x_1 + 2x_2 - x_3 - 5x_4 = 4,$$
$$x_1 + 3x_2 - 2x_3 - 7x_4 = 5.$$

3.
$$2x_1 - 2x_2 - x_3 + 5x_4 + x_5 = 7,$$
$$3x_1 - 3x_2 + 2x_3 + 4x_4 + 2x_5 = 15,$$
$$x_1 - x_2 + x_3 + x_4 + x_5 = 6.$$

In each of Exercises 4–7, solve the given system of linear homogeneous equations over the rational field and find a basis for the vector space of all solutions.

4.
$$x_1 - x_2 + 2x_3 = 0,$$
$$2x_1 + x_2 - 5x_3 = 0,$$
$$x_1 - 4x_2 + 11x_3 = 0.$$

5.
$$x_1 + 3x_2 - 4x_3 - 4x_4 + 9x_5 = 0,$$
$$x_1 + x_2 - 2x_3 - x_4 + 2x_5 = 0,$$
$$2x_1 - x_2 + 2x_3 + 4x_4 - 8x_5 = 0.$$

6.
$$4x_1 + 2x_2 - x_3 + 3x_4 = 0,$$
$$x_1 - 2x_2 + 2x_3 - x_4 = 0,$$
$$2x_1 + 6x_2 - 5x_3 + 5x_4 = 0,$$
$$3x_1 + 14x_2 - 12x_3 + 11x_4 = 0.$$

7.
$$2x_1 + 3x_2 + x_3 - x_4 = 0,$$
$$3x_1 - 2x_2 - x_3 + x_4 = 0.$$

8. Use Corollary 11.40 to show that any $n + 1$ vectors of a vector space $V_n(F)$ are linearly dependent (10.19).

9. Show that if T is one solution of the system 11.33 of linear equations, every solution of the system is of the form $T + S$, where S is a solution of the system 11.36 of linear homogeneous equations.

12

Determinants

The theory of determinants, to be introduced in this chapter, had its origin in the study of systems of linear equations, but it has other applications as well. We shall establish some of the more fundamental properties of determinants and also give a new characterization of the rank of a matrix. Finally, we shall show how determinants may be used in solving a system of linear equations. A few other applications of the theory of determinants will be found in the following chapter.

12.1 PRELIMINARY REMARKS

The purpose of this section is to motivate the general definition of a determinant to be given in the next section, and to introduce some convenient notation.

The concept of a determinant arises in the attempt to find general *formulas* for the solution of a system of linear equations with the same number of equations as unknowns. Suppose, first, that we have the following system of two equations in two unknowns over a field F:

$$a_{11}x_1 + a_{12}x_2 = b_1,$$
$$a_{21}x_1 + a_{22}x_2 = b_2.$$

If, by the familiar methods of elementary algebra, we eliminate x_2 from these two equations, the resulting equation takes the form

$$(a_{11}a_{22} - a_{12}a_{21})x_1 = b_1a_{22} - b_2a_{12}.$$

Similarly, if we eliminate x_1, we obtain the equation

$$(a_{11}a_{22} - a_{12}a_{21})x_2 = b_2a_{11} - b_1a_{12}.$$

The expression $a_{11}a_{22} - a_{12}a_{21}$, which occurs as the coefficient of x_2 in this last equation, and also as the coefficient of x_1 in the preceding equation, is called the *determinant* of the matrix of coefficients of the given system of equations.

The case of two equations in two unknowns is too simple to furnish much of a hint about the general case, so let us briefly consider a system of three equations in three unknowns. Such a system may be written in the form

2.1
$$a_{11}x_1 + a_{12}x_2 + a_{13}x_3 = b_1,$$
$$a_{21}x_1 + a_{22}x_2 + a_{23}x_3 = b_2,$$
$$a_{31}x_1 + a_{32}x_2 + a_{33}x_3 = b_3.$$

It can be shown by direct calculations, although in this case the calculations would be fairly tedious, that if we eliminate any *two* of the unknowns, the coefficient of the remaining unknown in the resulting equation is as follows:

2.2 $\quad a_{11}a_{22}a_{33} - a_{11}a_{23}a_{32} - a_{12}a_{21}a_{33} + a_{12}a_{23}a_{31} + a_{13}a_{21}a_{32} - a_{13}a_{22}a_{31}.$

This expression is called the *determinant* of the matrix of coefficients of the system 12.1. For convenience, let A be this matrix of coefficients; that is, let

$$A = \begin{bmatrix} a_{11} & a_{12} & a_{13} \\ a_{21} & a_{22} & a_{23} \\ a_{31} & a_{32} & a_{33} \end{bmatrix}.$$

Then the determinant of A, defined by 12.2, may be denoted by $|A|$.

Let us now make a few observations about $|A|$. Clearly, $|A|$ is an element of F associated with the matrix A over F. Moreover, $|A|$ consists of an algebraic sum of six terms, each of which is a product of three elements of the matrix A. In each of these products, the integers 1, 2, 3 occur, in this order, as the first subscripts; also, these three integers occur, in some order, as the second subscripts. That is, each product is a product of elements of A, one from each row and one from each column. Another way of expressing this fact is to say that a typical term of 12.2 is of the form $\pm a_{1i_1}a_{2i_2}a_{3i_3}$, where i_1, i_2, and i_3 are the integers 1, 2, and 3 in some order. Using the notation for permutations, introduced in Chapter 9, let α be the permutation of the set $\{1, 2, 3\}$ defined by $1\alpha = i_1$, $2\alpha = i_2$, $3\alpha = i_3$. Then a typical term of 12.2 can be written in the form

12.3 $$\pm a_{1\,1\alpha}\, a_{2\,2\alpha}\, a_{3\,3\alpha}.$$

Now the symmetric group S_3 on three symbols has six elements, and since there are six terms in 12.2, we see that for every α in S_3 a term of the form 12.3 occurs as a summand.

Let us now discuss the choice of sign in a term 12.3. Since, in 12.2, three of the terms are prefixed by a "$+$" sign and the other three by a "$-$" sign, it is clear that the choice of sign must depend in some way on the permutation α. We recall that a permutation is called *even* or *odd* according as it can be expressed as a product of an even or an odd number of transpositions. Moreover, we have proved, in Theorem 9.46, that half of the permutations of any symmetric group S_n are even, and half are odd. As suggested by these remarks, it is true that the choice of sign in a term 12.3 depends only on whether α is an even or an odd permutation. Before stating this fact in a more precise form, let us make the following convenient definition.

12.4 Definition. If α is a permutation of a finite set, we define

$$sign\ \alpha = \begin{cases} + 1 \text{ if } \alpha \text{ is an even permutation,} \\ - 1 \text{ if } \alpha \text{ is an odd permutation.} \end{cases}$$

Using this notation, we now assert that

12.5 $$|A| = \sum_{\alpha \in S_3} (\text{sign } \alpha) a_{1\,1\alpha}\, a_{2\,2\alpha}\, a_{3\,3\alpha},$$

it being understood that the sum is to be taken over all elements α of S_3. Since there are six elements in S_3, there will be six terms in this sum. To verify that this sum is exactly the expression 12.2, we need only verify that the signs of the terms are correct. For example, let us consider the product $a_{13}a_{22}a_{31}$. For this product, we have $1\alpha = 3$, $2\alpha = 2$, $3\alpha = 1$; and it follows that α is the transposition (13). Hence, this α is odd and therefore sign $\alpha = -1$. Accordingly, in the sum on the right of 12.5 we would have $- a_{13}a_{22}a_{31}$, and this product appears, with this same sign, in the expression 12.2. In like manner all the other terms may be verified. (See Exercise 4 in the next set of exercises.)

In the next section we shall give the definition of the determinant of an $n \times n$ matrix. The definition is a natural generalization of 12.5, and this is the reason that we have here gone to so much trouble to express 12.2 in the simple form 12.5.

12.2 GENERAL DEFINITION OF DETERMINANT

Unless otherwise stated, throughout this chapter the matrices with which we shall be concerned will be *square* matrices, that is, $n \times n$ matrices for some positive integer n. It is often convenient to call an $n \times n$ matrix a matrix of *order n*. Although a considerable part of what we shall do would remain valid if the elements of the matrices were elements of a commutative ring, for simplicity we shall always assume that the elements are from a field F. A matrix A, of order n, over a field F may be written in the following explicit form:

12.6
$$A = \begin{bmatrix} a_{11} & a_{12} & \cdots & a_{1n} \\ a_{21} & a_{22} & \cdots & a_{2n} \\ \cdot & \cdot & \cdots & \cdot \\ a_{n1} & a_{n2} & \cdots & a_{nn} \end{bmatrix},$$

it being understood that $a_{ij} \in F$ $(i, j = 1, 2, \cdots, n)$. If the order n is apparent from the context and therefore does not need to be mentioned explicitly, it is sometimes convenient to indicate the above matrix A by writing simply $A = (a_{ij})$.

The line joining the upper left-hand element of a square matrix and the lower right-hand element is often called the *principal diagonal* of the matrix. The elements $a_{11}, a_{22}, \cdots, a_{nn}$ of the matrix A are the elements on its principal diagonal.

We shall continue to denote by S_n the set (actually a group) of all permutations of the set $\{1, 2, \cdots, n\}$. Then, as suggested by the discussion of the preceding section, we shall make the following definition.

12.7 Definition. If A is the matrix 12.6 of order n over a field F, the *determinant* of A, denoted by $|A|$, is defined as follows:

12.8
$$|A| = \sum_{\alpha \in S_n} (\text{sign } \alpha) a_{1 1\alpha} \, a_{2 2\alpha} \cdots a_{n n\alpha}.$$

The determinant of A may also be denoted by $|a_{ij}|$, or by

$$\begin{vmatrix} a_{11} & a_{12} & \cdots & a_{1n} \\ a_{21} & a_{22} & \cdots & a_{2n} \\ \cdot & \cdot & \cdots & \cdot \\ a_{n1} & a_{n2} & \cdots & a_{nn} \end{vmatrix}.$$

Since the symmetric group S_n has $n!$ elements, we see that if A is a square matrix of order n, $|A|$ is a sum of $n!$ terms, each of which is a product of n elements, one from each row and one from each column of A. Moreover, half of these terms will have a "+" sign and the other half a "−" sign prefixed. We may make one other observation as follows.

If in 12.8 we consider the term obtained when α is the identity permutation, which is an even permutation, we see that one of the terms is the product of the elements on the principal diagonal of A.

We shall presently develop methods for computing the determinant of a given matrix that will be much simpler than applying the definition directly. Before proceeding to do so, we shall present two simple examples to illustrate some of the ideas presented so far.

Example 1. Suppose that the matrix A is of order 5, and let us find the sign of the term involving the product $a_{13}a_{24}a_{35}a_{42}a_{51}$ in $|A|$. For this term, we have $1\alpha = 3$, $2\alpha = 4$, $3\alpha = 5$, $4\alpha = 2$, $5\alpha = 1$. Using the notation of cycles, we find that α can be expressed in the form $\alpha = (135)(24) = (13)(15)(24)$. Hence α is an odd permutation and sign $\alpha = -1$. Accordingly, one of the terms in $|A|$ is $-a_{13}a_{24}a_{35}a_{42}a_{51}$.

Example 2. Suppose that the matrix A is of order 6 and let us find the sign of the term involving the product $a_{45}a_{31}a_{12}a_{64}a_{23}a_{56}$ in $|A|$. In order to apply the definition of determinant let us first rearrange this product so that the first (row) subscripts appear in their natural order. Of course, we can do so because multiplication is commutative in F. We get in this way the product $a_{12}a_{23}a_{31}a_{45}a_{56}a_{64}$. For this product, we have $1\alpha = 2$, $2\alpha = 3$, $3\alpha = 1$, $4\alpha = 5$, $5\alpha = 6$, $6\alpha = 4$; and it follows that $\alpha = (123)(456)$. This is an even permutation and therefore sign $\alpha = +1$. Accordingly, the given product occurs with a "$+$" sign.

EXERCISES

1. If A is a matrix of order 5, find the sign of the term in $|A|$ which involves each of the following products:

   (a) $a_{15}a_{24}a_{33}a_{42}a_{51}$,

   (b) $a_{13}a_{21}a_{32}a_{45}a_{54}$,

   (c) $a_{11}a_{25}a_{32}a_{43}a_{54}$,

   (d) $a_{14}a_{25}a_{33}a_{41}a_{52}$,

   (e) $a_{52}a_{41}a_{34}a_{25}a_{13}$,

   (f) $a_{24}a_{45}a_{12}a_{53}a_{31}$.

2. If the matrix B is obtained from the matrix A of order n by multiplying all elements of one row by the element c of F, show that $|B| = c\,|A|$.

3. Apply Definition 12.7 to show that
$$\begin{vmatrix} a & b \\ c & d \end{vmatrix} = ad - bc.$$

4. Apply Definition 12.7 to show that the expression 12.2 is actually the determinant of the matrix $A = (a_{ij})$ of order three.

5. Show that if all the elements of one row, or of one column, of a matrix A are zero, then $|A| = 0$.

6. Suppose that for the matrix A, exhibited in 12.6, all the elements above the principal diagonal are zero. Show that in this case the determinant of A is just the product of the elements on the principal diagonal.

12.3 SOME FUNDAMENTAL PROPERTIES

In the definition of the determinant of a matrix A, the rows play a role somewhat different from that of the columns. That is, we have written each term as a product of elements with the row (first) subscripts in their natural order, and have then determined the sign of the term by a consideration of the column (second) subscripts. However, we shall now show that in this definition we could just as well reverse the roles of the rows and the columns.

In the preceding chapter we have defined the *transpose* C' of any matrix C to be the matrix obtained from C by interchanging rows and columns. We shall now prove the following theorem.

2.9 Theorem. *If A' is the transpose of the square matrix A, then* $|A'| = |A|$.

Let $A = (a_{ij})$ be the matrix of order n exhibited in 12.6. It will be helpful to set $b_{ji} = a_{ij}$ $(i, j = 1, 2, \cdots, n)$, so that $A' = (b_{ij})$ or, in more detail,

$$A' = \begin{bmatrix} b_{11} & b_{12} & \cdots & b_{1n} \\ b_{21} & b_{22} & \cdots & b_{2n} \\ \cdot & \cdot & \cdots & \cdot \\ b_{n1} & b_{n2} & \cdots & b_{nn} \end{bmatrix}.$$

Applying Definition 12.8, we see that

2.10
$$|A'| = \sum_{\alpha \in S_n} (\text{sign } \alpha) b_{1\,1\alpha} b_{2\,2\alpha} \cdots b_{n\,n\alpha}.$$

For the moment, let α be a fixed element of S_n and let us consider the following term in this sum:

2.11
$$(\text{sign } \alpha) b_{1\,1\alpha} b_{2\,2\alpha} \cdots b_{n\,n\alpha}.$$

Since multiplication is commutative in F, we can rearrange the order of the factors in this product in any way we wish. That is, if β is an arbitrary permutation of $\{1, 2, \cdots, n\}$, we can write the expression 12.11 in the form

12.12
$$(\text{sign } \alpha)b_{1\beta\ 1\beta\alpha}\ b_{2\beta\ 2\beta\alpha} \cdots b_{n\beta\ n\beta\alpha}.$$

In particular, let us choose $\beta = \alpha^{-1}$. Then, since, by a remark preceding the statement of Theorem 9.46, sign $\beta =$ sign α, this expression 12.12 can be written as follows:

12.13
$$(\text{sign } \beta)b_{1\beta\ 1}\ b_{2\beta\ 2} \cdots b_{n\beta\ n}.$$

Now if α_1 and α_2 are elements of the group S_n, we know that $\alpha_1^{-1} = \alpha_2^{-1}$ if and only if $\alpha_1 = \alpha_2$. It follows that *every* element of S_n is uniquely expressible in the form α^{-1} for $\alpha \in S_n$. By the equality of the expressions 12.11 and 12.13, we can therefore rewrite 12.10 as follows:

$$|A'| = \sum_{\beta \in S_n} (\text{sign } \beta)b_{1\beta\ 1}\ b_{2\beta\ 2} \cdots b_{n\beta\ n}.$$

However, using the fact that $b_{ji} = a_{ij}$, it then follows that

$$|A'| = \sum_{\beta \in S_n} (\text{sign } \beta)a_{1\ 1\beta}\ a_{2\ 2\beta} \cdots a_{n\ n\beta}.$$

The sum on the right is clearly $|A|$, and we have therefore proved that $|A'| = |A|$.

In the next theorem we shall determine the effect on $|A|$ of an elementary operation on the square matrix A, as defined in 11.24.

12.14   Theorem.   *The effect of an elementary operation of each of the three types may be described as follows:*

Type 1.   If the matrix B is obtained from the matrix A by interchanging two rows (columns), then $|B| = -|A|$.

Type 2.   If the matrix C is obtained from the matrix A by multiplying all elements of one row (column) by the nonzero element r of F, then $|C| = r|A|$.

Type 3.   If the matrix D is obtained from the matrix A by multiplying all elements of one row (column) by an element of F and adding them to the corresponding elements of a different row (column), then $|D| = |A|$.

First, let us observe that an elementary column operation on a matrix A induces an elementary row operation of the same type on the transpose A' of A. Hence, the preceding theorem assures us that in proving the present theorem we may limit ourselves to elementary *row* operations only.

Proof for Type 1.   Suppose that the matrix B is obtained from the matrix A by interchanging rows k and l, $k < l$. Then $B = (b_{ij})$, where $b_{ij} = a_{ij}$ if $i \neq k$ and $i \neq l$; $b_{kj} = a_{lj}$, $b_{lj} = a_{kj}$. Then, by the definition of determinant, we have

$$|B| = \sum_{\alpha \in S_n} (\text{sign } \alpha) b_{1\,1\alpha} \cdots b_{k\,k\alpha} \cdots b_{l\,l\alpha} \cdots b_{n\,n\alpha}$$

$$= \sum_{\alpha \in S_n} (\text{sign } \alpha) a_{1\,1\alpha} \cdots a_{l\,k\alpha} \cdots a_{k\,l\alpha} \cdots a_{n\,n\alpha}$$

$$= \sum_{\alpha \in S_n} (\text{sign } \alpha) a_{1\,1\alpha} \cdots a_{k\,l\alpha} \cdots a_{l\,k\alpha} \cdots a_{n\,n\alpha}.$$

In this last sum we have merely changed the order of the factors in each product by interchanging $a_{l\,k\alpha}$ and $a_{k\,l\alpha}$ so that the first subscripts are in their natural order.

Now if $\alpha \in S_n$, let us set $\beta = (kl)\alpha$ so that $i\beta = i\alpha$ if $i \neq k$ and $i \neq l$; $k\beta = l\alpha$, $l\beta = k\alpha$. It is clear that sign $\beta = -$ sign α and, moreover, every element of S_n is expressible uniquely in the form $(kl)\alpha$ with $\alpha \in S_n$. Using all these facts, and referring to the last form for $|B|$ given above, we see that

$$|B| = -\sum_{\beta \in S_n} (\text{sign } \beta) a_{1\,1\beta} \cdots a_{k\,k\beta} \cdots a_{l\,l\beta} \cdots a_{n\,n\beta} = -|A|,$$

and the proof is completed.

Before proceeding to the proof of the other two parts of the theorem, we point out the following consequence of what we have just proved.

2.15 Corollary. *If a matrix A has two rows (columns) that are identical, then $|A| = 0$.*

Suppose, for convenience of statement, that the first two rows of A are alike. If B is obtained from A by interchanging the first two rows, clearly A and B are identical and therefore $|B| = |A|$. However, by the first part of the preceding theorem, we have $|B| = -|A|$. Accordingly, $|A| = -|A|$, and we conclude that $|A| = 0$. In this final argument we have tacitly assumed that the characteristic of the field F is different from 2. The statement of Corollary 12.15 remains true even for this case, but the proof must make direct use of the definition of a determinant. However, this case is not a very important one for our purposes, and we shall omit its proof.

We now return to a consideration of the other parts of Theorem 12.14.

Proof for Type 2. Since each term in the sum which defines a determinant contains exactly one element from each row, the desired result follows almost immediately from the definition. Actually, the argument holds equally well even if r happens to be zero although, by the definition of elementary operations on a matrix, this would not be an elementary operation. We can, however, conclude that if all the elements of one row (column) of a matrix are zero, then the determinant of the matrix is zero. (*Cf.* Exercises 2 and 5 of the preceding set.)

Proof for Type 3. The same argument would apply in general but, for simplicity, let us assume that the matrix D is obtained from the matrix A by multiplying the elements of the second row by $s \in F$ and adding them to the corresponding elements of the first row. If $D = (d_{ij})$, then for $j = 1, 2, \cdots, n$ we have $d_{ij} = a_{ij}$ if $i \neq 1$; $d_{1j} = a_{1j} + sa_{2j}$. Accordingly,

$$|D| = \sum_{\alpha \in S_n} (\text{sign } \alpha)\, d_{11\alpha}\, d_{22\alpha} \cdots d_{nn\alpha}$$

$$= \sum_{\alpha \in S_n} (\text{sign } \alpha)(a_{11\alpha} + sa_{21\alpha})a_{22\alpha} \cdots a_{nn\alpha}$$

$$= \sum_{\alpha \in S_n} (\text{sign } \alpha)a_{11\alpha}\, a_{22\alpha} \cdots a_{nn\alpha}$$

$$+ s \sum_{\alpha \in S_n} (\text{sign } \alpha)a_{21\alpha}\, a_{22\alpha}\, a_{33\alpha} \cdots a_{nn\alpha}$$

$$= |A| + s \sum_{\alpha \in S_n} (\text{sign } \alpha)a_{21\alpha}\, a_{22\alpha}\, a_{33\alpha} \cdots a_{nn\alpha}.$$

Now this last sum is the determinant of a matrix obtained from A by replacing the first row by the second row. Since two rows are identical, the determinant of the matrix is zero by Corollary 12.15. The above calculations therefore show that $|D| = |A|$, and the proof of the theorem is completed.

If the row vectors of a matrix A are linearly dependent, a finite sequence of elementary row operations of Type 3 will reduce the matrix to one which has a zero row. The determinant of such a matrix is zero and, since the value of a determinant is not changed by elementary row operations of this type, we conclude that also $|A| = 0$. We have therefore proved the following result.

12.16 Corollary. *If the row vectors (column vectors) of the square matrix A are linearly dependent, then $|A| = 0$.*

Theorem 12.14 is exceedingly useful in actually computing the value of the determinant of a given matrix. However, this theorem is usually used in conjunction with the principal theorem of the following section, and we shall therefore postpone any further discussion of these matters until that theorem has also been established.

12.4 EXPANSION IN TERMS OF A ROW OR COLUMN

Let us make the following convenient definitions.

2.17 Definition. (i) A matrix obtained from a given matrix (not necessarily a square matrix) by deleting certain rows or columns, or both, is called a *submatrix* of the given matrix.

(ii) If A is a square matrix of order n, the square submatrix M_{ij} of order $n-1$ obtained by deleting the ith row and the jth column of A is called the *minor of the element a_{ij}*.

(iii) If A is a square matrix, the *cofactor A_{ij}* of a_{ij} in $|A|$ is defined as follows: $A_{ij} = (-1)^{i+j} |M_{ij}|$.

In order to illustrate these concepts, suppose that A is the following matrix of order 4:

2.18
$$A = \begin{bmatrix} a_{11} & a_{12} & a_{13} & a_{14} \\ a_{21} & a_{22} & a_{23} & a_{24} \\ a_{31} & a_{32} & a_{33} & a_{34} \\ a_{41} & a_{42} & a_{43} & a_{44} \end{bmatrix}.$$

Then the minor of the element a_{43} in this matrix is the matrix

2.19
$$M_{43} = \begin{bmatrix} a_{11} & a_{12} & a_{14} \\ a_{21} & a_{22} & a_{24} \\ a_{31} & a_{32} & a_{34} \end{bmatrix},$$

and the cofactor A_{43} of a_{43} in $|A|$ is given by:

$$A_{43} = (-1)^7 |M_{43}| = -|M_{43}|.$$

We may emphasize that a minor is a *matrix*, whereas a cofactor is an element of the underlying field F.

The reason for the name *cofactor* will be suggested by the following result.

2.20 Lemma. *If $A = (a_{ij})$ is a square matrix of order n, the sum of all the terms in $|A|$ which contain the arbitrary fixed element a_{ij} of A is $a_{ij}A_{ij}$.*

We shall first prove this lemma for the special case in which $i = 1$ and $j = 1$. In $|A|$, the sum of all the terms which contain a_{11} can be written in the form

$$a_{11} \sum_{\substack{\alpha \in S_n \\ 1\alpha = 1}} (\text{sign } \alpha) a_{2\,2\alpha}\, a_{3\,3\alpha} \cdots a_{n\,n\alpha},$$

it being understood that the sum is over all permutations α of S_n such that $1\alpha = 1$. Of course, if we let S_{n-1} be the set of all permutations of the set $\{2, 3, \cdots, n\}$, this sum can be written in the form

$$a_{11} \sum_{\gamma \in S_{n-1}} (\text{sign } \gamma) a_{2\,2\gamma}\, a_{3\,3\gamma} \cdots a_{n\,n\gamma}.$$

Moreover, although the notation is slightly different from that which we have previously used, the sum occurring here is just the determinant of the matrix

$$\begin{bmatrix} a_{22} & a_{23} & \cdots & a_{2n} \\ a_{32} & a_{33} & \cdots & a_{3n} \\ \cdot & \cdot & \cdots & \cdot \\ a_{n2} & a_{n3} & \cdots & a_{nn} \end{bmatrix}.$$

Now this is the minor M_{11} of the element a_{11} of the matrix A; hence the sum of all the terms in $|A|$ which contain a_{11} is $a_{11}|M_{11}|$. Since, by Definition 12.17 (iii), $A_{11} = (-1)^2 |M_{11}| = |M_{11}|$, the sum of all these terms is $a_{11}A_{11}$. This proves the lemma for the special case in which $i = 1$ and $j = 1$. For later reference, let us restate what we have proved in the following form. *In the determinant of an arbitrary square matrix, the sum of the terms which contain the element in the upper left-hand corner of the matrix is just this element times the determinant of its minor.* We shall make use of this fact in the proof of the lemma for the case in which i and j are arbitrary. However, let us first illustrate the method to be used by an example.

For the moment, let A be the matrix of order 4 given in 12.18, and let us show that the sum of the terms in $|A|$ which contain the element a_{43} is $a_{43}A_{43}$, where $A_{43} = -|M_{43}|$. We proceed to perform on A a finite sequence of elementary operations of Type 1 to get a matrix with a_{43} in the upper left-hand corner and, moreover, in such a way that the minor of a_{43} in this new matrix is the same as its minor in A. More specifically, we first interchange rows 3 and 4, then rows 2 and 3, and then rows 1 and 2. This gives us the following matrix in which the element a_{43} now occurs in the first row:

$$\begin{bmatrix} a_{41} & a_{42} & a_{43} & a_{44} \\ a_{11} & a_{12} & a_{13} & a_{14} \\ a_{21} & a_{22} & a_{23} & a_{24} \\ a_{31} & a_{32} & a_{33} & a_{34} \end{bmatrix}.$$

We now interchange columns 2 and 3 in this matrix, and finally columns 1 and 2. We then have the matrix B given by

$$B = \begin{bmatrix} a_{43} & a_{41} & a_{42} & a_{44} \\ a_{13} & a_{11} & a_{12} & a_{14} \\ a_{23} & a_{21} & a_{22} & a_{24} \\ a_{33} & a_{31} & a_{32} & a_{34} \end{bmatrix}.$$

Now the minor of the element a_{43} *of this matrix B* is obtained by deleting the row and column which contain a_{43}, that is, the first row and first column. This minor is therefore as follows:

$$\begin{bmatrix} a_{11} & a_{12} & a_{14} \\ a_{21} & a_{22} & a_{24} \\ a_{31} & a_{32} & a_{34} \end{bmatrix}.$$

It will be seen that this matrix is exactly the minor M_{43} of the element a_{43} *in the matrix A*, as given in 12.19. Moreover, the special case of the lemma which we have already proved, as applied to the matrix B, shows that the sum of the terms in $|B|$ which contain a_{43} is $a_{43}|M_{43}|$. To obtain the matrix B from A we applied five elementary operations of Type 1, each of which changed the sign of the determinant. Hence, $|A| = -|B|$ and the sum of all the terms in $|A|$ which contain a_{43} is $-a_{43}|M_{43}| = a_{43}A_{43}$.

Of course, it would have been possible to get from A a matrix with a_{43} in the upper left-hand corner merely by interchanging the first and fourth rows, and the first and third columns. However, had we done so, the minor of a_{43} in the matrix so obtained would not have been M_{43} and we would have had to do some more work before reaching the desired conclusion.

To complete the proof of the lemma, we use the same method as in this illustration. Again, let A be a matrix of order n, and let i and j be fixed integers, distinct or identical, from the set $\{1, 2, \cdots, n\}$. By $i - 1$ successive interchanges of adjacent rows and $j - 1$ successive interchanges of adjacent columns we can obtain a matrix C with the element a_{ij} in the upper left-hand corner and with the further important property that the minor of a_{ij} in the matrix C is exactly the minor M_{ij} of the element a_{ij} in the given matrix A. Clearly, $|C| = (-1)^{i+j-2}|A| = (-1)^{i+j}|A|$. Now, applying the special case of the lemma which has already been proved, we see that the sum of all the terms in $|C|$ which contain the element a_{ij} is $a_{ij}|M_{ij}|$. Hence, the sum of all the terms in $|A|$ which contain the element a_{ij} is $(-1)^{i+j}a_{ij}|M_{ij}| = a_{ij}A_{ij}$. This completes the proof of the lemma.

Since, by the definition of a determinant, every term contains exactly one element from the first row. it is clear that every term in $|A|$ contains exactly one of the elements $a_{11}, a_{12}, \cdots, a_{1n}$. It follows at once from the lemma that

$$|A| = a_{11}A_{11} + a_{12}A_{12} + \cdots + a_{1n}A_{1n}.$$

It is obvious that a similar argument applies to the elements of any fixed row or column, and we therefore have the following important result.

12.21 Theorem. *Let $A = (a_{ij})$ be a matrix of order n over a field. Then*

12.22
$$|A| = \sum_{j=1}^{n} a_{kj} A_{kj}, \qquad (k = 1, 2, \cdots, n),$$

and also

12.23
$$|A| = \sum_{i=1}^{n} a_{il} A_{il}, \qquad (l = 1, 2, \cdots, n).$$

It is customary to say that 12.22 gives the expansion of $|A|$ in terms of the kth row, and 12.23 the expansion in terms of the lth column. Since the cofactor of an element in $|A|$ is the determinant of a matrix of order $n - 1$, these expansions express the determinant of a matrix of order n in terms of determinants of matrices of order $n - 1$. This fact is of great value in computing the determinant of a given matrix. We shall presently give some examples, but first let us establish another result which follows easily from Theorem 12.21 and is of considerable interest in itself.

12.24 Theorem. *Let $A = (a_{ij})$ be a matrix of order n over a field. Then, if $k \neq l$, we have*

12.25
$$\sum_{j=1}^{n} a_{kj} A_{lj} = 0,$$

and

12.26
$$\sum_{i=1}^{n} a_{ik} A_{il} = 0.$$

Theorem 12.21 states that the sum of the products of the elements of any row (column) of a matrix by their respective cofactors is the determinant of the matrix. This theorem states that the sum of the products of the elements of any row (column) by the cofactors of the corresponding elements of a *different* row (column) is always zero.

To prove 12.25, let k and l be distinct integers of the set $\{1, 2, \cdots, n\}$, and let D be the matrix obtained from A by deleting its lth row and replacing it by its kth row. Since two rows of D are identical, Corollary 12.15 assures us that $|D| = 0$. Moreover, the cofactor of an element a_{kj} of the lth row of D coincides with A_{lj}, the cofactor of the corresponding element a_{lj} of A. Accordingly, the sum appearing in 12.25 is, by the preceding theorem applied to D, the expansion of $|D|$ in terms of its lth row. Since $|D| = 0$, this proves 12.25. A similar argument, using columns instead of rows, will establish 12.26.

We now proceed to give examples which may help to clarify the theory that has been presented so far. In particular, we shall give illustrations of how certain of our results may be used in actually computing the determinant of a given matrix. It will be understood that the elements are from the field of rational numbers.

Example 1. Find the value of the following determinant:

$$\begin{vmatrix} 1 & 3 & 2 \\ -2 & 1 & -1 \\ 0 & 1 & 4 \end{vmatrix}.$$

We shall compute the value of this determinant in two different ways. First, let us use 12.22 to expand the determinant in terms of its first row as follows:

$$\begin{vmatrix} 1 & 3 & 2 \\ -2 & 1 & -1 \\ 0 & 1 & 4 \end{vmatrix} = 1 \cdot \begin{vmatrix} 1 & -1 \\ 1 & 4 \end{vmatrix} - 3 \cdot \begin{vmatrix} -2 & -1 \\ 0 & 4 \end{vmatrix} + 2 \cdot \begin{vmatrix} -2 & 1 \\ 0 & 1 \end{vmatrix}.$$

Of course, the minus sign in the second term is caused by the fact that the cofactor of an element in the first row and second column is $(-1)^3$ times its minor. Now it was observed in Exercise 3 at the end of Section 12.2 that

$$\begin{vmatrix} a & b \\ c & d \end{vmatrix} = ad - bc,$$

and hence it is easy to find the value of each of our determinants of order two. Doing so, we obtain as the value of the given determinant

$$1 \cdot (4+1) - 3(-8) + 2(-2) = 25.$$

Now let us carry out the calculation in a different way using an elementary operation as follows. If we multiply the first row by 2 and add to the second, we know by Theorem 12.14 that the determinant is unchanged. We then expand in terms of the first column. The calculations are as follows:

$$\begin{vmatrix} 1 & 3 & 2 \\ -2 & 1 & -1 \\ 0 & 1 & 4 \end{vmatrix} = \begin{vmatrix} 1 & 3 & 2 \\ 0 & 7 & 3 \\ 0 & 1 & 4 \end{vmatrix} = 1 \cdot \begin{vmatrix} 7 & 3 \\ 1 & 4 \end{vmatrix} = 25.$$

Example 2. Find the value of the following determinant:

$$\begin{vmatrix} 5 & -3 & 12 & 2 \\ 6 & 4 & 8 & 6 \\ 3 & -1 & 8 & -1 \\ 4 & 2 & 12 & 4 \end{vmatrix}.$$

Of course, it would be possible to expand this determinant in terms of some row or column and then proceed to evaluate each of the four determinants of order three that would be involved. However, it is much less work to use elementary operations in such a way as to get all elements but one of some row or column equal to zero, and then to expand in terms of that particular row or column. One possible way to apply this procedure is indicated by the following calculations, which we shall explain briefly below:

$$
\begin{vmatrix} 5 & -3 & 12 & 2 \\ 6 & 4 & 8 & 6 \\ 3 & -1 & 8 & -1 \\ 4 & 2 & 12 & 4 \end{vmatrix} = 2 \begin{vmatrix} 5 & -3 & 12 & 2 \\ 3 & 2 & 4 & 3 \\ 3 & -1 & 8 & -1 \\ 4 & 2 & 12 & 4 \end{vmatrix} = 8 \begin{vmatrix} 5 & -3 & 3 & 2 \\ 3 & 2 & 1 & 3 \\ 3 & -1 & 2 & -1 \\ 4 & 2 & 3 & 4 \end{vmatrix}
$$

$$
= 8 \begin{vmatrix} -4 & -9 & 0 & -7 \\ 3 & 2 & 1 & 3 \\ -3 & -5 & 0 & -7 \\ -5 & -4 & 0 & -5 \end{vmatrix} = -8 \begin{vmatrix} 4 & 9 & 0 & 7 \\ 3 & 2 & 1 & 3 \\ 3 & 5 & 0 & 7 \\ 5 & 4 & 0 & 5 \end{vmatrix} = 8 \begin{vmatrix} 4 & 9 & 7 \\ 3 & 5 & 7 \\ 5 & 4 & 5 \end{vmatrix}
$$

$$
= 8 \begin{vmatrix} 1 & 4 & 0 \\ 3 & 5 & 7 \\ 5 & 4 & 5 \end{vmatrix} = 8 \begin{vmatrix} 1 & 0 & 0 \\ 3 & -7 & 7 \\ 5 & -16 & 5 \end{vmatrix} = 8 \begin{vmatrix} -7 & 7 \\ -16 & 5 \end{vmatrix} = 8(77) = 616.
$$

We have first used the second part of Theorem 12.14 to factor 2 from each element of the second row, then have factored 4 from each element of the third column. Next we used elementary operations of Type 3, which did not change the value of the determinant, to get all elements but one of the third column equal to zero. In order to avoid so many minus signs we then multiplied the first, third, and fourth rows by −1. Since each of these operations changed the sign of the determinant, we had to place a minus sign in front. We then expanded in terms of the third column. To evaluate the determinant of order three, we subtracted the second row from the first (multiplied by −1 and added to the first). This was done merely to get 1 in some position. The rest of the calculation should be obvious.

Example 3. Without expanding the determinants, show that

$$
\begin{vmatrix} a & b & c \\ d & e & f \\ g & h & i \end{vmatrix} = \begin{vmatrix} c & i & f \\ b & h & e \\ a & g & d \end{vmatrix}.
$$

The calculations are as follows, first using Theorem 12.9 and then using the first part of Theorem 12.14 twice:

$$
\begin{vmatrix} a & b & c \\ d & e & f \\ g & h & i \end{vmatrix} = \begin{vmatrix} a & d & g \\ b & e & h \\ c & f & i \end{vmatrix} = - \begin{vmatrix} c & f & i \\ b & e & h \\ a & d & g \end{vmatrix} = \begin{vmatrix} c & i & f \\ b & h & e \\ a & g & d \end{vmatrix}.
$$

1. Find the value of each of the following determinants over the rational field:

(a) $\begin{vmatrix} 1 & -3 & 2 \\ -2 & 4 & 3 \\ 3 & 1 & 2 \end{vmatrix}$,

(b) $\begin{vmatrix} 1 & 2 & 3 \\ 4 & 5 & 6 \\ 7 & 8 & 9 \end{vmatrix}$,

(c) $\begin{vmatrix} 6 & -4 & 8 \\ -2 & 3 & 5 \\ 10 & 4 & 14 \end{vmatrix}$,

(d) $\begin{vmatrix} \frac{1}{2} & \frac{2}{3} & -\frac{1}{2} \\ -\frac{2}{3} & -\frac{1}{2} & 2 \\ \frac{1}{6} & \frac{1}{2} & \frac{1}{3} \end{vmatrix}$,

(e) $\begin{vmatrix} 2 & 3 & -2 & -3 \\ 4 & 1 & 2 & 1 \\ 2 & -2 & 3 & 4 \\ 2 & 3 & -1 & 2 \end{vmatrix}$,

(f) $\begin{vmatrix} 2 & \frac{1}{2} & -\frac{1}{2} & 1 \\ \frac{2}{3} & \frac{1}{3} & -\frac{2}{3} & -\frac{1}{3} \\ 2 & -2 & 2 & -2 \\ 4 & 6 & 2 & 4 \end{vmatrix}$,

(g) $\begin{vmatrix} 2 & -3 & 1 & 2 & 3 \\ 1 & 2 & 2 & 3 & 4 \\ -1 & 1 & 1 & -1 & 1 \\ 2 & 4 & 6 & 4 & 2 \\ 3 & 2 & 1 & -3 & 2 \end{vmatrix}$.

2. Find the value of each of the following determinants over the field $I/(5)$:

(a) $\begin{vmatrix} 2 & 3 & 4 \\ 1 & 2 & 3 \\ 3 & 3 & 2 \end{vmatrix}$,

(b) $\begin{vmatrix} 3 & 0 & 4 \\ 1 & 2 & 4 \\ 4 & 3 & 2 \end{vmatrix}$,

(c) $\begin{vmatrix} 1 & 2 & 3 & 4 \\ 2 & 3 & 4 & 1 \\ 3 & 4 & 1 & 2 \\ 4 & 1 & 2 & 3 \end{vmatrix}$.

3. Without expansion of the determinants involved, verify the following (the elements are from any field):

$$\begin{vmatrix} a_1 & a_2 & a_3 \\ b_1 & b_2 & b_3 \\ c_1 & c_2 & c_3 \end{vmatrix} = \begin{vmatrix} c_1 + 2a_1 & b_1 & a_1 \\ c_3 + 2a_3 & b_3 & a_3 \\ c_2 + 2a_2 & b_2 & a_2 \end{vmatrix}.$$

12.5 THE DETERMINANT RANK OF A MATRIX

In this section we shall consider matrices that are not necessarily square. First we make the following definition.

12.27 Definition. An arbitrary matrix C over a field F is said to have *determinant rank r* if there exists a square submatrix of C of order r whose determinant is different from zero, whereas every square submatrix of C

of order $r + 1$ has zero determinant. If all elements of C are zero, we define its determinant rank to be zero.

We may notice that if the determinant rank of C is r, not only is the determinant of every square submatrix of order $r + 1$ equal to zero, but also the determinant of every square submatrix of order greater than r is necessarily zero. For example, consider a square submatrix M of order $r + 2$. If $|M|$ is expanded in terms of a row or column, every cofactor is, except possibly for sign, the determinant of a submatrix of C of order $r + 1$, and hence has the value zero. Accordingly, $|M| = 0$; that is, the determinant of every square submatrix of order $r + 2$ has the value zero. By the same kind of argument, the determinant of every square submatrix of order $r + 3$ must now be zero, and so on. Of course, a process of induction is actually involved here.

The following theorem justifies the use of the word *rank* in the above definition.

12.28 Theorem. *The determinant rank of an arbitrary matrix C over a field coincides with its rank as defined in 11.30.*

Let C be the $p \times q$ matrix given by

$$C = \begin{bmatrix} c_{11} & c_{12} & \cdots & c_{1q} \\ c_{21} & c_{22} & \cdots & c_{2q} \\ \cdot & \cdot & \cdot \cdot \cdot \cdot & \cdot \\ c_{p1} & c_{p2} & \cdots & c_{pq} \end{bmatrix},$$

and let us assume that C has determinant rank r. If $r = 0$, which means that all elements of C are zero, then the dimension of the row space (or column space) of C is also zero by definition of the dimension of a zero vector space. Hence, also, the rank of C is zero, and this case is easily disposed of. Henceforth we shall assume that $r > 0$, and shall complete the proof by showing that the row rank of C is r.

It is clear that interchanging rows (or columns) of C cannot affect its row (or column) rank, and also cannot affect its determinant rank since such operations would at most change the *sign* of certain determinants. Accordingly, by making such interchanges we can be sure that the square submatrix of order r in the upper left-hand corner is different from zero. As a matter of notation, let us assume that this is already true for the matrix C; that is, that the determinant of the matrix

12.29

$$\begin{bmatrix} c_{11} & c_{12} & \cdots & c_{1r} \\ c_{21} & c_{22} & \cdots & c_{2r} \\ \cdot & \cdot & \cdot \cdot \cdot \cdot & \cdot \\ c_{r1} & c_{r2} & \cdots & c_{rr} \end{bmatrix}$$

is different from zero. Now, by Corollary 12.16, the row vectors of this matrix are linearly independent; hence the first r row vectors of C must also be linearly independent. If $C_1, C_2, \cdots, C_p$ are the row vectors of C, we therefore know that the set $\{C_1, C_2, \cdots, C_r\}$ is linearly independent and we shall show that it is a basis of the row space of C. This is obviously true if $r = p$, so we henceforth assume that $r < p$. Let s be an arbitrary, but fixed, integer such that $r < s \leq p$, and let us show that C_s is a linear combination of $C_1, C_2, \cdots, C_r$. For each integer $t = 1, 2, \cdots, q$, let us consider the matrix $D(t)$ of order $r + 1$ defined as follows:

$$
D(t) = \begin{bmatrix}
c_{11} & c_{12} & \cdots & c_{1r} & c_{1t} \\
c_{21} & c_{22} & \cdots & c_{2r} & c_{2t} \\
\cdot & \cdot & \cdot & \cdot & \cdot \\
c_{r1} & c_{r2} & \cdots & c_{rr} & c_{rt} \\
c_{s1} & c_{s2} & \cdots & c_{sr} & c_{st}
\end{bmatrix}.
$$

If $t \leq r$, this matrix has two identical columns and hence $|D(t)| = 0$. On the other hand, if $t > r$, $D(t)$ is a square submatrix of C of order $r + 1$, and again $|D(t)| = 0$ since it is given that C has determinant rank r. Accordingly, $|D(t)| = 0$ for $t = 1, 2, \cdots, q$. If $d_1, d_2, \cdots, d_r, d_s$ are the cofactors of the elements of the last column of $D(t)$, it is clear that they do not depend on t, and if we expand $|D(t)|$ in terms of its last column, we find that

$$
c_{1t}d_1 + c_{2t}d_2 + \cdots + c_{rt}d_r + c_{st}d_s = 0, \qquad (t = 1, 2, \cdots, q).
$$

In terms of row vectors, this equation can be written in the form

$$
d_1C_1 + d_2C_2 + \cdots + d_rC_r + d_sC_s = 0.
$$

Moreover, $d_s \neq 0$ since it is the determinant of the matrix 12.29. It follows that C_s is a linear combination of $C_1, C_2, \cdots, C_r$. Since this is true for each s satisfying $r < s \leq p$, we have proved that $\{C_1, C_2, \cdots, C_r\}$ is indeed a basis of the row space of C, and hence that C has (row) rank r. The proof is therefore completed.

If A is a square matrix of order n, its determinant rank will be less than n if and only if $|A| = 0$. Moreover, the row (column) rank will be less than n if and only if the row vectors (column vectors) are linearly dependent. Accordingly, we have at once the following result, which completes the result of Corollary 12.16.

12.30 Corollary. *If A is a square matrix over a field, then $|A| = 0$ if and only if the row vectors (column vectors) of A are linearly dependent.*

In view of the equality of all the various ranks of a matrix, in the future we shall usually refer merely to the *rank* of a matrix to mean the row rank, the column rank, or the determinant rank.

12.6 SYSTEMS OF LINEAR EQUATIONS

We now briefly discuss applications of determinants to the problem of finding the solutions of a system of linear equations. We shall first consider a system with the same number of equations as unknowns. Let us therefore consider the following system of linear equations over a field F:

12.31
$$\sum_{j=1}^{n} a_{ij}x_j = b_i, \qquad (i = 1, 2, \cdots, n).$$

We shall denote by A the matrix of the coefficients in this system of equations and by A_{ij} the cofactor of a_{ij} in $|A|$. If $|A| \neq 0$, it follows that the matrix A has rank n and clearly the augmented matrix of the system also has rank n. We already know from Theorem 11.31 that in this case the system of equations will have a *unique* solution. As hinted at in Section 12.1, the theory of determinants gives us an easy way to write down the solution in this case. The procedure is as follows.

In order to find the value of an arbitrary unknown x_l, we multiply the first equation by A_{1l}, the second by A_{2l}, $\cdots$, the nth by A_{nl}, and add. In the resulting equation, the coefficient of x_l is

$$\sum_{i=1}^{n} a_{il}A_{il}$$

which, by Theorem 12.21, is just $|A|$. If $k \neq l$, the coefficient of x_k in this resulting equation is

$$\sum_{i=1}^{n} a_{ik}A_{il},$$

which is zero by 12.26. Accordingly, the equation takes the following form:

12.32
$$|A|\, x_l = \sum_{i=1}^{n} b_i A_{il}.$$

For convenience, let us define the matrix $B(l)$ to be the matrix of order n obtained from A by replacing the lth column by the column of constant terms in the system 12.31. It follows that the right side of 12.32 is the expansion of $|B(l)|$ in terms of its lth column. Using this fact, and observing that the above argument holds for each choice of l, we find that

12.33
$$|A|\, x_l = |B(l)|, \qquad (l = 1, 2, \cdots, n).$$

Up to this point the calculations remain valid even if $|A| = 0$, but we are here concerned with the case in which $|A| \neq 0$. In this case, the preceding equations yield at once the unique solution of our given system of equations in the following explicit form:

12.34
$$x_l = \frac{|B(l)|}{|A|}, \qquad (l = 1, 2, \cdots, n).$$

Actually, our calculations here merely show that *if* $|A| \neq 0$ and *if* the given system of equations has a solution, then that solution is given by 12.34. However, from previous results we know that if $|A| \neq 0$, the system does have a solution and it is therefore given by 12.34. It is also fairly easy to verify directly that 12.34 does furnish a solution (see Exercise 10 below). Our results may be summarized as follows.

12.35 Cramer's Rule. *If A is the matrix of the coefficients of a system 12.31 of n linear equations in n unknowns over a field, and if $|A| \neq 0$, then the system has the unique solution*

$$x_l = \frac{|B(l)|}{|A|}, \qquad (l = 1, 2, \cdots, n),$$

where $B(l)$ is the matrix obtained from A by replacing the lth column by the column of constant terms.

As an illustration of the use of Cramer's Rule, let us solve the following system of equations over the rational field:

$$\begin{aligned}
3x_1 + x_2 - x_3 &= 2, \\
x_1 + 2x_2 + x_3 &= 3, \\
-x_1 + x_2 + 4x_3 &= 9.
\end{aligned}$$

For this system, using the notation introduced above, we have

$$A = \begin{bmatrix} 3 & 1 & -1 \\ 1 & 2 & 1 \\ -1 & 1 & 4 \end{bmatrix}, \quad B(1) = \begin{bmatrix} 2 & 1 & -1 \\ 3 & 2 & 1 \\ 9 & 1 & 4 \end{bmatrix}, \quad B(2) = \begin{bmatrix} 3 & 2 & -1 \\ 1 & 3 & 1 \\ -1 & 9 & 4 \end{bmatrix},$$

and

$$B(3) = \begin{bmatrix} 3 & 1 & 2 \\ 1 & 2 & 3 \\ -1 & 1 & 9 \end{bmatrix}.$$

We omit the details but the values of the determinants of these matrices are: $|A| = 13$, $|B(1)| = 26$, $|B(2)| = -13$, and $|B(3)| = 39$. The solution of the system is therefore $x_1 = 2$, $x_2 = -1$, $x_3 = 3$.

Although Cramer's Rule applies to the solution of a system of equations involving the same number of equations as unknowns, and then only if the determinant of the coefficients is different from zero, it can frequently be used in a somewhat more general situation as follows.

Suppose that we have the following system of r linear equations in n unknowns, for which the rank of the matrix of the coefficients is also r:

12.36
$$\sum_{j=1}^{n} a_{ij}x_j = b_i, \qquad (i = 1, 2, \cdots, r).$$

If $r = n$, we may apply Cramer's Rule at once, so let us assume that $r < n$. The matrix of the coefficients must have a square submatrix of order r whose determinant is different from zero. Suppose, for simplicity, that this submatrix is made up of the *first* r columns. In this case, we rewrite the system 12.36 in the following form:

12.37
$$a_{11}x_1 + a_{12}x_2 + \cdots + a_{1r}x_r = b_1 - a_{1\ r+1}x_{r+1} - \cdots - a_{1n}x_n,$$
$$a_{21}x_1 + a_{22}x_2 + \cdots + a_{2r}x_r = b_2 - a_{2\ r+1}x_{r+1} - \cdots - a_{2n}x_n,$$
$$\cdots \cdots \cdots \cdots \cdots \cdots \cdots \cdots \cdots \cdots \cdots \cdots \cdots \cdots$$
$$a_{r1}x_1 + a_{r2}x_2 + \cdots + a_{rr}x_r = b_r - a_{r\ r+1}x_{r+1} - \cdots - a_{rn}x_n.$$

We then replace $x_{r+1}, \cdots, x_n$ by arbitrary elements of the underlying field and since the matrix of the coefficients of $x_1, \cdots, x_r$ has nonzero determinant, we can use Cramer's Rule to solve for the corresponding values of $x_1, \cdots, x_r$. All solutions of the system 12.37, and therefore of the system 12.36, can be obtained in this way.

We may point out that, by Theorem 11.34, any system of equations that has a solution is equivalent to a system of the form 12.36 so that, at least in theory, the present method is always available.

Let us illustrate how to solve a system of the form 12.36 by considering the following system of linear equations over the rational field:

12.38
$$x_1 + 2x_2 - x_3 + x_4 = 4,$$
$$- x_1 + x_2 + 3x_3 + x_4 = - 2,$$
$$x_1 + 5x_2 + x_3 + x_4 = 2.$$

It may be verified that the matrix of the coefficients has rank 3; also that the determinant of the submatrix consisting of the first three columns is zero. However, the matrix consisting of the first, third, and fourth columns has nonzero determinant. Accordingly, we replace x_2 by the arbitrary rational number s and solve the following system by Cramer's Rule:

$$x_1 - x_3 + x_4 = 4 - 2s,$$
$$- x_1 + 3x_3 + x_4 = - 2 - s,$$
$$x_1 + x_3 + x_4 = 2 - 5s.$$

We omit the details but the solution turns out to be as follows:

$$x_1 = \frac{2 - 7s}{2}, \qquad x_2 = s, \qquad x_3 = -\frac{2 + 3s}{2}, \qquad x_4 = 2.$$

Every solution of the given system 12.38 is then of this form.

In this section we have considered applications of the theory of determinants to the problem of solving a given system of linear equations. Of course, there is no reason why the use of determinants may not be combined with the methods of the preceding chapter. In particular, it may be helpful first to simplify the system somewhat by use of elementary operations, and then at some appropriate stage to apply Cramer's Rule.

———————————————————— E X E R C I S E S

In each of Exercises 1–9, apply Cramer's Rule to solve the given system of linear equations over the rational field.

1. $3x_1 - 5x_2 = 25,$
$x_1 + 4x_2 = -3.$

2. $3x_1 + 6x_2 = -15,$
$x_1 + 4x_2 = 1.$

3. $2x_1 - x_2 + x_3 = 0,$
$x_1 + 2x_2 - 2x_3 = 10,$
$3x_1 - 3x_2 - 5x_3 = 2.$

4. $2x_1 - 4x_2 + x_3 = 4,$
$x_1 + 3x_2 - x_3 = 5,$
$4x_1 - 2x_2 + 3x_3 = 6.$

5. $x_1 - 3x_2 + x_3 = 2,$
$3x_1 + x_2 + x_3 = 1.$
$5x_1 + x_2 + 3x_3 = 3.$

6. $2x_1 + x_2 + 3x_3 - x_4 = 1,$
$x_1 - x_2 + x_3 - x_4 = -5,$
$3x_1 + 2x_2 + 2x_3 - 3x_4 = 1,$
$-x_1 + 3x_2 - x_3 + 2x_4 = 14.$

7. $2x_1 - x_2 + 3x_3 = 4,$
$3x_1 + x_2 - 2x_3 = 3.$

8. $x_1 - 2x_2 + x_3 - x_4 = 2,$
$2x_1 + x_2 - x_3 + 2x_4 = 1,$
$x_1 + x_2 + 3x_3 - 3x_4 = 3.$

9. $x_1 - x_2 + 2x_3 - x_4 = 2,$
$2x_1 + x_2 - 3x_3 + 3x_4 = 0,$
$4x_1 - x_2 + x_3 + 2x_4 = 1.$

10. Verify that 12.33 actually gives a solution of the *first* equation of the system 12.31. [Hint: By expanding in terms of the first row, show that the determinant

$$\begin{vmatrix} b_1 & a_{11} & a_{12} & \cdots & a_{1n} \\ b_1 & a_{11} & a_{12} & \cdots & a_{1n} \\ b_2 & a_{21} & a_{22} & \cdots & a_{2n} \\ \cdot & \cdot & \cdot & \cdot \cdot \cdot \cdot \cdot & \cdot \\ b_n & a_{n1} & a_{n2} & \cdots & a_{nn} \end{vmatrix}$$

has the value

$$b_1 |A| - a_{11} |B(1)| - a_{12} |B(2)| - \cdots - a_{1n} |B(n)|.]$$

13

Linear Transformations and Matrices

In this chapter we introduce the important class of mappings of a vector space $V(F)$ into itself which are called *linear transformations*. Under appropriate definitions of addition, multiplication, and scalar multiplication, the set L of all linear transformations of a vector space $V(F)$ is a ring and is also itself a vector space over F. Such a system is an example of an *algebra* over F, according to the definition to be given in Section 13.2. For our purposes, the most important case is that in which $V(F)$ has finite dimension n, and in this case we shall show how to set up a one-one mapping of the set L onto the set F_n of all matrices of order n over F. This leads naturally to definitions of addition, multiplication, and scalar multiplication in F_n in such a way that F_n becomes an algebra over F which is isomorphic to the algebra L. We then proceed to establish a few properties of this algebra of matrices.

The topics presented in this chapter play an important role in modern algebra and have been studied extensively. Our treatment gives merely a very brief introduction to the basic ideas and methods.

13.1 LINEAR TRANSFORMATIONS

Before giving the general definition of a linear transformation, we present a simple example as follows. Consider the vector space $V_2(K)$ over the field K of real numbers. If $X = (x_1, x_2)$ is an element of $V_2(K)$, let us define a corresponding element $Z = (z_1, z_2)$ of the same vector space by the following two equations:

13.1
$$z_1 = 2x_1 - 3x_2,$$
$$z_2 = x_1 + 2x_2.$$

Perhaps we should emphasize that x_1, x_2, z_1, z_2 are not indeterminates but real numbers related by these equations. The viewpoint we now wish to adopt is that Equations 13.1 define a mapping $X \to Z$ of $V_2(K)$ into $V_2(K)$. If we designate this mapping by α, then the mapping $X \to Z$ may also be written in the form $X\alpha = Z$ or

$$(x_1, x_2)\alpha = (2x_1 - 3x_2, x_1 + 2x_2).$$

It is not difficult to verify that addition and scalar multiplication are preserved under this mapping α, that is, that the following are true:

If $X, Y \in V_2(K)$, then $(X + Y)\alpha = X\alpha + Y\alpha$,

If $X \in V_2(K)$ and $c \in K$, then $(cX)\alpha = c(X\alpha)$.

According to the definition to be given below, any mapping of $V_2(K)$ into $V_2(K)$ having these two properties will be called a *linear transformation* of $V_2(K)$. The mapping α defined by Equations 13.1 is therefore a simple example of a linear transformation.

As suggested by the preceding remarks, we now give the following formal definition.

13.2 Definition. Let V be a vector space over a field F. A mapping α of V into V is called a *linear transformation* of V if it has the following two properties:

13.3 If $X, Y \in V$, then $(X + Y)\alpha = X\alpha + Y\alpha$,

13.4 If $X \in V$ and $c \in F$, then $(cX)\alpha = c(X\alpha)$.

There are several simple, but important, properties of linear transformations that follow almost immediately from this definition and the definition of a vector space. We collect them in the following theorem.

13.5 Theorem. *If α is a linear transformation of the vector space V over F, the following are true:*

(i)   *If $X \in V$, then $(-X)\mathfrak{a} = -(X\mathfrak{a})$,*

(ii) $0\mathfrak{a} = 0$,

(iii) *If $X_i \in V$ and $c_i \in F$ $(i = 1, 2, \cdots, n)$, then*

$$(c_1 X_1 + c_2 X_2 + \cdots + c_n X_n)\mathfrak{a} = c_1(X_1\mathfrak{a}) + c_2(X_2\mathfrak{a}) + \cdots + c_n(X_n\mathfrak{a}),$$

(iv) *If U is a subspace of V and we define $U\mathfrak{a} = \{X\mathfrak{a};\ X \in U\}$, then $U\mathfrak{a}$ is also a subspace of V.*

In view of 10.3 (v) and 10.6 (iii), we know that if $Y \in V$, then $(-1)Y = -Y$. Accordingly, the special case of 13.4 in which $c = -1$ shows that $(-X)\mathfrak{a} = -(X\mathfrak{a})$, and part (i) of the theorem is established.

To prove part (ii), we proceed as follows. If $X \in V$, we have

$$\begin{aligned}
0\mathfrak{a} &= [X + (-X)]\mathfrak{a} = X\mathfrak{a} + (-X)\mathfrak{a} &&\text{(by 13.3)}\\
&= X\mathfrak{a} - (X\mathfrak{a}) &&\text{(by 13.5 (i))}\\
&= 0.
\end{aligned}$$

We omit the proof of part (iii) since it follows in an almost obvious way by repeated use of 13.3 and 13.4.

Let us now consider part (iv) of the theorem. In view of Theorem 10.7, to prove that the set $U\mathfrak{a}$ is a subspace of V we need only show that it is closed under addition and scalar multiplication. Let $X\mathfrak{a}$ and $Y\mathfrak{a}$ be elements of $U\mathfrak{a}$, it being understood that $X, Y \in U$. Since U is a subspace of V, we know that $X + Y \in U$, and hence that $(X + Y)\mathfrak{a} \in U\mathfrak{a}$. In view of 13.3, it follows that $X\mathfrak{a} + Y\mathfrak{a}$ is an element of $U\mathfrak{a}$, and we see that $U\mathfrak{a}$ is therefore closed under addition. Similarly, if $X\mathfrak{a} \in U\mathfrak{a}$ with $X \in U$, and $c \in F$, then $cX \in U$ and hence $(cX)\mathfrak{a} \in U\mathfrak{a}$. It follows from 13.4 that $c(X\mathfrak{a}) \in U\mathfrak{a}$, and $U\mathfrak{a}$ is also closed with respect to scalar multiplication. This completes the proof of the theorem.

────────────────────────────── **EXERCISES**

1. Which of the following mappings of $V_2(K)$ into $V_2(K)$ are linear transformations of $V_2(K)$?

(a) $(x_1, x_2)\mathfrak{a} = (0, 0)$,

(b) $(x_1, x_2)\mathfrak{a} = (3x_1 + x_2, x_2)$,

(c) $(x_1, x_2)\mathfrak{a} = (x_1 + 1, x_1 + x_2)$,

(d) $(x_1, x_2)\mathfrak{a} = (x_2, x_1)$,

(e) $(x_1, x_2)\mathfrak{a} = (2x_1 - x_2, x_1 x_2)$,

(f) $(x_1, x_2)\mathfrak{a} = (x_1 - 3x_2, x_1 - 3x_2)$,

(g) $(x_1, x_2)\mathfrak{a} = (x_1, x_2)$.

2. Let V be the vector space of all polynomials in an indeterminate x over a field F (Example 4, Section 10.2). Verify that each of the following mappings of V into V is a linear transformation of V:

(a) $f(x)\alpha = -f(x),$

(b) $f(x)\alpha = 0,$

(c) $f(x)\alpha = f(x),$

(d) $f(x)\alpha = f(-x),$

(e) $f(x)\alpha = f(0),$

(f) $f(x)\alpha = f(x^2),$

(g) $f(x)\alpha = f(x) + f(-x).$

13.2 ALGEBRA OF LINEAR TRANSFORMATIONS

In this section we shall study the set L of all linear transformations of a vector space V over a field F. In order to have a convenient way to state our principal result, we first make the following definition.

13.6 Definition. Let S be a nonempty set on which there are defined binary operations of addition and multiplication, and also a scalar multiplication by elements of a field H. We shall call S an *algebra* over the field H if the following conditions are satisfied:

(i) S is a ring with respect to the operations of addition and multiplication,

(ii) S is a vector space over H with respect to the operations of addition and scalar multiplication,

(iii) If $u, v \in S$ and $a \in H$, then $(au)v = u(av) = a(uv).$

It will be observed that part (iii) of this definition is a condition which involves both multiplication and scalar multiplication.

We now proceed to introduce appropriate operations on the set L of all linear transformations of the vector space V over F, and shall eventually find that L is then an algebra over F.

First, let us define an operation of addition on the set L. If α, $\mathcal{B} \in L$, we define $\alpha + \mathcal{B}$ as follows:

13.7
$$X(\alpha + \mathcal{B}) = X\alpha + X\mathcal{B}, \qquad X \in V.$$

It is obvious that $\alpha + \mathcal{B}$ is then a mapping of V into V. The fact that it is a linear transformation of V, and therefore an element of L, follows easily from the defining properties (10.3) of a vector space and the definition (13.2) of a linear transformation. The proof goes as follows, where it is to be understood that $X, Y \in V$ and $c \in F$:

$$
\begin{aligned}
(X + Y)(\alpha + \mathcal{B}) &= (X + Y)\alpha + (X + Y)\mathcal{B} && \textit{(by 13.7)}\\
&= X\alpha + Y\alpha + X\mathcal{B} + Y\mathcal{B} && \textit{(by 13.3)}\\
&= X\alpha + X\mathcal{B} + Y\alpha + Y\mathcal{B} && \textit{(by 10.3 (i))}\\
&= X(\alpha + \mathcal{B}) + Y(\alpha + \mathcal{B}) && \textit{(by 13.7)},
\end{aligned}
$$

and
$$(cX)(\alpha + \mathcal{B}) = (cX)\alpha + (cX)\mathcal{B} \qquad \text{(by 13.7)}$$
$$= c(X\alpha) + c(X\mathcal{B}) \qquad \text{(by 13.4)}$$
$$= c(X\alpha + X\mathcal{B}) \qquad \text{(by 10.3 (ii))}$$
$$= c(X(\alpha + \mathcal{B})) \qquad \text{(by 13.7)}.$$

These calculations show that both of the defining properties 13.3 and 13.4 of a linear transformation are satisfied by the mapping $\alpha + \mathcal{B}$, and hence that $\alpha + \mathcal{B}$ is an element of L. Accordingly, we have defined an operation of addition on the set L.

Multiplication of mappings has already been defined in Section 9.3, where it was also shown that the associative law of multiplication always holds. In accordance with the general definition of multiplication of mappings, we define the product $\alpha\mathcal{B}$ of elements of L as follows:

13.8 $$X(\alpha\mathcal{B}) = (X\alpha)\mathcal{B}, \qquad\qquad X \in V.$$

Certainly, $\alpha\mathcal{B}$ is a mapping of V into V, but we must show that it is in fact a linear transformation of V. In this case, the calculations are as follows where, again, $X, Y \in V$ and $c \in F$:

$$(X + Y)(\alpha\mathcal{B}) = ((X + Y)\alpha)\mathcal{B} \qquad \text{(by 13.8)}$$
$$= (X\alpha + Y\alpha)\mathcal{B} \qquad \text{(by 13.3)}$$
$$= (X\alpha)\mathcal{B} + (Y\alpha)\mathcal{B} \qquad \text{(by 13.3)}$$
$$= X(\alpha\mathcal{B}) + Y(\alpha\mathcal{B}) \qquad \text{(by 13.8)},$$

and
$$(cX)(\alpha\mathcal{B}) = ((cX)\alpha)\mathcal{B} \qquad \text{(by 13.8)}$$
$$= (c(X\alpha))\mathcal{B} \qquad \text{(by 13.4)}$$
$$= c((X\alpha)\mathcal{B}) \qquad \text{(by 13.4)}$$
$$= c(X(\alpha\mathcal{B})) \qquad \text{(by 13.8)}.$$

We have thus established the two defining properties of a linear transformation, and therefore $\alpha\mathcal{B} \in L$. Hence, 13.8 actually defines an operation of multiplication on the set L.

Finally, we introduce scalar multiplication of elements of L by elements of the field F. If $\alpha \in L$ and $r \in F$, we define $r\alpha$ as follows:

13.9 $$X(r\alpha) = (rX)\alpha, \qquad\qquad X \in V.$$

Once more it is clear that $r\alpha$ is a mapping of V into V, and we show as follows that it is a linear transformation of V:

$$(X + Y)(r\alpha) = (r(X + Y))\alpha \qquad \text{(by 13.9)}$$
$$= (rX + rY)\alpha \qquad \text{(by 10.3 (ii))}$$
$$= (rX)\alpha + (rY)\alpha \qquad \text{(by 13.3)}$$
$$= X(r\alpha) + Y(r\alpha) \qquad \text{(by 13.9)},$$

and

$$(cX)(r\alpha) = (r(cX))\alpha \qquad \text{(by 13.9)}$$
$$= ((rc)X)\alpha \qquad \text{(by 10.3 (iv))}$$
$$= ((cr)X)\alpha$$
$$= (c(rX))\alpha \qquad \text{(by 10.3 (iv))}$$
$$= c((rX)\alpha) \qquad \text{(by 13.4)}$$
$$= c(X(r\alpha)) \qquad \text{(by 13.9).}$$

We conclude that $r\alpha$ is a linear transformation of V, and we therefore have a scalar multiplication of elements of L by elements of the field F.

We may now state the following important result.

13.10 Theorem. *Using the respective Definitions 13.7, 13.8, and 13.9 of addition, multiplication, and scalar multiplication, the set L of all linear transformations of the vector space V over F is an algebra over F.*

The properties of addition in a vector space are precisely those properties of addition in a ring. Accordingly, to establish this theorem we need only verify the defining properties of a ring, parts (ii)–(v) of the Definition 10.3 of a vector space, and the property 13.6 (iii). We shall prove that L has some of these properties and leave the proofs of the others as exercises.

Let us first make a remark about the meaning of equality of linear transformations. Since linear transformations are mappings, the general definition of equality of mappings, as given in Section 9.3, is applicable. That is, if α, $\beta \in L$, then $\alpha = \beta$ if and only if $X\alpha = X\beta$ for every X in V.

Since the vector space V is an abelian group with respect to the operation of addition, if α, $\beta \in L$ and $X \in V$, we have

$$X\alpha + X\beta = X\beta + X\alpha$$

and therefore, by 13.7, it follows that

$$X(\alpha + \beta) = X(\beta + \alpha).$$

Hence $\alpha + \beta = \beta + \alpha$, and the commutative law of addition therefore holds in L.

Let us now prove the associative law of addition. If α, β, $c \in L$, for each vector X in V we have the following:

$$X((\alpha + \beta) + c) = X(\alpha + \beta) + Xc \qquad \text{(by 13.7)}$$
$$= (X\alpha + X\beta) + Xc \qquad \text{(by 13.7)}$$
$$= X\alpha + (X\beta + Xc)$$
$$= X\alpha + X(\beta + c) \qquad \text{(by 13.7)}$$
$$= X(\alpha + (\beta + c)) \qquad \text{(by 13.7).}$$

This implies that $(\mathfrak{A} + \mathfrak{B}) + \mathfrak{C} = \mathfrak{A} + (\mathfrak{B} + \mathfrak{C})$, and the associative law of addition is therefore established.

It is easily seen that the mapping $\mathfrak{O}$ of V into V defined by

13.11 $$X\mathfrak{O} = 0, \qquad\qquad X \in V,$$

is a linear transformation of V, and therefore an element of L. Moreover, this element $\mathfrak{O}$ of L is the zero of the algebra L since if $\mathfrak{A} \in L$, we have

$$X(\mathfrak{A} + \mathfrak{O}) = X\mathfrak{A} + X\mathfrak{O} = X\mathfrak{A}, \qquad\qquad X \in V,$$

and hence $\mathfrak{A} + \mathfrak{O} = \mathfrak{A}$.

Now if $\mathfrak{A} \in L$ and 1 is the unity of F, for each X in V we have the following:

$$
\begin{aligned}
X(\mathfrak{A} + (-1)\mathfrak{A}) &= X\mathfrak{A} + X((-1)\mathfrak{A}) && \textit{(by 13.7)} \\
&= X\mathfrak{A} + (-1)(X\mathfrak{A}) && \textit{(by 13.9, 13.4)} \\
&= X\mathfrak{A} - (X\mathfrak{A}) \\
&= 0.
\end{aligned}
$$

This implies that $X(\mathfrak{A} + (-1)\mathfrak{A}) = X\mathfrak{O}$, from which it follows that $\mathfrak{A} + (-1)\mathfrak{A} = \mathfrak{O}$. Hence, $(-1)\mathfrak{A}$ is the additive inverse of $\mathfrak{A}$, and in the future we may conform with our usual notation and write $-\mathfrak{A}$ in place of $(-1)\mathfrak{A}$.

We have now proved all the required properties of addition, and we remarked earlier that the associative law of multiplication holds in L. To show that L is a ring there remains only to prove both distributive laws. We shall leave the proof of these laws as an exercise.

Let us now prove one of the additional properties required for a vector space; for example, the property 10.3 (ii). If $\mathfrak{A}, \mathfrak{B} \in L$ and $c \in F$, we see that for each X in V,

$$
\begin{aligned}
X(c(\mathfrak{A} + \mathfrak{B})) &= (cX)(\mathfrak{A} + \mathfrak{B}) && \textit{(by 13.9)} \\
&= (cX)\mathfrak{A} + (cX)\mathfrak{B} && \textit{(by 13.7)} \\
&= X(c\mathfrak{A}) + X(c\mathfrak{B}) && \textit{(by 13.9)} \\
&= X(c\mathfrak{A} + c\mathfrak{B}) && \textit{(by 13.7)}.
\end{aligned}
$$

Hence $c(\mathfrak{A} + \mathfrak{B}) = c\mathfrak{A} + c\mathfrak{B}$, as required. We omit the proofs of 10.3 (iii, iv, v), and the proof of 13.6 (iii).

It is quite easy to verify that the mapping $\mathcal{E}$ of V into V defined by

13.12 $$X\mathcal{E} = X, \qquad\qquad X \in V,$$

is a linear transformation and hence an element of L. Moreover, if

$\alpha \in L$, we have that $\alpha \mathcal{E} = \mathcal{E}\alpha = \alpha$, and hence the algebra L has $\mathcal{E}$ as unity.

One characterization of the elements of L that have multiplicative inverses is given in the following theorem.

13.13 Theorem. *An element α of L has a multiplicative inverse α^{-1} in L if and only if α is a one-one mapping of V onto V.*

Suppose, first, that α is a linear transformation of V which is a one-one mapping of V onto V. Then every element of V is uniquely expressible in the form $X\alpha$ for $X \in V$. Exactly as in 9.12, it follows that the mapping α^{-1} defined by

13.14
$$(X\alpha)\alpha^{-1} = X, \qquad\qquad X \in V,$$

is also a one-one mapping of V onto V. Moreover, as in the proof of Theorem 9.14, we know that

$$\alpha\alpha^{-1} = \alpha^{-1}\alpha = \mathcal{E}.$$

To show that α^{-1} is indeed the multiplicative inverse of α in L, we need only show that α^{-1} is a linear transformation, and is therefore an element of L. Let $X\alpha$ and $Y\alpha$ be any elements of V. Then

$$
\begin{aligned}
(X\alpha + Y\alpha)\alpha^{-1} &= ((X+Y)\alpha)\alpha^{-1} & \text{(by 13.3)}\\
&= X + Y & \text{(by 13.14)}\\
&= (X\alpha)\alpha^{-1} + (Y\alpha)\alpha^{-1} & \text{(by 13.14)}.
\end{aligned}
$$

This establishes for α^{-1} the property 13.3 of a linear transformation. Likewise, if $X\alpha \in V$ and $c \in F$, we have

$$
\begin{aligned}
(c(X\alpha))\alpha^{-1} &= ((cX)\alpha)\alpha^{-1} & \text{(by 13.4)}\\
&= cX & \text{(by 13.14)}\\
&= c((X\alpha)\alpha^{-1}) & \text{(by 13.14)}.
\end{aligned}
$$

Hence property 13.4 is also satisfied by the mapping α^{-1}, and we have therefore shown that α^{-1} is a linear transformation.

Conversely, suppose that α is an element of L which has a multiplicative inverse α^{-1} in L, and let us show that α is a one-one mapping of V onto V. First, we see that if $X \in V$, then $(X\alpha^{-1})\alpha = X(\alpha^{-1}\alpha) = X$, and it is clear that the mapping α is therefore a mapping of V onto V. Moreover, if $X, Y \in V$ such that $X\alpha = Y\alpha$, it follows at once that $(X\alpha)\alpha^{-1} = (Y\alpha)\alpha^{-1}$. In turn, this implies that $X(\alpha\alpha^{-1}) = Y(\alpha\alpha^{-1})$ or that $X = Y$. Hence, the mapping α is a one-one mapping, and the proof of the theorem is completed.

1. Let α and $\mathcal{B}$ be linear transformations of the vector space $V_2(K)$ defined as follows:

$$(x_1, x_2)\alpha = (2x_1 + x_2, x_1 - x_2),$$
$$(x_1, x_2)\mathcal{B} = (x_1, x_1 + 3x_2).$$

Exhibit in a similar manner each of the following linear transformations of $V_2(K)$: $\alpha + \mathcal{B}$, $\alpha\mathcal{B}$, $\mathcal{B}\alpha$, 5α, $-\alpha$, α^2.

2. If α is as in the preceding exercise, verify that $\alpha^2 - \alpha = 3\mathcal{E}$, where $\mathcal{E}$ is the unity of the algebra of all linear transformations of $V_2(K)$.

3. Find nonzero linear transformations $\mathcal{C}$ and $\mathcal{D}$ of $V_2(K)$ such that $\mathcal{C}\mathcal{D} = \mathcal{O}$.

4. Complete the proof of Theorem 13.10 by doing the following:

    (i)   Prove that both of the distributive laws hold in L.

    (ii)   Prove that L has Properties 10.3 (iii), (iv), and (v).

    (iii)   Prove that L has Property 13.6 (iii).

5. If L is the algebra of all linear transformations of a vector space V over F, verify that the set of all elements of L that are one-one mappings of V onto V is a group with respect to the operation of multiplication.

13.3 THE FINITE-DIMENSIONAL CASE

Heretofore, we have considered linear transformations of an entirely arbitrary vector space V over a field F. In this section we shall restrict V to have finite dimension $n > 0$. Of course, this restriction assures us that V has a basis consisting of n vectors, and we shall exploit the existence of a basis in obtaining the results to follow.

First of all, we shall prove the following theorem.

13.15   **Theorem.**   *If $\{X_1, X_2, \cdots, X_n\}$ is a basis of V and $Z_1, Z_2, \cdots, Z_n$ are arbitrary elements of V, there exists exactly one linear transformation α of V such that*

13.16 $$X_i\alpha = Z_i, \qquad\qquad (i = 1, 2, \cdots, n).$$

We begin by showing that there does exist such a linear transformation, and we shall then show that there is only one such linear transformation.

Since every element of V is uniquely expressible as a linear combination of the elements of a basis, let us *define* a mapping α of V into V as follows:

13.17 $(c_1 X_1 + c_2 X_2 + \cdots + c_n X_n)\alpha = c_1 Z_1 + c_2 Z_2 + \cdots + c_n Z_n,$

it being understood that the c's are arbitrary elements of F. If, in particular, we set $c_1 = 1$ and $c_i = 0$ $(i > 1)$, Equation 13.17 shows that $X_1\alpha = Z_1$. In a similar way, it follows that the mapping α, defined by Equation 13.17, satisfies all the conditions 13.16. There remains to show that the mapping α is actually a linear transformation of V. We shall exhibit the necessary calculations, leaving it to the reader to justify each step. For convenience, let us write "$\sum$" in place of the more explicit symbol "$\sum\limits_{i=1}^{n}$". If $X = \sum a_i X_i$ and $Y = \sum b_i X_i$ are arbitrary elements of V, we have

$$
\begin{aligned}
(X + Y)\alpha = \left(\sum (a_i + b_i)X_i\right)\alpha &= \sum (a_i + b_i)(X_i\alpha) \\
&= \sum (a_i + b_i)Z_i \\
&= \sum a_i Z_i + \sum b_i Z_i \\
&= X\alpha + Y\alpha.
\end{aligned}
$$

Also, if $r \in F$, we have

$$
\begin{aligned}
(rX)\alpha = \left(\sum (ra_i)X_i\right)\alpha &= \sum (ra_i)(X_i\alpha) \\
&= \sum (ra_i)Z_i \\
&= r\sum a_i Z_i \\
&= r(X\alpha).
\end{aligned}
$$

Hence, both defining properties of a linear transformation are satisfied and the mapping α, given by 13.17, is a linear transformation of V.

Suppose, now, that $\mathcal{B}$ is a linear transformation of V such that $X_i\mathcal{B} = Z_i$ $(i = 1, 2, \cdots, n)$. It follows from Theorem 13.5 (iii) that

$$(c_1 X_1 + c_2 X_2 + \cdots + c_n X_n)\mathcal{B} = c_1 Z_1 + c_2 Z_2 + \cdots + c_n Z_n.$$

Since every element X of V is expressible as a linear combination of the elements of a basis, a comparison of this equation with Equation 13.17 shows that $X\alpha = X\mathcal{B}$ for every X in V. We therefore conclude that $\alpha = \mathcal{B}$, and hence there is only one linear transformation which satisfies conditions 13.16. This completes the proof of the theorem.

As in the preceding section, we shall continue to let L denote the algebra of all linear transformations of the vector space V.

13-3 · The Finite-Dimensional Case

277

We have proved in Theorem 13.5 (iv) that if U is a subspace of the vector space V and $\alpha \in L$, then $U\alpha$ is also a subspace of V. We can now say something as follows about the dimensions of these subspaces.

13.18 Theorem. *If U is a subspace of the vector space V of finite dimension and $\alpha \in L$, then dim $(U\alpha) \leq dim\ U$. Moreover, if α has a multiplicative inverse α^{-1} in L, then dim $(U\alpha) = dim\ U$.*

We may remark that the theorem remains true for an arbitrary vector space V provided only that the subspace U has finite dimension. However, our assumption that V has finite dimension assures us that every subspace of V necessarily has finite dimension.

Suppose that dim $U = k$ and that $\{X_1, X_2, \cdots, X_k\}$ is a basis of U, so that every element of U is expressible in the form

$$c_1X_1 + c_2X_2 + \cdots + c_kX_k, \qquad\qquad c_i \in F\ (i = 1, 2, \cdots, k).$$

Since, by Theorem 13.5 (iii),

$$(c_1X_1 + c_2X_2 + \cdots + c_kX_k)\alpha = c_1(X_1\alpha) + c_2(X_2\alpha) + \cdots + c_k(X_k\alpha),$$

it follows at once that $U\alpha$ is generated by the k vectors $X_1\alpha, X_2\alpha, \cdots, X_k\alpha$. That is, in the notation of Chapter 10, we have

$$U\alpha = [X_1\alpha, X_2\alpha, \cdots, X_k\alpha].$$

Hence dim $(U\alpha) \leq k$, and since dim $U = k$, we see immediately that dim $(U\alpha) \leq$ dim U.

Now if α has a multiplicative inverse α^{-1} in L, we apply the result just established with U replaced by $U\alpha$ and α by α^{-1}. Accordingly, we find that

$$dim\ U = dim\ ((U\alpha)\alpha^{-1} \leq dim\ (U\alpha)).$$

Since we proved above that always dim $(U\alpha) \leq$ dim U, we conclude that dim $(U\alpha) = $ dim U, and the proof is completed.

The dimension of the subspace $V\alpha$ of V gives some important information about the linear transformation α. For convenience of reference, we therefore make the following definition.

13.19 Definition. Suppose that dim $V = n$ and let α be a linear transformation of V. Then dim $(V\alpha)$ is called the *rank* of the linear transformation α. If the rank of α is less than n, α is said to be *singular*; if the rank of α is n, α is said to be *nonsingular*.

In the next section we shall show how matrices are related to linear transformations, and eventually we shall justify the use of the word "rank" in terms of the previous definition of rank of a matrix.

We now proceed to prove the following theorem.

13.20 Theorem. *If V is a vector space of finite dimension and $\alpha \in L$, the following are equivalent:*

    (i)   *α is a one-one mapping of V onto V,*

    (ii)   *α has a multiplicative inverse α^{-1} in L,*

    (iii) *α is nonsingular,*

    (iv) *$V\alpha = V$,*

    (v)   *If $X \in V$ such that $X\alpha = 0$, then $X = 0$.*

By saying that these statements are equivalent, we mean that each implies all the others. We have already proved in Theorem 13.13 that (i) and (ii) are equivalent without any restriction on V. Suppose, henceforth, that dim $V = n$. If (iv) holds, clearly dim $(V\alpha) = n$, and therefore (iii) holds. If (iii) holds, then dim $(V\alpha) = n$ and (iv) holds by Theorem 10.25. This proves that (iii) and (iv) are equivalent.

We next prove that (i) and (v) are equivalent. Let us assume that (i) holds and that $X \in V$ such that $X\alpha = 0$. Since, by 13.5 (ii), $0\alpha = 0$, we have $X\alpha = 0\alpha$. Since we are assuming that α is a one-one mapping, we conclude that $X = 0$, and (v) is established. Conversely, let us now assume (v) and prove (i). We first show that α maps V onto V. If $\sum c_i(X_i\alpha) = 0$, it follows that $(\sum c_i X_i)\alpha = 0$ and (v) assures us that $\sum c_i X_i = 0$. Using this fact, it follows easily that if $\{X_1, X_2, \cdots, X_n\}$ is a basis of V, then the set $\{X_1\alpha, X_2\alpha, \cdots, X_n\alpha\}$ is a linearly independent set and therefore also a basis of V. Hence, if $X \in V$, we have $X = \sum d_i(X_i\alpha) = (\sum d_i X_i)\alpha$, and α is a mapping of V onto V. Suppose, now, that $Y, Z \in V$ such that $Y\alpha = Z\alpha$. Using 13.5 (i), it follows that $(Y - Z)\alpha = 0$, and in view of (v), this assures us that $Y = Z$. Hence, α is a one-one mapping, and (i) is proved.

We shall complete the proof by showing that (ii) implies (iii) and that (iv) implies (v).

If statement (ii) holds, an application of Theorem 13.18 to the case in which $U = V$ shows that dim $(V\alpha) = $ dim $V = n$, and therefore (iii) holds.

Let us now assume the truth of statement (iv), and prove that (v) holds. If $\{X_1, X_2, \cdots, X_n\}$ is a basis of V, as in the proof of Theorem 13.18 it follows that

$$V\alpha = [X_1\alpha, X_2\alpha, \cdots, X_n\alpha].$$

Since it is given that $V\alpha = V$, Theorem 10.23 (iv) shows that the vectors $\{X_1\alpha, X_2\alpha, \cdots, X_n\alpha\}$ are linearly independent. Now in order to prove statement (v), let X be an element of V such that $X\mathcal{a} = 0$, and let us express X as follows as a linear combination of the basis vectors X_1, X_2, $\cdots$, X_n:

$$X = c_1 X_1 + c_2 X_2 + \cdots + c_n X_n.$$

Since $X\mathcal{a} = 0$, this equation implies that

$$c_1(X_1 \mathcal{a}) + c_2(X_2 \mathcal{a}) + \cdots + c_n(X_n \mathcal{a}) = 0.$$

However, we proved above that $\{X_1 \mathcal{a}, X_2 \mathcal{a}, \cdots, X_n \mathcal{a}\}$ is a linearly independent set, and therefore all the c's must be zero. Hence $X = 0$, and we have verified that statement (v) of the theorem is a consequence of statement (iv). This completes the proof of the theorem.

The next theorem will give some information about the rank of a product of linear transformations. For convenience, we shall designate the rank of the linear transformation $\mathcal{a}$ by "rank $\mathcal{a}$."

13.21 Theorem. (i) *If $\mathcal{a}$, $\mathcal{B} \in L$, then rank $(\mathcal{a}\mathcal{B}) \leq$ rank $\mathcal{a}$ and also rank $(\mathcal{a}\mathcal{B}) \leq$ rank $\mathcal{B}$.*

(ii) *If $\mathcal{a}$, $\mathcal{B} \in L$ and $\mathcal{a}$ is nonsingular, then*
$$rank \ (\mathcal{a}\mathcal{B}) = rank \ (\mathcal{B}\mathcal{a}) = rank \ \mathcal{B}.$$

Let us first apply Theorem 13.18 with U replaced by $V\mathcal{a}$ and $\mathcal{a}$ by $\mathcal{B}$. We then have dim $((V\mathcal{a})\mathcal{B}) \leq$ dim $(V\mathcal{a})$. But, by the definition of the product of linear transformations, $(V\mathcal{a})\mathcal{B} = V(\mathcal{a}\mathcal{B})$. Accordingly, we see that rank $(\mathcal{a}\mathcal{B}) \leq$ rank $\mathcal{a}$.

Since $V\mathcal{a} \subseteq V$, it follows that $V(\mathcal{a}\mathcal{B}) = (V\mathcal{a})\mathcal{B} \subseteq V\mathcal{B}$. Hence, dim $(V(\mathcal{a}\mathcal{B})) \leq$ dim $(V\mathcal{B})$, that is, rank $(\mathcal{a}\mathcal{B}) \leq$ rank $\mathcal{B}$. We have thus established part (i) of the theorem.

To prove the second part, suppose that $\mathcal{a}$ is nonsingular. Then, by the preceding theorem, $\mathcal{a}$ has a multiplicative inverse $\mathcal{a}^{-1}$, and we can write $\mathcal{B} = \mathcal{a}^{-1}(\mathcal{a}\mathcal{B})$. Now the part of the theorem already proved assures us that the rank of a product does not exceed the rank of either factor. Hence, rank $\mathcal{B} \leq$ rank $(\mathcal{a}\mathcal{B})$. On the other hand, we know from part (i) of the theorem that rank $(\mathcal{a}\mathcal{B}) \leq$ rank $\mathcal{B}$, and we conclude that rank $(\mathcal{a}\mathcal{B}) =$ rank $\mathcal{B}$. To show that also rank $(\mathcal{B}\mathcal{a}) =$ rank $\mathcal{B}$, we need only write $\mathcal{B} = (\mathcal{B}\mathcal{a})\mathcal{a}^{-1}$, and apply a similar argument.

The following important result is a special case of the second part of the theorem just proved, and is also an easy consequence of the equivalence of statements (i) and (iii) of Theorem 13.20.

13.22 Corollary. *The product of two nonsingular linear transformations of a vector space V is itself a nonsingular linear transformation of V.*

If $\mathcal{a}$ is an arbitrary linear transformation, it follows easily from the definition of a linear transformation that the set of all vectors X of V

such that $X\alpha = 0$ is a *subspace* of V. The following terminology is convenient and suggestive.

13.23 Definition. If $\alpha \in L$, the subspace of V consisting of all vectors X of V such that $X\alpha = 0$ is called the *null space* of α. The dimension of the null space of α is called the *nullity* of α.

The equivalence of conditions (iii) and (v) of Theorem 13.20 shows that if α is nonsingular (that is, has rank n), then the nullity of α is zero. This is a special case of the following theorem.

13.24 Theorem. *If* $\dim V = n$ *and* α *is a linear transformation of* V *of rank* r, *then* α *has nullity* $n - r$.

In view of the preceding remarks we may restrict attention to the case in which the nullity k of α is positive. Let $\{Y_1, \cdots, Y_k\}$ be a basis of the null space of α, and let us extend this set to a basis

$$\{Y_1, \cdots, Y_k, \cdots, Y_n\}$$

of V. Since $Y_i\alpha = 0$ $(i = 1, 2, \cdots, k)$, it follows easily that

$$V\alpha = [Y_{k+1}\alpha, \cdots, Y_n\alpha].$$

We shall now show that $\{Y_{k+1}\alpha, \cdots, Y_n\alpha\}$ is a linearly independent set and hence a basis of $V\alpha$. Suppose that

$$c_{k+1}(Y_{k+1}\alpha) + \cdots + c_n(Y_n\alpha) = 0,$$

where $c_{k+1}, \cdots, c_n$ are elements of F. It follows that

$$(c_{k+1}Y_{k+1} + \cdots + c_nY_n)\alpha = 0,$$

and hence that

$$c_{k+1}Y_{k+1} + \cdots + c_nY_n$$

is in the null space of α. Hence, this vector is a linear combination of the basis elements $Y_1, Y_2, \cdots, Y_k$ of this null space. However, since $\{Y_1, \cdots, Y_n\}$ is a linearly independent set, we conclude that $c_{k+1} = 0$, $\cdots, c_n = 0$. This shows that $\{Y_{k+1}\alpha, \cdots, Y_n\alpha\}$ is a linearly independent set, and therefore a basis of $V\alpha$. Accordingly, $\dim (V\alpha) = n - k$. Since $r = \dim (V\alpha)$, it follows that $r = n - k$ or $k = n - r$, and the proof of the theorem is completed.

_____ **E X E R C I S E S**

1. In each of the following, find the rank of the linear transformation α of $V_3(K)$ and find a basis for the null space of α:

(a) $(x_1, x_2, x_3)\alpha = (x_1 + 2x_2 - x_3, 2x_1 + x_2 + x_3, x_2 - x_3)$,

(b) $(x_1, x_2, x_3)\alpha = (2x_1 - x_2 + x_3, x_1 + 2x_2 - x_3, x_1 + 7x_2 - 4x_3)$,

(c) $(x_1, x_2, x_3)\alpha = (x_1 + x_2, x_1 + x_2, x_1 + x_2)$.

2. If c is a nonzero element of F and $\alpha \in L$, show that rank $(c\alpha)$ = rank α.

3. If $\alpha, \mathcal{B} \in L$, prove that rank $(\alpha + \mathcal{B}) \leq$ rank $\alpha +$ rank $\mathcal{B}$. [Hint: Using the Definition 10.26 of the sum of two subspaces, observe that $V(\alpha + \mathcal{B}) \subseteq V\alpha + V\mathcal{B}$.]

13.4 ALGEBRA OF MATRICES

We continue to let V be a vector space of dimension $n > 0$ over a field F, and L the algebra of all linear transformations of V. Moreover, throughout this section we shall let $\{X_1, X_2, \cdots, X_n\}$ be a *fixed* basis of V.

Suppose, now, that $\alpha \in L$ and that $X_i\alpha = Z_i$ $(i = 1, 2, \cdots, n)$. Since each of the vectors Z_i is *uniquely* expressible as a linear combination of the basis elements, we see that there exist elements a_{ij} $(i, j = 1, 2, \cdots, n)$ of F, uniquely determined by α, such that

$$X_1\alpha = a_{11}X_1 + a_{12}X_2 + \cdots + a_{1n}X_n,$$
$$X_2\alpha = a_{21}X_1 + a_{22}X_2 + \cdots + a_{2n}X_n,$$
$$\cdot \quad \cdot \quad \cdot \quad \cdot \quad \cdot \quad \cdot \quad \cdot \quad \cdot \quad \cdot \quad \cdot \quad \cdot \quad \cdot \quad \cdot \quad \cdot \quad \cdot$$
$$X_n\alpha = a_{n1}X_1 + a_{n2}X_2 + \cdots + a_{nn}X_n.$$

Of course, we may also write these equations in the following condensed form:

13.25
$$X_i\alpha = \sum_{j=1}^{n} a_{ij}X_j, \qquad (i = 1, 2, \cdots, n).$$

Let us restate what we have just observed in the following way. Each linear transformation α of V has associated with it, by Equations 13.25, a unique matrix $A = (a_{ij})$ of order n over F. Conversely, if $A = (a_{ij})$ is a given matrix of order n over F, Theorem 13.15 shows that there exists a unique linear transformation α of V such that α and A are related as in Equations 13.25.

Let us henceforth denote by F_n the set of all matrices of order n over F. To avoid any possible confusion, perhaps we should state that two elements of F_n are considered as equal only if they are identical. That is, if (a_{ij}) and (b_{ij}) are elements of F_n, $(a_{ij}) = (b_{ij})$ means that $a_{ij} = b_{ij}$ for all $i, j = 1, 2, \cdots, n$.

We can now state in the following precise way what we have observed above. The mapping

13.26
$$\alpha \rightarrow A = (a_{ij}),$$

defined by Equations 13.25, is a one-one mapping of L onto F_n.

Inasmuch as L is an algebra over F, it is almost obvious that we can use this one-one mapping of L onto F_n to define operations of addition, multiplication, and scalar multiplication on F_n in such a way that F_n will be an algebra over F, which is isomorphic to L. We proceed to consider each of these operations in turn.

First, let us consider addition, and let $A = (a_{ij})$ and $B = (b_{ij})$ be elements of F_n. Suppose, further, that under the mapping 13.26, $\alpha \to A$ and $\mathcal{B} \to B$. Then

$$X_i\alpha = \sum_{j=1}^{n} a_{ij}X_j, \qquad (i = 1, 2, \cdots, n),$$

and

$$X_i\mathcal{B} = \sum_{j=1}^{n} b_{ij}X_j, \qquad (i = 1, 2, \cdots, n).$$

Now, by the definition of addition of linear transformations, it follows that

$$X_i(\alpha + \mathcal{B}) = X_i\alpha + X_i\mathcal{B} = \sum_{j=1}^{n} (a_{ij} + b_{ij})X_j, \qquad (i = 1, 2, \cdots, n).$$

Accordingly, we see that under the mapping 13.26,

$$\alpha + \mathcal{B} \to (a_{ij} + b_{ij}).$$

This leads us to *define* addition in F_n as follows:

13.27 $$(a_{ij}) + (b_{ij}) = (a_{ij} + b_{ij}).$$

That is, the element of the matrix $A + B$ in any fixed position is obtained by adding the elements of A and of B that are in that position. Taking $n = 2$, and F to be the field of rational numbers, we have as an illustration:

$$\begin{bmatrix} 4 & 0 \\ -2 & 3 \end{bmatrix} + \begin{bmatrix} -1 & 2 \\ 1 & 2 \end{bmatrix} = \begin{bmatrix} 3 & 2 \\ -1 & 5 \end{bmatrix}.$$

We next consider multiplication, and let A and B be as above. Then, using first the definition of a product of linear transformations, we have the following:

$$X_i(\alpha\mathcal{B}) = (X_i\alpha)\mathcal{B} = \left(\sum_{k=1}^{n} a_{ik}X_k\right)\mathcal{B}$$

$$= \sum_{k=1}^{n} a_{ik}(X_k\mathcal{B})$$

$$= \sum_{k=1}^{n} a_{ik}\left(\sum_{j=1}^{n} b_{kj}X_j\right), \qquad (i = 1, 2, \cdots, n).$$

By rearranging the order of summation, this can be written in the form

$$X_i(\alpha\beta) = \sum_{j=1}^{n} \left(\sum_{k=1}^{n} a_{ik}b_{kj} \right) X_j, \qquad (i = 1, 2, \cdots, n).$$

Hence, under the mapping 13.26,

$$\alpha\beta \rightarrow \left(\sum_{k=1}^{n} a_{ik}b_{kj} \right).$$

Accordingly, we *define* multiplication in F_n as follows:

13.28 $$(a_{ij})(b_{ij}) = \left(\sum_{k=1}^{n} a_{ik}b_{kj} \right).$$

This definition may be stated in words as follows. The element in the ith row and jth column of the product AB is the sum of the products of the elements of the ith row of A by the corresponding elements of the jth column of B. This can be expressed in another way as follows. Let $A_1, A_2, \cdots, A_n$ be the row vectors of A; and let $B^1, B^2, \cdots, B^n$ be the column vectors of B. In terms of inner products of vectors, we may then write 13.28 in the following alternate form:

$$AB = (A_i \cdot B^j).$$

As a simple example of multiplication of matrices, using the same matrices as were used above to illustrate addition, we have

$$\begin{bmatrix} 4 & 0 \\ -2 & 3 \end{bmatrix} \begin{bmatrix} -1 & 2 \\ 1 & 2 \end{bmatrix} = \begin{bmatrix} 4(-1)+0(1) & 4(2)+0(2) \\ -2(-1)+3(1) & -2(2)+3(2) \end{bmatrix} = \begin{bmatrix} -4 & 8 \\ 5 & 2 \end{bmatrix}.$$

On the other hand, the reader may verify that

$$\begin{bmatrix} -1 & 2 \\ 1 & 2 \end{bmatrix} \begin{bmatrix} 4 & 0 \\ -2 & 3 \end{bmatrix} = \begin{bmatrix} -8 & 6 \\ 0 & 6 \end{bmatrix},$$

and clearly the commutative law of multiplication does not hold in F_n.

Finally, we consider scalar multiplication. If $c \in F$ and $\alpha \in L$, by the definition of scalar multiplication in L, we have

$$X_i(c\alpha) = c(X_i\alpha) = c \sum_{j=1}^{n} a_{ij}X_j = \sum_{j=1}^{n} (ca_{ij})X_j, \quad (i = 1, 2, \cdots, n).$$

This suggests that we *define* scalar multiplication in F_n as follows:

13.29 $$c(a_{ij}) = (ca_{ij}).$$

Otherwise expressed, if $A \in F_n$, cA is the matrix obtained by multiplying every element of A by c. As a simple example, we have

$$2 \begin{bmatrix} 4 & 0 \\ -2 & 3 \end{bmatrix} = \begin{bmatrix} 8 & 0 \\ -4 & 6 \end{bmatrix}.$$

We have now defined addition, multiplication, and scalar multiplication on F_n in such a way that all of these operations are preserved under the mapping 13.26. That is, if under this mapping $\alpha \to A$, and $\mathcal{B} \to B$, then $\alpha + \mathcal{B} \to A + B$, $\alpha\mathcal{B} \to AB$, and $c\alpha \to cA$ for $c \in F$. We have therefore established the following result, it being understood that an isomorphism of two algebras over F means an isomorphism as rings and also as vector spaces.

13.30 Theorem. *With addition, multiplication, and scalar multiplication defined respectively by 13.27, 13.28, and 13.29, the set F_n of all matrices of order n over F is an algebra over F. Moreover, this algebra is isomorphic to the algebra L of all linear transformations of a vector space V of dimension n over F.*

It follows easily from 13.27 that the zero element of the algebra F_n is the matrix of order n *all* of whose elements are zero. We shall usually designate this zero matrix by the familiar symbol "0". Of course, this matrix is the image of the zero linear transformation under the mapping 13.26.

If $\mathcal{E}$ is the unity of L, we have $X_i \mathcal{E} = X_i$ $(i = 1, 2, \cdots, n)$, and the image of $\mathcal{E}$ under the mapping 13.26 is the matrix with 1's on the principal diagonal and zeros elsewhere. This matrix must then be the unity of F_n, as can also be verified by use of 13.28. The unity of F_n may be denoted by "I". Heretofore, we have used this symbol for the ring of integers, but there will be no confusion since we shall not again need to refer to this ring. For example, if $n = 3$, we have

$$0 = \begin{bmatrix} 0 & 0 & 0 \\ 0 & 0 & 0 \\ 0 & 0 & 0 \end{bmatrix}, \quad \text{and} \quad I = \begin{bmatrix} 1 & 0 & 0 \\ 0 & 1 & 0 \\ 0 & 0 & 1 \end{bmatrix}.$$

In closing this section we may observe that the isomorphism of the algebra L onto the algebra F_n, which we obtained above, was defined in terms of a fixed basis of the vector space V. By choice of a different basis of V, we could similarly obtain a different isomorphism of L onto F_n. Thus there are many different isomorphisms of L onto F_n.

_____ **E X E R C I S E S**

1. Let A and B be the following matrices of order 3 over R:

$$A = \begin{bmatrix} 1 & -1 & 2 \\ 0 & 1 & 3 \\ 2 & 1 & -2 \end{bmatrix}, \quad B = \begin{bmatrix} 1 & -2 & 3 \\ 2 & 1 & -1 \\ 1 & 0 & 1 \end{bmatrix}.$$

Compute each of the following: AB, BA, A^2, B^2, $(A + B)^2$.

2. If A is the matrix of the preceding exercise, verify that
$A^3 - 10A + 15I = 0$.

3. If A is the same matrix as above, and

$$C = -\tfrac{1}{15}\begin{bmatrix} -5 & 0 & -5 \\ 6 & -6 & -3 \\ -2 & -3 & 1 \end{bmatrix},$$

verify that $AC = CA = I$, and hence that $C = A^{-1}$.

4. If B is an element of F_n which has an inverse B^{-1} in F_n, verify that the mapping $A \rightarrow B^{-1}AB$ $(A \in F_n)$ is an isomorphism of the algebra F_n onto itself.

5. If L is the set of all linear transformations of a vector space of dimension n over a field F, what is the dimension of L considered as a vector space over F?

6. Show that the subset of F_n consisting of those matrices all of whose elements below the principal diagonal are zero is a subalgebra of the algebra F_n.

7. If D is any element of F_n, let D' be the *transpose* of D. Prove that if $A, B \in F_n$, then $(A + B)' = A' + B'$ and $(AB)' = B'A'$. Prove also that if A has a multiplicative inverse, then A' has a multiplicative inverse and that $(A^{-1})' = (A')^{-1}$.

13.5   LINEAR TRANSFORMATIONS OF $V_n(F)$

The results of the preceding section take a particularly simple form if we restrict V to be a vector space $V_n(F)$ and use as the fixed basis the unit vectors E_i $(i = 1, 2, \cdots, n)$, as defined in Section 10.4. If L is the algebra of all linear transformations of $V_n(F)$, the isomorphism 13.26 of L onto F_n is now given by

$$\mathcal{Q} \rightarrow A = (a_{ij}),$$

where

13.31 $$E_i\mathcal{Q} = \sum_{j=1}^{n} a_{ij}E_j = (a_{i1}, a_{i2}, \cdots, a_{in}), \qquad (i = 1, 2, \cdots, n).$$

That is, $E_i\mathcal{Q}$ is just the ith row vector of the matrix A. If we let the row vectors of A be $A_1, A_2, \cdots, A_n$, we can write 13.31 in the simpler form:

13.32 $$E_i\mathcal{Q} = A_i, \qquad (i = 1, 2, \cdots, n).$$

Now an arbitrary element X of $V_n(F)$ can be written in the form:

$$X = (x_1, x_2, \cdots, x_n) = \sum_{i=1}^{n} x_i E_i.$$

It follows from 13.32 that

13.33
$$X\mathcal{C} = \left(\sum_{i=1}^{n} x_i E_i\right)\mathcal{C} = \sum_{i=1}^{n} x_i(E_i\mathcal{C}) = \sum_{i=1}^{n} x_i A_i.$$

This shows that the subspace $(V_n(F))\mathcal{C}$ of $V_n(F)$ is just the set of all linear combinations of the row vectors of A. Since the rank of the linear transformation $\mathcal{C}$ is the dimension of $(V_n(F))\mathcal{C}$, and the row rank of the matrix A is the dimension of the row space of A, we have therefore established the following result.

13.34   Theorem.   *The rank of the linear transformation $\mathcal{C}$ is equal to the rank of the corresponding matrix A.*

There is still another way, as follows, of writing 13.33 in terms of the inner product of X with the column vectors $A^1, A^2, \cdots, A^n$ of A:

13.35
$$X\mathcal{C} = (X \cdot A^1, X \cdot A^2, \cdots, X \cdot A^n).$$

So far we have carefully distinguished between linear transformations and matrices. However, since L and F_n are isomorphic algebras, we could very well use an identical notation for these concepts. Henceforth, let us consider that a matrix A *is* the corresponding linear transformation $\mathcal{C}$ of $V_n(F)$ relative to the basis of unit vectors. In particular, in the future we shall write "A" in place of "$\mathcal{C}$". For example, 13.35 may then be written as follows:

13.36
$$XA = (X \cdot A^1, X \cdot A^2, \cdots, X \cdot A^n).$$

It will thus be observed that XA can be computed by using a "row by column" multiplication of the *vector* X of $V_n(F)$ by the *matrix* A of F_n.

Let us illustrate the use of this notation by an example. Suppose that

$$A = \begin{bmatrix} 1 & -1 & 2 \\ 0 & 1 & -1 \\ 3 & 2 & 1 \end{bmatrix}$$

is considered as a linear transformation of the vector space $V_3(R)$.

Then the image of the vector $(2, -1, 3)$ under the mapping A, as given by 13.36, is computed as follows:

$$(2, -1, 3) \begin{bmatrix} 1 & -1 & 2 \\ 0 & 1 & -1 \\ 3 & 2 & 1 \end{bmatrix}$$

$$= (2 \cdot 1 + (-1)0 + 3 \cdot 3, \; 2(-1) + (-1)1 + 3 \cdot 2,$$
$$2 \cdot 2 + (-1)(-1) + 3 \cdot 1) = (11, 3, 8).$$

Inasmuch as we are now identifying matrices with linear transformations, we can apply to matrices some of the terminology that has heretofore been defined for linear transformations. We shall say that a *matrix of F_n* is *singular* or *nonsingular* according as its rank is less than n or equal to n. Also, we may refer to the set of all vectors X of $V_n(F)$ such that $XA = 0$ as the *null space* of the matrix A of F_n. The dimension of this null space is the *nullity* of A. Moreover, Theorems 13.21 and 13.24 may henceforth be considered as theorems about matrices as well as linear transformations.

By Theorem 13.20, we know that a matrix A of F_n has a multiplicative inverse A^{-1} in F_n if and only if it is nonsingular. Moreover, by Theorem 12.28, A is nonsingular if and only if $|A| \neq 0$. We now proceed to show how determinants may be used to compute the multiplicative inverse of a nonsingular matrix.

If $A = (a_{ij}) \in F_n$, we use the notation of the preceding chapter and let A_{ij} denote the cofactor of the element a_{ij} in $|A|$. That is, $A_{ij} = (-1)^{i+j}|M_{ij}|$, where M_{ij} is the minor of a_{ij} in the matrix A. We now consider a certain matrix whose elements are cofactors of elements of A. It will be convenient to make the following definition.

13.37 Definition. If $A \in F_n$, the *adjoint* of A (which we shall write as adj A) is the transpose of the matrix (A_{ij}) of F_n; that is,

$$\text{adj } A = \begin{bmatrix} A_{11} & A_{21} & \cdots & A_{n1} \\ A_{12} & A_{22} & \cdots & A_{n2} \\ \cdot & \cdot \cdot \cdot \cdot \cdot \cdot \cdot & \cdot \\ A_{1n} & A_{2n} & \cdots & A_{nr} \end{bmatrix}.$$

We shall now prove the following result.

13.38 Theorem. *If $A \in F_n$, then*

$$A(\text{adj } A) = (\text{adj } A)A = |A| \cdot I.$$

Moreover, if A is nonsingular, then

$$A^{-1} = |A|^{-i} \text{ adj } A.$$

By the definition of the product of two matrices, we see that the element in the pth row and qth column of $A(\text{adj } A)$ is $\sum_{k=1}^{n} a_{pk}A_{qk}$. By 12.25 and 12.22, this element has the value zero if $p \neq q$, and is just $|A|$ if $p = q$. Hence, each element of the principal diagonal of the matrix $A(\text{adj } A)$ is $|A|$, and all other elements are zero. That is,

$$A(\text{adj } A) = |A| \cdot I,$$

where I is the unity of F_n. A similar argument, using 12.23 and 12.26, will show that also

$$(\text{adj } A)A = |A| \cdot I,$$

and the first statement of the theorem is established. Using this result and the Definition 13.29 of scalar multiplication of matrices, we now see that

$$A(|A|^{-1} \text{adj } A) = (|A|^{-1} \text{adj } A)A = I,$$

and hence that $A^{-1} = |A|^{-1} \text{adj } A$. This completes the proof of the theorem.

As an illustration of this theorem, let C be the matrix

$$\begin{bmatrix} 1 & -1 & 2 \\ 0 & 1 & 2 \\ 1 & -3 & -4 \end{bmatrix}$$

of order three over R. Then a calculation shows that

$$\text{adj } C = \begin{bmatrix} 2 & -10 & -4 \\ 2 & -6 & -2 \\ -1 & 2 & 1 \end{bmatrix}.$$

The reader may now verify that

$$C(\text{adj } C) = (\text{adj } C)C = \begin{bmatrix} -2 & 0 & 0 \\ 0 & -2 & 0 \\ 0 & 0 & -2 \end{bmatrix} = -2I.$$

Accordingly, we have that

$$C^{-1} = -\tfrac{1}{2} \text{adj } C = \begin{bmatrix} -1 & 5 & 2 \\ -1 & 3 & 1 \\ \tfrac{1}{2} & -1 & -\tfrac{1}{2} \end{bmatrix}.$$

Now that we have available the concept of the inverse of a matrix, it may be of interest to give a brief indication of how matrix methods may be used, in place of Cramer's Rule, to solve a system of n linear equations in n unknowns over a field F. Suppose that we have the following system of equations:

$$\sum_{j=1}^{n} a_{ij}x_j = b_i, \qquad (i = 1, 2, \cdots, n).$$

Let $A = (a_{ij})$ be the matrix of coefficients in this system of equations. Moreover, let us set $B = (b_1, b_2, \cdots, b_n)$ and $X = (x_1, x_2, \cdots, x_n)$, where we may now consider $x_1, x_2, \cdots, x_n$ as unknown elements of F. Then it may be verified that the above system can be written in the following simple form

13.39 $$XA' = B,$$

it being understood that A' is the transpose of A. Let us now assume that A is nonsingular. Hence, also, A' is nonsingular (why?), and if we multiply the preceding equation on the right by the multiplicative inverse of A', we obtain

$$(XA')(A')^{-1} = B(A')^{-1}.$$

However,

$$(XA')(A')^{-1} = X(A'(A')^{-1}) = X,$$

and therefore

13.40 $$X = B(A')^{-1}.$$

This, then, is the solution of the system 13.39. Of course, it is the same solution as would be obtained by use of Cramer's Rule (12.35).

As an example of the use of this notation, suppose that we have the following system of three linear equations in three unknowns over R:

$$\begin{aligned} x_1 \quad\; + x_3 &= \quad\; 1, \\ -x_1 + x_2 - 3x_3 &= -2, \\ 2x_1 + 2x_2 - 4x_3 &= \quad\; 3. \end{aligned}$$

This system can be written in the form 13.39 as follows:

$$(x_1, x_2, x_3) \begin{bmatrix} 1 & -1 & 2 \\ 0 & 1 & 2 \\ 1 & -3 & -4 \end{bmatrix} = (1, -2, 3).$$

The matrix appearing here is the matrix C whose inverse was computed above, and the solution 13.40 is therefore obtained by the following calculation:

$$(x_1, x_2, x_3) = (1, -2, 3) \begin{bmatrix} -1 & 5 & 2 \\ -1 & 3 & 1 \\ \frac{1}{2} & -1 & -\frac{1}{2} \end{bmatrix} = (5/2, -4, -3/2).$$

The unique solution is therefore $x_1 = 5/2$, $x_2 = -4$, $x_3 = -3/2$.

1. Let the matrix

$$A = \begin{bmatrix} 1 & 2 & 1 \\ -1 & 1 & -4 \\ -1 & 4 & -7 \end{bmatrix}$$

over R be considered as a linear transformation of $V_3(R)$. Verify that under this linear transformation both of the vectors $(2, 1, 3)$ and $(1, -1, 4)$ map into the vector $(-2, 17, -23)$. What does this fact tell us about the matrix A? Find a basis of the null space of A.

2. Find the adjoint and, if the matrix is nonsingular, the multiplicative inverse of each of the following matrices over R:

(a) $\begin{bmatrix} 1 & 2 \\ 2 & -3 \end{bmatrix}$,　(b) $\begin{bmatrix} -2 & 1 \\ 0 & 2 \end{bmatrix}$,　(c) $\begin{bmatrix} 1 & -1 & 1 \\ -1 & 1 & 1 \\ 1 & 1 & -1 \end{bmatrix}$.

(d) $\begin{bmatrix} 2 & -1 & 0 \\ 1 & 3 & -2 \\ 2 & 1 & 1 \end{bmatrix}$,　(e) $\begin{bmatrix} 2 & -1 & 3 \\ 1 & 2 & -1 \\ 1 & -8 & 9 \end{bmatrix}$.

(f) $\begin{bmatrix} 0 & 0 & 2 \\ 1 & 0 & 3 \\ 3 & 4 & 2 \end{bmatrix}$,　(g) $\begin{bmatrix} 1 & 0 & -1 & 0 \\ 0 & 2 & 0 & -3 \\ 2 & 0 & 0 & 1 \\ 1 & 0 & 1 & 2 \end{bmatrix}$.

3. Use the method illustrated above to solve the following system of linear equations over R:

$$\begin{aligned} 2x_1 - x_2 + x_3 &= 2, \\ 3x_1 + x_2 - 2x_3 &= -1, \\ x_1 + 2x_2 + 3x_3 &= 3. \end{aligned}$$

4. Of the sixteen matrices of order two over the field $I/(2)$, verify that ten are singular and six are nonsingular.

5. Apply Theorem 13.24 to obtain a new proof of Theorem 11.37 for the case in which there are the same number of equations as unknowns.

13.6　EQUIVALENT MATRICES

All matrices considered will be $n \times n$ matrices over a field F, that is, elements of F_n. We now study again the elementary row and column operations, as defined in 11.24. These are of three types, and we begin by introducing some notation that will be helpful in referring to specific elementary operations.

Let "$\mathcal{R}_{ij}$" stand for the operation of interchanging the ith and jth rows, let "$\mathcal{R}_i(c)$" stand for the operation of multiplying the ith row by the nonzero element c of F, and let "$\mathcal{R}_{ij}(d)$" stand for the operation of adding to the jth row d times the ith row, where $d \in F$.

In like manner, let "$\mathcal{C}_{ij}$", "$\mathcal{C}_i(c)$", and "$\mathcal{C}_{ij}(d)$" represent the corresponding *column* operations.

When we speak of an elementary operation, we shall mean either an elementary row operation or an elementary column operation.

It is an important fact that the effect of an elementary operation can always be canceled by an elementary operation. Suppose, first, that matrix B is obtained from matrix A by applying an elementary operation $\mathcal{R}_{ij}$. Then, it is clear that the same operation $\mathcal{R}_{ij}$ applied to B will yield A again. Likewise, if the operation $\mathcal{R}_i(c)$ applied to A gives B, the operation $\mathcal{R}_i(c^{-1})$ applied to B gives A. In like manner, if $\mathcal{R}_{ij}(d)$ applied to A yields B, then $\mathcal{R}_{ij}(-d)$ applied to B yields A. Of course, similar statements apply to the column operations as well.

We now make the following definition.

13.41 Definition. If A, $B \in F_n$, we say that A is *equivalent* to B, and write $A \sim B$, if it is possible to pass from A to B by a finite sequence of elementary operations.

From the observations just made it follows easily that if $A \sim B$, then $B \sim A$. This is one of the defining properties (1.7) of an equivalence relation. The other two properties are obviously satisfied, and hence "$\sim$" is an equivalence relation defined on F_n.

Now that we have an equivalence relation defined on F_n, we may consider the equivalence sets relative to this equivalence relation. The main part of this section will be devoted to the determination of these equivalence sets. Otherwise expressed, we shall find conditions under which two elements of F_n will be equivalent. For convenience of reference, let us first state the following fact, which is a consequence of Theorem 11.25 and Definition 11.30.

13.42 Lemma. If $A \sim B$, then rank $A =$ rank B.

We shall presently prove the converse of this lemma, from which it will follow that the elements of an equivalence set are just those matrices with some specified rank. Before proving this converse, we shall establish one more lemma.

If r is an integer ($0 \leq r \leq n$), let us denote by I_r the element of F_n which has a 1 in the first r places of the principal diagonal and zeros elsewhere. Clearly, I_0 is the zero and I_n the unity I of F_n. As an illustration of this notation, if $n = 3$, we have

$$I_1 = \begin{bmatrix} 1 & 0 & 0 \\ 0 & 0 & 0 \\ 0 & 0 & 0 \end{bmatrix} \text{ and } I_2 = \begin{bmatrix} 1 & 0 & 0 \\ 0 & 1 & 0 \\ 0 & 0 & 0 \end{bmatrix}.$$

We are now in a position to state the following result.

13.43 Lemma. *If $A \in F_n$ and rank $A = r$, then $A \sim I_r$.*

The method of proof of this lemma is suggested by the procedure used in Chapter 11 to reduce a system of linear equations to an echelon system. However, we can here carry the simplification somewhat further since we may use column operations as well as row operations.

Before proceeding, we give an example to illustrate the method of proof and also to clarify the notation and terminology introduced so far. Let us consider the following matrix over the rational field R:

$$D = \begin{bmatrix} 1 & 2 & -1 \\ 3 & 1 & 2 \\ 2 & -1 & 3 \end{bmatrix}.$$

First, we perform the operations $\mathcal{R}_{12}(-3)$ and $\mathcal{R}_{13}(-2)$. That is, we multiply the first row by -3 and add it to the second row, then multiply the first row by -2 and add it to the third row. Next, we perform the column operations $\mathcal{C}_{12}(-2)$ and $\mathcal{C}_{13}(1)$. At this stage, we have a 1 in the upper left-hand corner and zeros in all other positions of the first row and first column. Actually, we have the matrix

$$\begin{bmatrix} 1 & 0 & 0 \\ 0 & -5 & 5 \\ 0 & -5 & 5 \end{bmatrix}.$$

We now proceed to perform elementary operations that do not involve the first row or first column. In particular, the operation $\mathcal{R}_{23}(-1)$ makes the last row zero, and then the operation $\mathcal{R}_2(-1/5)$ places a 1 in the second row and second column. Finally, the column operation $\mathcal{C}_{23}(1)$ gives us the matrix I_2. We have therefore showed that $D \sim I_2$. Moreover, the elementary operations that we performed were as follows, and in this order:

13.44 $\mathcal{R}_{12}(-3)$, $\mathcal{R}_{13}(-2)$, $\mathcal{C}_{12}(-2)$, $\mathcal{C}_{13}(1)$, $\mathcal{R}_{23}(-1)$, $\mathcal{R}_2(-1/5)$, $\mathcal{C}_{23}(1)$.

As a matter of fact, we could have obtained the same result by first performing all the specified row operations in the order in which they appear above, *followed* by the column operations in their specified order (or vice versa). However, we are here only concerned with the fact that there is at least one sequence of elementary operations by which we can pass from D to I_2.

Let us return to the proof of the lemma and let $A = (a_{ij})$ be an element of F_n. If $r = 0$, then $A = 0$, and the result is trivial; hence we assume that $r > 0$. Then A has at least one nonzero element. If necessary, we can use suitable operations $\mathcal{R}_{ij}$ and $\mathcal{C}_{ij}$ (interchanging rows and interchanging columns) in order to get a nonzero element in the upper left-hand corner. For convenience, let us assume that a_{11} itself is different from zero. Then a matrix of the form

$$B = \begin{bmatrix} 1 & 0 & 0 & \cdots & 0 \\ 0 & b_{22} & b_{23} & \cdots & b_{2n} \\ 0 & b_{32} & b_{33} & \cdots & b_{3n} \\ \cdot & \cdot & \cdot & \cdot & \cdot & \cdot & \cdot \\ 0 & b_{n2} & b_{n3} & \cdots & b_{nn} \end{bmatrix}$$

can be obtained from A by the following sequence of elementary operations: $\mathcal{R}_1(a_{11}^{-1})$, $\mathcal{R}_{12}(-a_{21})$, $\mathcal{R}_{13}(-a_{31})$, $\cdots$, $\mathcal{R}_{1n}(-a_{n1})$, $\mathcal{C}_{12}(-a_{11}^{-1}a_{12})$, $\mathcal{C}_{13}(-a_{11}^{-1}a_{13})$, $\cdots$, $\mathcal{C}_{1n}(-a_{11}^{-1}a_{1n})$.

If some element b_{ij} of B ($i \le 2 \le n$, $j \le 2 \le n$) is different from zero, we can get such a nonzero element in the second row and second column by suitable interchange of rows and of columns. Then, proceeding as above, working only with rows and columns other than the first, we can apply elementary operations to B and get a matrix of the form

$$C = \begin{bmatrix} 1 & 0 & 0 & \cdots & 0 \\ 0 & 1 & 0 & \cdots & 0 \\ 0 & 0 & c_{33} & \cdots & c_{3n} \\ 0 & 0 & c_{43} & \cdots & c_{4n} \\ \cdot & \cdot & \cdot & \cdot & \cdot & \cdot & \cdot \\ 0 & 0 & c_{n3} & \cdots & c_{nn} \end{bmatrix}.$$

If some c_{ij} is different from zero, this process can be repeated. We thus finally obtain a matrix of the form I_s with $s \le n$. Now it was given that the rank of A is r, and it is obvious that the rank of I_s is s. Since we have $A \sim I_s$, Lemma 13.42 assures us that $r = s$, and the proof is completed.

We are now ready to prove the following result.

13.45 Theorem. *If $A, B \in F_n$, then $A \sim B$ if and only if rank $A = $ rank B.*

Of course, one part of this theorem is merely Lemma 13.42. To prove the other part, suppose that rank $A = $ rank $B = r$. Then, by the preceding lemma, $A \sim I_r$ and $B \sim I_r$. By the symmetric and transitive properties of the equivalence relation "$\sim$", it follows at once that $A \sim B$.

We have now obtained one characterization of the equivalence sets relative to the equivalence relation "$\sim$." The elements of an equivalence set $[A]$ are precisely those elements of F_n that have the same rank as A. A little later we shall obtain another characterization of these equivalence sets.

It is a fact of considerable importance in the theory of matrices that elementary operations can be effected by matrix multiplication. We shall briefly indicate how this is done, and then give a few simple consequences of this fact.

We begin by defining certain matrices of F_n as follows. Let E_{ij}, $E_i(c)$, and $E_{ij}(d)$ be the matrices obtained by applying the respective elementary operations $\mathcal{R}_{ij}$, $\mathcal{R}_i(c)$, and $\mathcal{R}_{ij}(d)$ to the matrix I. As examples, if $n = 3$, we have the following:

$$E_{12} = \begin{bmatrix} 0 & 1 & 0 \\ 1 & 0 & 0 \\ 0 & 0 & 1 \end{bmatrix}, \quad E_2(c) = \begin{bmatrix} 1 & 0 & 0 \\ 0 & c & 0 \\ 0 & 0 & 1 \end{bmatrix}, \quad E_{12}(d) = \begin{bmatrix} 1 & 0 & 0 \\ d & 1 & 0 \\ 0 & 0 & 1 \end{bmatrix}.$$

We now make the following definition.

13.46 Definition. A matrix of the form E_{ij}, $E_i(c)$, or $E_{ij}(d)$ is called an *elementary matrix*. It is understood that i and j are distinct integers from the set $\{1, 2, \cdots, n\}$, that c is a nonzero element of F, and that $d \in F$.

We now assert that an elementary row (column) operation on a matrix A can be achieved by multiplying A on the left (right) by an elementary matrix. More precisely, we have the following theorem.

13.47 Theorem. *The result of applying an elementary row operation $\mathcal{R}_{ij}$, $\mathcal{R}_i(c)$, or $\mathcal{R}_{ij}(d)$ to a matrix A is to obtain the matrix $E_{ij}A$, $E_i(c)A$, or $E_{ij}(d)A$, respectively. The result of applying an elementary column operation $\mathcal{C}_{ij}$, $\mathcal{C}_i(c)$, or $\mathcal{C}_{ij}(d)$ to a matrix A is to obtain the matrix AE_{ij}, $AE_i(c)$, or $AE_{ji}(d)$, respectively.*

If $A = (a_{ij})$ and $n = 3$, we may illustrate certain parts of this theorem by the following calculations. In each case, the matrix product is obviously the matrix obtained from A by the corresponding elementary operation:

$$E_{12}A = \begin{bmatrix} 0 & 1 & 0 \\ 1 & 0 & 0 \\ 0 & 0 & 1 \end{bmatrix} \begin{bmatrix} a_{11} & a_{12} & a_{13} \\ a_{21} & a_{22} & a_{23} \\ a_{31} & a_{32} & a_{33} \end{bmatrix} = \begin{bmatrix} a_{21} & a_{22} & a_{23} \\ a_{11} & a_{12} & a_{13} \\ a_{31} & a_{32} & a_{33} \end{bmatrix},$$

$$E_{12}(d)A = \begin{bmatrix} 1 & 0 & 0 \\ d & 1 & 0 \\ 0 & 0 & 1 \end{bmatrix} \begin{bmatrix} a_{11} & a_{12} & a_{13} \\ a_{21} & a_{22} & a_{23} \\ a_{31} & a_{32} & a_{33} \end{bmatrix}$$

$$= \begin{bmatrix} a_{11} & a_{12} & a_{13} \\ a_{21} + da_{11} & a_{22} + da_{12} & a_{23} + da_{13} \\ a_{31} & a_{32} & a_{33} \end{bmatrix},$$

$$AE_{12} = \begin{bmatrix} a_{11} & a_{12} & a_{13} \\ a_{21} & a_{22} & a_{23} \\ a_{31} & a_{32} & a_{33} \end{bmatrix} \begin{bmatrix} 0 & 1 & 0 \\ 1 & 0 & 0 \\ 0 & 0 & 1 \end{bmatrix} = \begin{bmatrix} a_{12} & a_{11} & a_{13} \\ a_{22} & a_{21} & a_{23} \\ a_{32} & a_{31} & a_{33} \end{bmatrix},$$

$$AE_{12}(d) = \begin{bmatrix} a_{11} & a_{12} & a_{13} \\ a_{21} & a_{22} & a_{23} \\ a_{31} & a_{32} & a_{33} \end{bmatrix} \begin{bmatrix} 1 & 0 & 0 \\ d & 1 & 0 \\ 0 & 0 & 1 \end{bmatrix} = \begin{bmatrix} a_{11} + da_{12} & a_{12} & a_{13} \\ a_{21} + da_{22} & a_{22} & a_{23} \\ a_{31} + da_{32} & a_{32} & a_{33} \end{bmatrix}.$$

By a separate consideration of each of the cases involved, the reader should have no difficulty in convincing himself of the truth of Theorem 13.47, or even in supplying a formal proof. Accordingly, we shall omit the proof.

Suppose, now, that we can pass from a matrix A to a matrix B by a finite sequence of elementary operations. The preceding theorem says that B can be obtained from A by successive multiplications by elementary matrices. As an example, consider the matrix D which is transformed into I_2 by the elementary operations 13.44. After applying $\Re_{12}(-3)$ to D we have the matrix $E_{12}(-3)D$, after applying $\Re_{13}(-2)$ to this matrix we have $E_{13}(-2)E_{12}(-3)D$, after applying the column operation $\mathcal{C}_{12}(-2)$ to this matrix we have $E_{13}(-2)E_{12}(-3)DE_{21}(-2)$, and so on. We finally obtain in this way that

13.48 $\quad E_2(-1/5)E_{23}(-1)E_{13}(-2)E_{12}(-3)DE_{21}(-2)E_{31}(1)E_{32}(1) = I_2.$

Now each elementary matrix is nonsingular since it is obtained from the nonsingular matrix I by an elementary operation. Moreover, we know by Corollary 13.22 that a product of nonsingular matrices is nonsingular. Hence, if we set

$$S = E_2(-1/5)E_{23}(-1)E_{13}(-2)E_{12}(-3)$$

and

$$T = E_{21}(-2)E_{31}(1)E_{32}(1),$$

S and T are nonsingular matrices and Equation 13.48 can be written in the form

13.49 $$SDT = I_2.$$

This is an illustration of one part of the following general theorem.

13.50 Theorem. *If* $A, B \in F_n$, *then* $A \sim B$ *if and only if there exist nonsingular matrices* P *and* Q *such that* $B = PAQ$.

If $B = PAQ$, where P and Q are nonsingular, it follows from Theorem 13.21 (ii) that A and B have the same rank, and Theorem 13.45 then shows that $A \sim B$.

Conversely, let us assume that $A \sim B$. In view of Theorem 13.47, this implies that there exist elementary matrices $P_1, P_2, \cdots, P_k$ and $Q_1, Q_2, \cdots, Q_l$ such that

$$B = P_k \cdots P_2 P_1 A Q_1 Q_2 \cdots Q_l.$$

If we set $P = P_k \cdots P_2 P_1$ and $Q = Q_1 Q_2 \cdots Q_l$, P and Q are nonsingular since they are products of nonsingular matrices, and $B = PAQ$ as required. The proof of the theorem is therefore completed.

This theorem shows that the equivalence set $[A]$ consists of all those elements of F_n of the form PAQ, where P and Q are nonsingular elements of F_n.

An important special case of some of the preceding results is that in which A is taken to be the unity I of F_n. Since I is nonsingular, Theorem 13.45 asserts that $I \sim B$ if and only if B is nonsingular. Moreover, Theorem 13.47, as applied in the proof of the preceding theorem, shows that $I \sim B$ if and only if B is expressible as a product of elementary matrices. We have then the following result.

13.51 Corollary. *A matrix is expressible as a product of elementary matrices if and only if it is nonsingular.*

13.7 THE DETERMINANT OF A PRODUCT

The results of the preceding section enable us to prove the following theorem about determinants.

13.52 Theorem. *If* $A, B \in F_n$, *then* $|AB| = |A| \cdot |B|$.

First, we dispose of the case in which A is singular. In view of Theorem 12.28, this means that $|A| = 0$. Moreover, by Theorem 13.21, we see that rank $(AB) < n$, so that also $|AB| = 0$. Hence, the theorem is true in this case.

We next show that the desired result is true if A is an elementary matrix. Let us state this special case as follows.

13.53 Lemma. *If* E *is an elementary matrix, then* $|EB| = |E| \cdot |B|$.

To prove this lemma, we consider, in turn, each of the three types of elementary matrices. Since each such matrix is obtained from I by an elementary operation, and $|I| = 1$, it follows from Theorem 12.14 that $|E_{ij}| = -1$, $|E_i(c)| = c$, and $|E_{ij}(d)| = 1$. Then, by again applying the same theorem and Theorem 13.47, we can verify each of the following:

$$|E_{ij}B| = -|B| = |E_{ij}| \cdot |B|,$$
$$|E_i(c)B| = c|B| = |E_i(c)| \cdot |B|,$$
$$|E_{ij}(d)B| = |B| = |E_{ij}(d)| \cdot |B|,$$

and the lemma is established.

Suppose now that A is an arbitrary nonsingular matrix. Corollary 13.51 then assures us that it can be expressed as a product of elementary matrices. The desired result is now easily completed by induction. Let S_m be the statement "For every matrix B of F_n, and for every matrix A of F_n which can be expressed as a product of m elementary matrices, we have $|AB| = |A| \cdot |B|$." Then S_1 is true by the preceding lemma. Let us now assume that S_k is true and prove that S_{k+1} is true. Suppose, then, that $A = E_1 E_2 \cdots E_{k+1}$, where these are elementary matrices. It follows that

$$
\begin{aligned}
|AB| = |E_1(E_2 E_3 \cdots E_{k+1}B)| &= |E_1| \cdot |E_2 E_3 \cdots E_{k+1}B| && \text{(by } S_1) \\
&= |E_1| \cdot |E_2 E_3 \cdots E_{k+1}| \cdot |B| && \text{(by } S_k) \\
&= |E_1 E_2 \cdots E_{k+1}| \cdot |B| && \text{(by } S_1) \\
&= |A| \cdot |B|.
\end{aligned}
$$

Hence, S_{k+1} is true, and it follows that S_m is true for every positive integer m. The theorem is therefore established.

EXERCISES

1. For each of the following matrices over R, write down a sequence of elementary operations that will reduce it to the form I_r:

(a) $\begin{bmatrix} 1 & -1 \\ 2 & 3 \end{bmatrix}$,
(b) $\begin{bmatrix} 2 & -1 \\ 4 & -2 \end{bmatrix}$,

(c) $\begin{bmatrix} 0 & -1 & 2 \\ 1 & 2 & -1 \\ 1 & -1 & 5 \end{bmatrix}$,
(d) $\begin{bmatrix} 1 & -2 & 3 \\ 2 & 1 & 4 \\ -2 & 1 & 2 \end{bmatrix}$.

2. Show that the multiplicative inverse of each elementary matrix is also an elementary matrix.

3. Let $E_1 E_2 \cdots E_s$ be a product of elementary matrices. Since $E_1 E_2 \cdots E_s = E_1 E_2 \cdots E_s I$, Theorem 13.47 says that we can compute this product by first applying the elementary row operation corresponding to E_s to the matrix I, then the elementary

row operation corresponding to E_{s-1} to this new matrix, and so on. Use this method to compute the matrices S and T occurring in 13.49.

4. For each matrix A of Exercise 1, find nonsingular matrices P and Q such that $PAQ = I_r$.

5. Express each of the nonsingular matrices of Exercise 1 as a product of elementary matrices.

6. By actual calculation of the determinants involved, verify Theorem 13.52 for the following matrices:

$$A = \begin{bmatrix} 3 & -1 & 0 \\ 1 & 0 & 3 \\ -2 & 1 & 1 \end{bmatrix}, \qquad B = \begin{bmatrix} 2 & 1 & -3 \\ 0 & 1 & 2 \\ 1 & 3 & 2 \end{bmatrix}.$$

7. Let us write $A \equiv B$ if there exist nonsingular matrices P and Q such that $B = PAQ$. Use this definition to verify that "$\equiv$" is an equivalence relation on F_n. (Of course, Theorem 13.50 shows indirectly that "$\equiv$" coincides with the equivalence relation "$\sim$".)

8. Let us define $A \approx B$ to mean that it is possible to pass from A to B by a finite sequence of elementary *row* operations. Prove each of the following:

   (*a*) "$\approx$" is an equivalence relation defined on F_n,
   (*b*) $A \approx B$ if and only if there exists a nonsingular matrix P such that $B = PA$,
   (*c*) If A is nonsingular, then $A \approx I$.

9. Show that if A can be reduced to I by a sequence of elementary *row* operations, then A^{-1} is the matrix obtained by starting with the matrix I and applying in turn the same sequence of elementary row operations.

10. Use the method of the previous problem to compute the multiplicative inverse of the following matrix over R:

$$\begin{bmatrix} 3 & 1 & -2 \\ 2 & 0 & 3 \\ -1 & 1 & -6 \end{bmatrix}.$$

Index

Matrix (*Contd*)
  row rank, 233
  singular, 288
  transpose, 237
Minor, 255
Monic polynomial, 139
Multiple, 48, 135
Multiples, 30
Multiplication, 9
  of complex numbers, 113
  of integers, 87
  of linear transformations, 272
  of matrices, 284
  of natural numbers, 47
  of polynomials, 128
  of rational numbers, 80
  of real numbers, 98
Multiplicative inverse, 24
  of a linear transformation, 275, 279
  of a matrix, 288
Multiplicity of root, 144

N

Natural numbers, 46
Negative elements of ordered domain, 37
Nonsingular linear transformation, 278
Nonsingular matrix, 288
Null space, 281, 288
Nullity, 281, 288

O

Octic group, 180
Odd permutation, 193
One-one mapping, 5
Operation, 9
Order:
  of a group, 182
  of a group element, 182
  of a matrix, 249
Ordered field, 83
Ordered integral domain, 37
Ordered pairs, 3

P

Partial fractions, 162
Peano Axioms, 46
Permutation, 175
  even, 193
  odd, 193
Permutation group, 178
Polynomial, 127
Polynomial ring, 127

Positive elements of ordered domain, 37
Prime integer, 49
Prime polynomial, 142, 147, 152, 153
Primitive nth root, 125
Primitive Pythagorean triple, 64
Principal diagonal, 249
Principal nth root, 105
Product of mappings, 173
Product set, 3
Proper subset, 2
Pythagorean triple, 63

Q

Quadratic formulas, 150
Quotient, 51, 136
Quotient field, 86

R

Rank:
  of linear transformation, 278
  of matrix, 233, 238, 261
Rational form, 162
Rational numbers, 83
Rational roots, 145
Real numbers, 99
Recursive definition, 28, 43
Reflexive property of equivalence, 7
Relation, 7
Relatively prime, 58, 141
Remainder, 51, 136
Remainder Theorem, 137
Ring, 12
  of integers modulo n, 69
  of polynomials, 127
  of polynomials modulo $s(x)$, 155
  of subsets of a set, 18
  with unity, 13
Roots, 105, 122
  of a polynomial, 133
  of unity, 124, 125
Row rank, 233
Row space, 233
Row vectors, 224, 233

S

Scalar, 197
Scalar multiplication, 197
Set, 1
Sign of permutation, 248
Singular linear transformation, 278
Singular matrix, 288
Standard form of an integer, 61
Subgroup, 170